Basic Linear Algebra

BASIC LINEAR ALGEBRA

PAUL W. HAGGARD
East Carolina University

ALLYN AND BACON, INC. BOSTON

Contents

Preface

BASIC LINEAR ALGEBRA provides the student with a methodological as well as a theoretical approach to linear algebra. The author feels that if linear algebra is to be useful in agriculture, economics, engineering, the physical and social sciences, and also provide helpful background for multivariable calculus and differential equations, techniques need to be emphasized as well as principles. To this end, the author has devoted the first four chapters and Chapter 7 to methodology, while Chapters 5 and 6 provide a more theoretical approach to the subject. Also, throughout the book, the student will find completely worked out example problems. If these problems are studied and understood, the principles involved will be clear.

Chapter 1 provides a concrete beginning for the course. Vectors, lines, and planes are discussed. The vector spaces E^2, R^2, and R^3 are our first examples of vector spaces. The concepts of linear independence, linear dependence, and basis are introduced as they apply to R^2 and R^3.

Chapter 2 gives an introduction to matrices. The algebra of matrices is developed and some special matrices are discussed. Matrices are then used as a tool in Chapter 3 to solve systems of linear equations.

In Chapter 4 a short traditional treatment of determinants is presented, without the theory of permutations. The basic properties of determinants are given and determinants are used to obtain the inverse of a nonsingular matrix and to solve systems of linear equations.

Vector spaces over a field and linear mappings are discussed in Chapters 5 and 6. To help offset the natural abstractness of these concepts, many examples of vector spaces and linear mappings are given. Also, the basic theory presented is developed in a simple, straightforward way.

A Problem Set follows each section, and some sections have more than one Problem Set. These Problem Sets are extensive and supply an ample number of problems. Many problems are of a computational type, but carefully selected problems involving theory are also included. Answers to approximately one-half of the problems are given at the back of the book. The remaining answers are available in an Instructor's Supplement. The Instructor's Supplement also contains comments to the teacher, complete solutions for all proof-type problems, review questions, and sample tests, with solutions, for each chapter. In an appendix to the Instructor's Supplement, several simple computer programs are provided for such problems as solving systems of linear equations, reducing a matrix, obtaining the inverse of a nonsingular matrix, evaluating the determinant of a 3×3 matrix, and obtaining equations of the least squares line and least squares plane.

BASIC LINEAR ALGEBRA contains sufficient material for a one-semester course in linear algebra. The course may be taken between the first two semesters of calculus or it can be taken concurrently with the second semester of calculus.

The author wishes to gratefully acknowledge David Outcalt of the University of California, at Santa Barbara, and Harvey Keynes of the University of Minnesota for the contributions made in their reviews of the manuscript. Special thanks is here given to Mrs. Marie M. Davis and Mrs. Connie Maynor who, from handwritten copy, typed the entire manuscript promptly and expertly.

Greenville, North Carolina   PAUL W. HAGGARD

Basic Linear Algebra

1

Geometric Vectors

Vectors in a plane can be interpreted either geometrically or algebraically. The geometry of vectors provides concrete problems and also provides help in solving purely algebraic problems. The algebraic interpretation of vectors will be discussed later, after we have examined the geometric interpretation of vectors.

To a physicist, a vector is a directed line segment or an arrow that represents an acceleration, a force, a velocity, or any other quantity having both a direction and a magnitude. We will use a directed line segment as our first interpretation of a vector. For the setting let us use a Euclidean plane K consisting of points and lines that satisfy the familiar postulates of plane Euclidean geometry. We know that every pair of distinct points A and B in K determines exactly one straight line segment with endpoints A and B. If the line segment is from A to B, then A is called the *initial point* and B is called the *terminal point* of the segment. We will call such a directed line segment a *vector in* K and denote it in boldface as $\mathbf{AB}$. If A and B are not distinct points, we still consider $\mathbf{AB}$ to be a vector. This vector is called a *zero vector* at A (at B) and is denoted by $\mathbf{0}$. A zero vector is not assigned any particular direction. If the usual rectangular coordinate system is imposed on K, the

1

distance formula can be applied. The distance between points A and B is the *magnitude*, (or *length*), of **AB**. The magnitude is designated by $|\mathbf{AB}|$.

The set of all vectors in a Euclidean plane is signified by E^2. (See Appendix for a review of sets.) The vectors of E^2 are said to be *free vectors;* they can be moved in the plane, provided magnitudes and directions are not changed. Thus, two nonzero vectors **AB** and **CD** are *equal* if and only if $|\mathbf{AB}| = |\mathbf{CD}|$ and **AB** and **CD** are parallel and have the same direction (see Fig. 1–1.1). If we agree that a line is parallel to itself, then **AB** and **CD** are parallel means that the lines (line) containing them are parallel. The vectors have the same direction provided the arrows point the same way along the parallel lines. Also, it may be said that any two zero vectors are considered to be equal. If two vectors are equal, either one can replace the other in any discussion. We further agree that a zero vector is parallel to every vector.

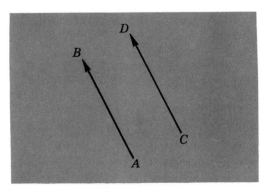

Figure 1–1.1

Let us now consider a planar displacement of an object from one position to another as a vector. Since a planar displacement along a straight line segment involves both distance and direction, we can interpret a displacement as a vector. If an object is moved first from A to B and then from B to C, the result is that the object is moved from A to C (see Fig. 1–1.2). We interpret this result as the

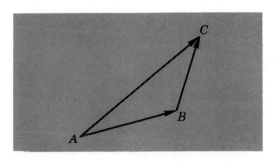

Figure 1–1.2

vector addition $\mathbf{AB} + \mathbf{BC} = \mathbf{AC}$. The same result is obtained if **AB** and **BC** represent forces acting simultaneously on an object at A. These two forces produce the same effect as the single force **AC**. As a third interpretation, let **AB** denote the velocity produced by an airplane's engines and let **BC** denote the velocity of the wind. In this case, **AC** is the sum of the two velocities.

The last sentence leads to a digression. Notice that we did *not* say that the magnitude of **AC** is the sum of the magnitudes of the other two vectors, see *property iv* below. In fact, the basic proper-ties of the distance function are

i. $|\mathbf{AB}| \geq 0$,

ii. $|\mathbf{AB}| = 0$, if and only if A and B are not distinct points,

iii. $|\mathbf{AB}| = |\mathbf{BA}|$, and

iv. $|\mathbf{AB}| + |\mathbf{BC}| \geq |\mathbf{AC}|$ *The Triangle Inequality*

The first three of these clearly hold. Notice that *property iv* holds for A, B, and C noncollinear, since the sum of two sides of a triangle is greater than the third side. When does equality hold?

Suppose we wish to add two vectors **AB** and **CD**. Let $\mathbf{CD} = \mathbf{BE}$, a vector with initial point B. Now, the previous addition holds and $\mathbf{AB} + \mathbf{CD} = \mathbf{AB} + \mathbf{BE} = \mathbf{AE}$ (see Fig. 1-1.3). We can interpret this addition as the result of moving **CD** such that C coincides with B.

Figure 1-1.3

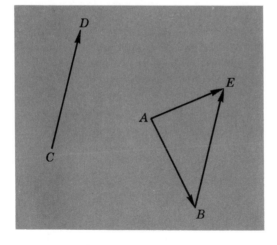

To add nonparallel vectors **AB** and **AC** with the same initial points, we can always complete the parallelogram having **AB** and **AC** as adjacent sides (see Fig. 1-1.4). Since $\mathbf{BD} = \mathbf{AC}$, we have $\mathbf{AB} + \mathbf{AC} = \mathbf{AB} + \mathbf{BD} = \mathbf{AD}$. This method of adding vectors is called the *parallelogram law*. Notice that since $\mathbf{CD} = \mathbf{AB}$, we also have $\mathbf{AC} + \mathbf{AB} = \mathbf{AC} + \mathbf{CD} = \mathbf{AD}$. Thus,

$$\mathbf{AB} + \mathbf{AC} = \mathbf{AC} + \mathbf{AB} \qquad \textit{Commutative Law}$$

3

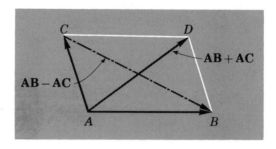

Figure 1-1.4

Vector addition has several other interesting and useful prop-
erties. If **AB**, **BC**, and **CD** are vectors in E^2, then $(\mathbf{AB} + \mathbf{BC}) +$
$\mathbf{CD} = \mathbf{AC} + \mathbf{CD} = \mathbf{AD}$ and $\mathbf{AB} + (\mathbf{BC} + \mathbf{CD}) = \mathbf{AB} + \mathbf{BD} =$
AD (see Fig. 1-1.5). Therefore,

$$(\mathbf{AB} + \mathbf{BC}) + \mathbf{CD} = \mathbf{AB} + (\mathbf{BC} + \mathbf{CD}) \qquad \textit{Associative Law}$$

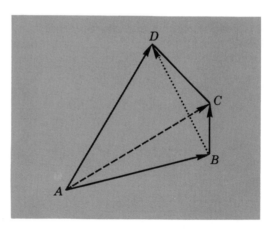

Figure 1-1.5

If $\mathbf{AB} \in E^2$ (**AB** is an element of, or a member of, E^2, see Appendix A), vector addition gives

$$\mathbf{AB} + \mathbf{0} = \mathbf{0} + \mathbf{AB} = \mathbf{AB} \qquad \textit{Additive Identity}$$

Next, if $\mathbf{AB} \in E^2$, then $\mathbf{BA} \in E^2$. Notice that $|\mathbf{BA}| = |\mathbf{AB}|$ and
if $\mathbf{AB} \neq \mathbf{0}$, the direction of **BA** is opposite that of **AB**, that is, **AB**
is directed from A to B while **BA** is directed from B to A. Thus,

$$\mathbf{AB} + \mathbf{BA} = \mathbf{BA} + \mathbf{AB} = \mathbf{0} \qquad \textit{Additive Inverse}$$

The vector **BA** is called an *additive inverse* of **AB**, and is sometimes
expressed as $-\mathbf{AB}$. The computation $\mathbf{CB} = \mathbf{CA} + \mathbf{AB} = -\mathbf{AC} +$
$\mathbf{AB} = \mathbf{AB} + (-\mathbf{AC})$ leads to the vector subtraction

$$\mathbf{AB} - \mathbf{AC} = \mathbf{AB} + (-\mathbf{AC}) \qquad \textit{Definition of Subtraction}$$

This result can be obtained geometrically from the parallelogram $ABDC$ (see Fig. 1-1.4) as the alternate diagonal directed from C to B. Furthermore, notice that $\mathbf{AC} - \mathbf{AB} = \mathbf{BC}$.

The addition of vectors leads to *scalar multiplication*, that is, multiplication of a vector by a real number. A scalar is simply a real number. If $\mathbf{AB} \neq \mathbf{0}$, $\mathbf{AB} + \mathbf{AB}$ is a vector having the direction of $\mathbf{AB}$ but having twice the length of $\mathbf{AB}$. Thus, we naturally write $\mathbf{AB} + \mathbf{AB} = 2\mathbf{AB}$. With this notation, $\mathbf{BA} + \mathbf{BA} = 2\mathbf{BA} = 2(-\mathbf{AB})$, which may be expressed as $-2\mathbf{AB}$. Thus, $-2\mathbf{AB}$ is a vector with the opposite direction of $\mathbf{AB}$ and has twice the length of $\mathbf{AB}$. With these interpretations, we may state the following:

1. if $\mathbf{AB} \neq \mathbf{0}$ and $c > 0$, then $c\mathbf{AB}$ is a vector with direction that of $\mathbf{AB}$ and $|c\mathbf{AB}| = |c| |\mathbf{AB}|$,
2. if $\mathbf{AB} \neq \mathbf{0}$ and $c < 0$, then $c\mathbf{AB}$ is a vector with direction opposite that of $\mathbf{AB}$ and $|c\mathbf{AB}| = |c| |\mathbf{AB}|$,
3. if $\mathbf{AB} \in E^2$ and $c = 0$, then $c\mathbf{AB} = \mathbf{0}$, and
4. if $\mathbf{AB} = \mathbf{0}$ and $c \in R$, then $c\mathbf{AB} = \mathbf{0}$.

Notice that $|\mathbf{AB}|$ denotes the length of $\mathbf{AB}$ while $|c|$, a scalar, denotes the absolute value of the real number c. For $\mathbf{AB} \neq \mathbf{0}$, the preceding definition is illustrated in Fig. 1-1.6. The symbol R in the above definition denotes the set of all real numbers.

Figure 1-1.6

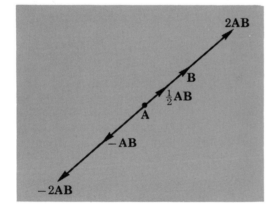

From the definition of scalar multiplication, clearly $1\mathbf{AB} = \mathbf{AB}$ for every $\mathbf{AB} \in E^2$. Some other important results that hold for c, $d \in R$ and $\mathbf{AB}$, $\mathbf{CD} \in E^2$ are:

i. $(cd)\mathbf{AB} = c(d\mathbf{AB})$,
ii. $(c + d)\mathbf{AB} = c\mathbf{AB} + d\mathbf{AB}$, and
iii. $c(\mathbf{AB} + \mathbf{CD}) = c\mathbf{AB} + c\mathbf{CD}$.

Properties i and ii are easily proved for $c > 0$ and $d > 0$, and the properties hold for all c, $d \in R$. In the following illustration assume that *properties i* and *ii* hold.

5

Illustration 1

If $c > 0$, prove that $c(\mathbf{AB} + \mathbf{CD}) = c\mathbf{AB} + c\mathbf{CD}$. If $\mathbf{AB} = \mathbf{0}$ or $\mathbf{CD} = \mathbf{0}$, the proof is immediate. If $\mathbf{AB}$ and $\mathbf{CD}$ are parallel and neither is $\mathbf{0}$, then $\mathbf{CD} = r\mathbf{AB}$ for some $r \in R$. Then,

$$
\begin{aligned}
c(\mathbf{AB} + \mathbf{CD}) &= c(\mathbf{AB} + r\mathbf{AB}) \\
&= c\,[(1 + r)\,\mathbf{AB}\,] \\
&= [\,c(1 + r)\,]\,\mathbf{AB} \\
&= (c + cr)\,\mathbf{AB} \qquad \text{\textit{Provide all reasons.}}\\
&= c\mathbf{AB} + (cr)\,\mathbf{AB} \\
&= c\mathbf{AB} + c(r\mathbf{AB}) \\
&= c\mathbf{AB} + c\mathbf{CD}
\end{aligned}
$$

Consequently, the result holds in this case. If $\mathbf{AB}$ and $\mathbf{CD}$ are not parallel, let $\mathbf{CD} = \mathbf{BE}$. Then, there exist points B' and E' such that $\mathbf{AB'} = c\mathbf{AB}$ and $\mathbf{AE'} = c\mathbf{AE}$ (see Fig. 1–1.7). Since the triangles ABE and $AB'E'$ are similar triangles, segment $B'E'$ is parallel to segment BE and has

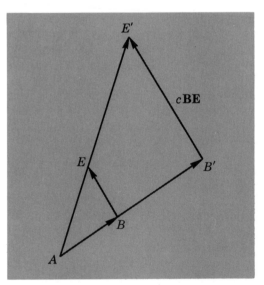

Figure 1–1.7

length $|c|$ times the length of BE. In terms of vectors, $\mathbf{B'E'} = c\mathbf{BE}$. Now, the computation

$$
\begin{aligned}
c(\mathbf{AB} + \mathbf{CD}) &= c(\mathbf{AB} + \mathbf{BE}) \\
&= c\mathbf{AE} \\
&= \mathbf{AE'} \\
&= \mathbf{AB'} + \mathbf{B'E'} \qquad \text{\textit{Provide all reasons.}}\\
&= c\mathbf{AB} + c\mathbf{BE} \\
&= c\mathbf{AB} + c\mathbf{CD}
\end{aligned}
$$

provides the required result.

Among the properties mentioned for geometric vectors are all the properties of a *vector space over R.*

DEFINITION 1–1.1.   *A set V, along with equality, addition, and multiplication of elements of V by real numbers, and satisfying for all c, d $\in$ R and all* **u, v, w** $\in$ *V,*

a. **u + v** *is a unique element of* V

b. **u + v = v + u**   *Commutative Law*

c. **(u + v) + w = u + (v + w)**   *Associative Law*

d. *there exists an element* **0** $\in$ V *such that* **v + 0 = v**   *Additive Identity*

e. *for each* **v** $\in$ V *there exists an element* **−v** $\in$ V *such that* **v + (−v) = 0**   *Additive Inverse*

f. *c***v** *is a unique element of* V

g. $(cd)\mathbf{v} = c(d\mathbf{v})$

h. $(c + d)\mathbf{v} = c\mathbf{v} + d\mathbf{v}$

i. $c(\mathbf{u} + \mathbf{v}) = c\mathbf{u} + c\mathbf{v}$, *and*

j. $1\mathbf{v} = \mathbf{v}$

is a vector space over R.

With this definition we can state the following result.

THEOREM 1–1.1. E^2 *is a vector space over R.*

In leading to the definition of a vector space over R we stressed the algebraic properties of geometric vectors. The following illustrations show how geometric vectors can be applied to two familiar geometric problems.

Illustration 2

Show that the line segment with endpoints at the midpoints of two sides of a triangle is parallel to the third side and is half the length of the third side. Let the triangle have vertices A, B, and C and let D and E be the midpoints of the segments AB and AC, respectively (see Fig. 1–1.8). Notice that the problem will be solved if we show that **DE** = $\frac{1}{2}$**BC**. Now,

$$\begin{aligned} \mathbf{DE} &= \mathbf{AE} - \mathbf{AD} \\ &= \tfrac{1}{2}\mathbf{AC} - \tfrac{1}{2}\mathbf{AB} \\ &= \tfrac{1}{2}(\mathbf{AC} - \mathbf{AB}) \\ &= \tfrac{1}{2}\mathbf{BC} \end{aligned}$$

Provide all reasons.

7

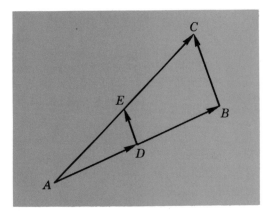

Figure 1-1.8

Illustration 3

Argue that the diagonals of a parallelogram bisect each other. Let $ABCD$ be a parallelogram and let E be the midpoint of the diagonal AC (see Fig. 1-1.9). We will show that E is the midpoint of the diagonal BD. First, $\mathbf{AE} = \mathbf{EC}$. Since opposite sides of a parallelogram are parallel and equal in length, we have $\mathbf{AB} = \mathbf{DC}$. Then,

$$\begin{aligned} \mathbf{BE} &= \mathbf{AE} - \mathbf{AB} \\ &= \mathbf{EC} - \mathbf{DC} \\ &= \mathbf{EC} + \mathbf{CD} \\ &= \mathbf{ED} \end{aligned}$$

Provide all reasons.

Thus, B, D, and E are collinear (why?) and E is the midpoint of $\mathbf{BD}$. Therefore, the diagonals bisect each other.

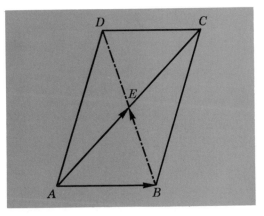

Figure 1-1.9

8

Problem Set 1-1

1. If $c > 0$ and $d > 0$, argue that $(c + d)\mathbf{AB} = c\mathbf{AB} + d\mathbf{AB}$.
2. If $c > 0$ and $d > 0$, show that $(cd)\mathbf{AB} = c(d\mathbf{AB})$.
3. Prove that $c(\mathbf{AB} - \mathbf{CD}) = c\mathbf{AB} - c\mathbf{CD}$.
4. If the diagonals of a quadrilateral bisect each other, argue that the quadrilateral is a parallelogram.
5. Prove that the figure formed by connecting the midpoints of the adjacent sides of a quadrilateral with straight line segments is a parallelogram.
6. Show that the line segments that join the midpoints of opposite sides of a quadrilateral bisect each other.
7. If ABC is a triangle and D is the midpoint of side BC, prove that $\mathbf{AD} = \frac{1}{2}(\mathbf{AB} + \mathbf{AC})$.
8. Devise a method to divide a vector $\mathbf{AB}$ internally such that $|\mathbf{AP}|/|\mathbf{AB}| = r$. Will the result also hold for any external division?

1-2. OTHER INTERPRETATIONS OF VECTORS

Suppose a rectangular coordinate system is imposed on a Euclidean plane K. Recall that E^2 is the set of all vectors in K. We know that a vector $\mathbf{AB}$ in E^2 is equal to some vector $\mathbf{OC}$, a vector in *standard position*, that is, a vector with initial point at the origin (see Fig. 1-2.1). Furthermore, if the coordinates of A are (x_1, y_1) and those of B are (x_2, y_2), then the coordinates of C are $(x_2 - x_1, y_2 - y_1)$. This clearly holds if O, A, and B are collinear. If the points are not collinear consider the parallelogram $OABC$ and make use of congruent triangles. You are asked to supply the de-

Figure 1-2.1

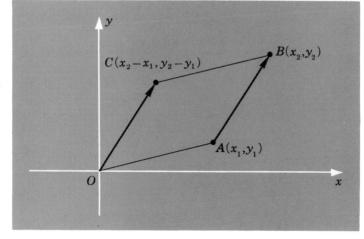
$C(x_2 - x_1, y_2 - y_1)$
$B(x_2, y_2)$
$A(x_1, y_1)$
O

tails in Problem 12. Thus, we can specify a nonzero vector in standard position by its terminal point. Also, a point P, not the origin, determines exactly one vector **OP** in standard position. We have shown that there is a natural pairing between the set of all nonzero vectors in standard position and the set of all points not the origin. If we denote the origin by **0**, we can interpret *any* vector as a *point* or as the *coordinates of the point*.

DEFINITION 1-2.1. *If* x, $y \in R$, *then* $\mathbf{v} = (x, y)$ *is a vector.*

If $\mathbf{v} = (x, y)$, the magnitude of **v** is $|\mathbf{v}| = \sqrt{x^2 + y^2}$. If $x = 0$ and $y \neq 0$, the orientation of **v** with respect to the x-axis (the angle as measured from the positive x-axis) is $\pi/2$ or $3\pi/2$, depending upon whether $y > 0$ or $y < 0$. If $x \neq 0$ and $y = 0$, then **v** is on the x-axis and the orientation of **v** is either 0 (for $x > 0$) or π (for $x < 0$). If $xy \neq 0$, the orientation of **v** is uniquely determined from $\tan \theta = y/x$ and the quadrant that contains the point (x, y). The quadrant is needed here because $-y/(-x) = y/x$ $(-y/x = y/(-x))$, although the corresponding vectors $(-x, -y)$ and (x, y) $((x, -y)$ and $(-x, y))$ are in quadrants III and I (IV and II), respectively. Notice that $\mathbf{v} = (x, y)$ is directed from the origin to the point (x, y) while the orientation of **v** with respect to the x-axis is an angle as described above. When we speak of the direction of **v**, we will mean the orientation of **v**. However, we say that two vectors have opposite directions provided the vectors as arrows point in opposite directions along parallel lines.

The next three definitions are made to agree with the corresponding definitions concerning vectors as directed line segments.

DEFINITION 1-2.2. *If* $\mathbf{u} = (a, b)$ *and* $\mathbf{v} = (x, y)$, *then* $\mathbf{u} = \mathbf{v}$ *if and only if* $a = x$ *and* $b = y$.

DEFINITION 1-2.3. *If* $\mathbf{u} = (a, b)$ *and* $\mathbf{v} = (x, y)$, *then the sum* $\mathbf{u} + \mathbf{v} = (a + x, b + y)$.

These two definitions certainly agree with the directed line segment interpretation of vectors. Two vectors in standard position are equal if and only if their terminal points coincide. The sum of two vectors clearly agrees with the parallelogram law. You will be asked to verify that the next definition agrees with the directed line segment interpretation of vectors.

DEFINITION 1-2.4. *If* $\mathbf{v} = (x, y)$ *and* $c \in R$, *then* $c\mathbf{v} = (cx, cy)$.

If $c = -1$, then $-1\mathbf{v} = (-x, -y)$, which is denoted by $-\mathbf{v}$. Also, subtraction is defined in the usual way as $\mathbf{u} - \mathbf{v} = \mathbf{u} + (-\mathbf{v})$.

Illustration 1

If $\mathbf{u} = (3, 4)$ and $\mathbf{v} = (3, -6)$, then $\mathbf{u} \neq \mathbf{v}$ since $4 \neq -6$

$$\mathbf{u} + \mathbf{v} = (3 + 3, 4 - 6) = (6, -2)$$
$$4\mathbf{u} = 4(3, 4) = (4 \cdot 3, 4 \cdot 4) = (12, 16)$$
$$-\mathbf{u} = (-3, -4)$$

and

$$\begin{aligned}
2\mathbf{u} - 3\mathbf{v} = 2(3, 4) - 3(3, -6) &= (6, 8) - (9, -18) \\
&= (6 - 9, 8 + 18) \\
&= (-3, 26)
\end{aligned}$$

With the definitions concerning points as vectors, the set of all points in a plane (or all ordered pairs of real numbers) is a vector space over R. This vector space is denoted by R^2.

Sometimes a proof is simplified by using vectors as points. For example, compare Illustration 1 of Section 1-1 with the following illustration.

Illustration 2

If $\mathbf{u} = (a, b)$, $\mathbf{v} = (x, y)$, and $c \in R$, prove that $c(\mathbf{u} + \mathbf{v}) = c\mathbf{u} + c\mathbf{v}$.
Now

$$\begin{aligned}
c(\mathbf{u} + \mathbf{v}) &= c[\,(a, b) + (x, y)\,] \\
&= c(a + x,\ b + y) \\
&= (c[a + x],\ c[b + y]) \\
&= (ca + cx,\ cb + cy) \qquad \textit{Provide all reasons.} \\
&= (ca, cb) + (cx, cy) \\
&= c(a, b) + c(x, y) \\
&= c\mathbf{u} + c\mathbf{v}
\end{aligned}$$

The vectors $\mathbf{i} = (1, 0)$ and $\mathbf{j} = (0, 1)$ are of particular importance. Since $|\mathbf{i}| = |\mathbf{j}| = 1$, $\mathbf{i}$ and $\mathbf{j}$ are *unit* vectors. The directions of $\mathbf{i}$ and $\mathbf{j}$ are those of the positive x and y-axes, respectively. Let $\mathbf{v} = (x, y)$ be a vector and project $\mathbf{v}$ onto the x and y-axes to obtain $\mathbf{u}$ and $\mathbf{w}$ (see Fig. 1-2.2). Now, $\mathbf{u} + \mathbf{w} = \mathbf{v}$. Also, $|\mathbf{u}| = |x|$ and

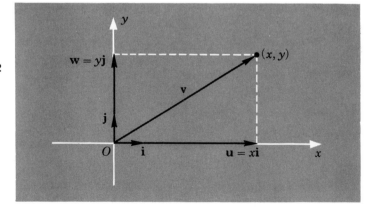

Figure 1-2.2

11

$|\mathbf{w}| = |y|$. Since $\mathbf{u}$ is a scalar multiple of $\mathbf{i}$ and $\mathbf{w}$ is a scalar multiple of $\mathbf{j}$, $\mathbf{u} = x\mathbf{i}$ and $\mathbf{w} = y\mathbf{j}$. Therefore, $\mathbf{v} = x\mathbf{i} + y\mathbf{j}$. Next, suppose $\mathbf{v} = x\mathbf{i} + y\mathbf{j}$. Since $x\mathbf{i}$ lies along the x-axis and $y\mathbf{j}$ lies along the y-axis, $\mathbf{v}$ is the diagonal of a rectangle. Consequently, the terminal point of $\mathbf{v}$ is (x, y). The cases where either $x = 0$ or $y = 0$ are easily proved. Thus, we have the following theorem.

THEOREM 1-2.1. *The vector $\mathbf{v}$ in standard position with terminal point (x, y) is $\mathbf{v} = x\mathbf{i} + y\mathbf{j}$, and the terminal point of $\mathbf{v} = x\mathbf{i} + y\mathbf{j}$ is the point (x, y).*

If $\mathbf{v} = x\mathbf{i} + y\mathbf{j}$, $\mathbf{v}$ is said to be a *linear combination* of $\mathbf{i}$ and $\mathbf{j}$. Since all vectors in R^2 are linear combinations of $\mathbf{i}$ and $\mathbf{j}$, then $\mathbf{i}$ and $\mathbf{j}$ are said to *span* R^2. The next illustration indicates that vectors expressed as linear combinations of $\mathbf{i}$ and $\mathbf{j}$ can be added by treating them as polynomials in $\mathbf{i}$ and $\mathbf{j}$.

Illustration 3

If $\mathbf{u} = a\mathbf{i} + b\mathbf{j}$ and $\mathbf{v} = x\mathbf{i} + y\mathbf{j}$, argue that $\mathbf{u} + \mathbf{v} = (a + x)\mathbf{i} + (b + y)\mathbf{j}$. Now,

$$\begin{aligned} \mathbf{u} + \mathbf{v} &= (a\mathbf{i} + b\mathbf{j}) + (x\mathbf{i} + y\mathbf{j}) \\ &= (a, b) + (x, y) \\ &= (a + x, b + y) \\ &= (a + x)\mathbf{i} + (b + y)\mathbf{j} \end{aligned}$$

Provide all reasons.

The obvious extensions hold. For example, $2(x\mathbf{i} + y\mathbf{j}) = 2x\mathbf{i} + 2y\mathbf{j}$, $|3\mathbf{i} - 4\mathbf{j}| = \sqrt{3^2 + (-4)^2} = \sqrt{25} = 5$, and $x\mathbf{i} - y\mathbf{j} = x\mathbf{i} + (-y)\mathbf{j}$. Also, since $0\mathbf{j} = \mathbf{0}$, we sometimes write $x\mathbf{i} + 0\mathbf{j}$ as $x\mathbf{i}$.

Problem Set 1-2

Problems 5, 9, and 10 involve new concepts and should be solved by everyone.

1. Determine the vector in standard position that is equal to the given vector.

	Initial point	Terminal point
(a)	(4, 3)	(7, −2)
(b)	(7, −2)	(4, 3)
(c)	(0, 0)	(0, 0)
(d)	(0, 0)	(−3, 5)
(e)	(−3, 5)	(0, 0)
(f)	(3, 0)	(4, 0)

2. Obtain the magnitude and direction of each given vector.
    (a) $(1, -\sqrt{3})$ (b) $(-1, \sqrt{3})$ (c) $(-\sqrt{3}, -1)$
    (d) $(4, 4)$ (e) $(-4, 4)$ (f) $(-4, -4)$

3. For each vector in Problem 2 obtain the terminal point of an equivalent vector with initial point $(5, 2)$.

4. For each vector in Problem 2 determine the initial point of an equivalent vector with terminal point $(4, -3)$.

5. If $\mathbf{u} \neq \mathbf{0}$, show that $\mathbf{u}/|\mathbf{u}|$ is a unit vector in the direction of $\mathbf{u}$.

6. For each vector in Problem 2 obtain a unit vector with direction that of the given vector. (See Problem 5.)

7. If $\mathbf{u} = (3, -5)$, $\mathbf{v} = (2, 0)$, $\mathbf{w} = (-4, 3)$, and $\mathbf{0} = (0, 0)$, evaluate:
   (a) $\mathbf{u} + \mathbf{v}$
   (b) $\mathbf{0} + \mathbf{w}$
   (c) $\mathbf{u} - \mathbf{v}$
   (d) $\mathbf{0} + \mathbf{0}$
   (e) $2\mathbf{u} + \mathbf{v}$
   (f) $5\mathbf{w}$
   (g) $-4\mathbf{u}$
   (h) $(\mathbf{u} + \mathbf{v}) + \mathbf{w}$
   (i) $\mathbf{u} + (\mathbf{v} + \mathbf{w})$
   (j) $3\mathbf{u} - 2\mathbf{v} + 4\mathbf{w}$
   (k) $-\mathbf{u} + 3\mathbf{v} - 5\mathbf{w}$
   (l) $3\mathbf{u} - \frac{1}{2}\mathbf{v} + \mathbf{w}$

8. Repeat Problem 7 for $\mathbf{u} = -2\mathbf{i} + \mathbf{j}$, $\mathbf{v} = 5\mathbf{i} - 3\mathbf{j}$, $\mathbf{w} = \mathbf{i} + 2\mathbf{j}$, and $\mathbf{0} = 0\mathbf{i} + 0\mathbf{j}$.

9. If $\mathbf{u} = 3\mathbf{i}$ and $\mathbf{v} = 2\mathbf{j}$, prove that $a\mathbf{u} + b\mathbf{v} = \mathbf{0}$ if and only if $a = 0$ and $b = 0$. Such vectors are said to be *linearly independent*. More generally, if $\mathbf{u}$ and $\mathbf{v}$ are any vectors, then $\mathbf{u}$ and $\mathbf{v}$ are linearly independent means that $a\mathbf{u} + b\mathbf{v} = \mathbf{0}$ if and only if $a = 0$ and $b = 0$. If $\mathbf{u}$ and $\mathbf{v}$ are not linearly independent, they are called *linearly dependent* vectors.

10. Prove that $\mathbf{i}$ and $\mathbf{j}$ are linearly independent. (See Problem 9.) Since $\mathbf{i}$ and $\mathbf{j}$ are linearly independent vectors that span R^2, $\mathbf{i}$ and $\mathbf{j}$ form a *basis* for R^2.

11. Argue that R^2 is a vector space over R.

12. If A has coordinates (x_1, y_1), B has coordinates (x_2, y_2), and $\mathbf{OC} = \mathbf{AB}$, argue that the coordinates of C are $(x_2 - x_1, y_2 - y_1)$.

13. Argue that Definition 1-2.4 agrees with the directed line segment interpretation of vectors.

1-3. PROJECTIONS

Before discussing projections and some of their applications, we need to define a certain product of vectors. Also, the concept of the angle between two vectors is needed.

DEFINITION 1-3.1. *If $\mathbf{u} = a\mathbf{i} + b\mathbf{j}$ and $\mathbf{v} = x\mathbf{i} + y\mathbf{j}$, the dot product $\mathbf{u} \cdot \mathbf{v} = ax + by$.*

Notice that $\mathbf{u} \cdot \mathbf{v}$ is a real number. Also, $\mathbf{u} \cdot \mathbf{u} = a^2 + b^2 = |\mathbf{u}|^2$, a nonnegative number. Later, a certain product of vectors that yields a vector will be discussed.

Illustration 1

If $\mathbf{u} = \sqrt{3}\mathbf{i} + \mathbf{j}$ and $\mathbf{v} = -\mathbf{i} - \sqrt{3}\mathbf{j}$, obtain $\mathbf{u} \cdot \mathbf{v}$. From the preceding definition we have immediately

$$\mathbf{u} \cdot \mathbf{v} = \sqrt{3}(-1) + 1(-\sqrt{3}) = -2\sqrt{3}$$

13

Next, let $\mathbf{u} = a\mathbf{i} + b\mathbf{j}$ and $\mathbf{v} = x\mathbf{i} + y\mathbf{j}$. If $\mathbf{u}$ and $\mathbf{v}$ are not collinear, let θ with $0 < \theta < \pi$ denote the smallest positive angle between $\mathbf{u}$ and $\mathbf{v}$ (see Fig. 1–3.1). Let $\mathbf{w}$ be the vector from the

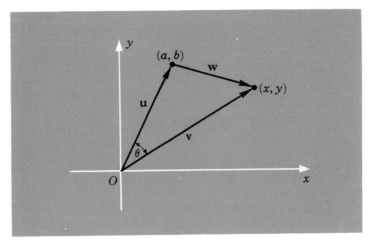

Figure 1–3.1

terminal point of $\mathbf{u}$ to the terminal point of $\mathbf{v}$. We know that $\mathbf{w} = \mathbf{v} - \mathbf{u} = (x - a, y - b)$. By the law of cosines, $|\mathbf{w}|^2 = |\mathbf{u}|^2 + |\mathbf{v}|^2 - 2|\mathbf{u}||\mathbf{v}| \cos \theta$. Then,

$$\cos \theta = \frac{|\mathbf{u}|^2 + |\mathbf{v}|^2 - |\mathbf{w}|^2}{2|\mathbf{u}||\mathbf{v}|}$$

Since

$$\begin{aligned}
|\mathbf{u}|^2 + |\mathbf{v}|^2 - |\mathbf{w}|^2 &= (a^2 + b^2) + (x^2 + y^2) \\
&\quad - [(x - a)^2 + (y - b)^2] \\
&= a^2 + b^2 + x^2 + y^2 - x^2 - y^2 \\
&\quad - a^2 - b^2 + 2ax + 2by \\
&= 2ax + 2by \\
&= 2(ax + by)
\end{aligned}$$

we have

$$\cos \theta = \frac{2(ax + by)}{2|\mathbf{u}||\mathbf{v}|} = \frac{ax + by}{|\mathbf{u}||\mathbf{v}|}$$

or

(1–3.1)
$$\cos \theta = \frac{\mathbf{u} \cdot \mathbf{v}}{|\mathbf{u}||\mathbf{v}|}$$

If $\theta = \pi/2$, then $\mathbf{u} \cdot \mathbf{v} = 0$. If $\mathbf{u} = \mathbf{0}$ or $\mathbf{v} = \mathbf{0}$, θ is not determined from Eq. (1–3.1). However, since $\mathbf{u} \cdot \mathbf{v} = 0$, if either $\mathbf{u} = \mathbf{0}$ or $\mathbf{v} = \mathbf{0}$ we agree that the angle between $\mathbf{0}$ and any vector is $\pi/2$. With this agreement, the two vectors $\mathbf{u}$ and $\mathbf{v}$ are perpendicular (*orthogonal*) if and only if $\mathbf{u} \cdot \mathbf{v} = 0$. Notice that $\mathbf{0}$ is considered both orthogonal to and parallel to any vector. If **u** and **v** have the same direction, then $\theta = 0$. However, if they have opposite directions, $\theta = \pi$.

Illustration 2

Determine the angle θ between $\mathbf{u} = \sqrt{3}\,\mathbf{i} + \mathbf{j}$ and $\mathbf{v} = -\mathbf{i} - \sqrt{3}\,\mathbf{j}$. First, $|\mathbf{u}| = 2 = |\mathbf{v}|$. From Illustration 1, $\mathbf{u} \cdot \mathbf{v} = -2\sqrt{3}$. Then, $\cos \theta = -2\sqrt{3}/(2)(2)$ and $\theta = 5\pi/6$.

Suppose $\mathbf{u} = a\mathbf{i} + b\mathbf{j}$ is projected onto $\mathbf{v} = x\mathbf{i} + y\mathbf{j} \neq \mathbf{0}$ (see Fig. 1-3.2). The *vector projection* of **u** on **v** is **OC** where **AC** is perpendicular to **v**. Now, $\mathbf{OC} = t\mathbf{v} = tx\mathbf{i} + ty\mathbf{j}$ for some $t \in R$. Thus, $\mathbf{AC} = \mathbf{OC} - \mathbf{u} = (tx - a)\mathbf{i} + (ty - b)\mathbf{j}$. Since $\mathbf{OC} \cdot \mathbf{AC} = 0$, we have

$$\begin{aligned} 0 &= tx(tx - a) + ty(ty - b) \\ &= t[\,t(x^2 + y^2) - (ax + by)\,] \qquad \textit{Provide all reasons.} \\ &= t(t\,|\mathbf{v}|^2 - \mathbf{u} \cdot \mathbf{v}) \end{aligned}$$

Now, $t = 0$ if and only if $\mathbf{u} \cdot \mathbf{v} = 0$. If $t \neq 0$, then $t = \dfrac{\mathbf{u} \cdot \mathbf{v}}{|\mathbf{v}|^2}$. This is also true in case $t = 0$. Therefore, the vector projection of **u** on **v** is

(1-3.2) $$\mathbf{OC} = \left[\frac{\mathbf{u} \cdot \mathbf{v}}{|\mathbf{v}|^2}\right]\mathbf{v}$$

and the *scalar projection* (the magnitude of the vector projection) is

(1-3.3) $$|\mathbf{OC}| = \frac{|\mathbf{u} \cdot \mathbf{v}|}{|\mathbf{v}|}$$

Figure 1-3.2

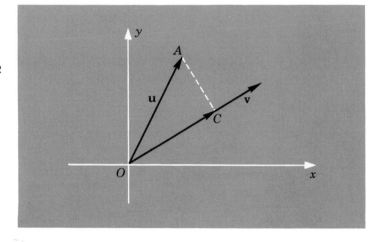

Illustration 3

Obtain the projections of (a) $\mathbf{u}_1 = 5\mathbf{i} + 7\mathbf{j}$, (b) $\mathbf{u}_2 = \mathbf{i} + 3\mathbf{j}$, (c) $\mathbf{u}_3 = -\mathbf{i} + 3\mathbf{j}$, and (d) $\mathbf{u}_4 = -4\mathbf{i} + 5\mathbf{j}$ onto $\mathbf{v} = 3\mathbf{i} + \mathbf{j}$. Since $\mathbf{u}_1 \cdot \mathbf{v} = 5(3) + 7(1) = 22$, $\mathbf{u}_2 \cdot \mathbf{v} = 1(3) + 3(1) = 6$, $\mathbf{u}_3 \cdot \mathbf{v} = -1(3) + 3(1) = 0$, $\mathbf{u}_4 \cdot \mathbf{v} = -4(3) + 5(1) = -7$, and $|\mathbf{v}| = \sqrt{3^2 + 1^2} = \sqrt{10}$, we have

(a) $\mathbf{OC}_1 = \frac{22}{10}(3\mathbf{i} + \mathbf{j}) = (\frac{33}{5})\mathbf{i} + (\frac{11}{5})\mathbf{j}$ and $|\mathbf{OC}_1| = 11\sqrt{10}/5$,

(b) $\mathbf{OC}_2 = \frac{6}{10}(3\mathbf{i} + \mathbf{j}) = (\frac{9}{5})\mathbf{i} + (\frac{3}{5})\mathbf{j}$ and $|\mathbf{OC}_2| = 3\sqrt{10}/5$,

(c) $\mathbf{OC}_3 = \frac{0}{10}(3\mathbf{i} + \mathbf{j}) = \mathbf{0}$ and $|\mathbf{OC}_3| = 0$, and

(d) $\mathbf{OC}_4 = \frac{-7}{10}(3\mathbf{i} + \mathbf{j}) = (\frac{-21}{10})\mathbf{i} - (\frac{7}{10})\mathbf{j}$ and $|\mathbf{OC}_4| = 7\sqrt{10}/10$.

Notice that $\mathbf{OC}_1$ and $\mathbf{OC}_2$ have the same direction as $\mathbf{v}$ while $\mathbf{OC}_4$ has direction opposite that of $\mathbf{v}$.

Next, consider the triangle ABC, as shown in Fig. 1–3.3. Let $\mathbf{AD}$ be the vector projection of $\mathbf{AB}$ onto $\mathbf{AC}$. Then, $|\mathbf{BD}| = |\mathbf{AB}| \sin \theta$ where θ is the angle between $\mathbf{AB}$ and $\mathbf{AC}$. The area of the triangle is $\frac{1}{2}|\mathbf{AC}||\mathbf{AB}| \sin \theta$. Furthermore, $|\mathbf{BD}|$ is the distance between the point B and the line that contains the points A and C.

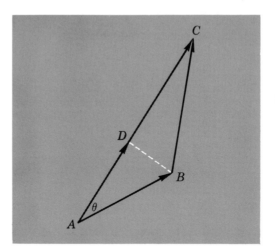

Figure 1–3.3

Illustration 4

Obtain the area of the triangle with vertices $A(2, 3)$, $B(1, 6)$, and $C(-3, -2)$. Now, $\mathbf{AC} = (-3 - 2)\mathbf{i} + (-2 - 3)\mathbf{j} = -5\mathbf{i} - 5\mathbf{j}$ and $\mathbf{AB} = (1 - 2)\mathbf{i} + (6 - 3)\mathbf{j} = -\mathbf{i} + 3\mathbf{j}$. To evaluate $\sin \theta$, we will first determine $\cos \theta = [(-1)(-5) + 3(-5)] / [\sqrt{10}(5\sqrt{2})] = -10/(5\sqrt{2} \times \sqrt{10}) = -\sqrt{5}/5$. Since $0 < \theta < \pi$, $\sin \theta = 2\sqrt{5}/5$. The required area is $\frac{1}{2}|\mathbf{AC}||\mathbf{AB}| \sin \theta = \frac{1}{2}\sqrt{50}\sqrt{10}(2\sqrt{5}/5) = 10$ square units.

Illustration 5

Determine the distance between the point $B(1, 6)$ and the line defined by $y = x + 1$. The idea is to obtain any two points A and C on the line. If **AB** is projected onto **AC** to yield the vector projection **AD**, we know that $|\mathbf{BD}| = |\mathbf{AB}| \sin \theta$ where θ is the angle between **AB** and **AC**. Since the points A and C of Illustration 4 are on the line, the desired distance is $|\mathbf{BD}| = \sqrt{10}(2\sqrt{5}/5) = 2\sqrt{2}$.

Problem Set 1-3

In Problems 1 through 6 let $\mathbf{u} = 3\mathbf{i} - 2\mathbf{j}$, $\mathbf{v} = \mathbf{i} + 4\mathbf{j}$, and $\mathbf{w} = -5\mathbf{i} + \mathbf{j}$. Perform the indicated operations.

1. (a) $\mathbf{u} \cdot \mathbf{v}$ (b) $\mathbf{u} \cdot \mathbf{w}$
2. (a) $\mathbf{w} \cdot \mathbf{u}$ (b) $(3\mathbf{u}) \cdot \mathbf{v}$
3. (a) $\mathbf{u} \cdot (\mathbf{v} + \mathbf{w})$ (b) $\mathbf{u} \cdot \mathbf{v} + \mathbf{u} \cdot \mathbf{w}$
4. (a) $(-3\mathbf{v}) \cdot \mathbf{w}$ (b) $\mathbf{w} \cdot (-3\mathbf{v})$
5. (a) $\mathbf{0} \cdot \mathbf{0}$ (b) $\mathbf{u} \cdot \mathbf{0}$
6. (a) $\mathbf{u} \cdot (\mathbf{v} - \mathbf{w})$ (b) $\mathbf{u} \cdot \mathbf{v} - \mathbf{u} \cdot \mathbf{w}$

In Problems 7 through 12 obtain the angle between the given vectors. Sketch each vector.

7. $\mathbf{u} = 5\mathbf{j}$, $\mathbf{v} = 2\mathbf{i} - 2\mathbf{j}$
8. $\mathbf{u} = 4\mathbf{i} + 3\mathbf{j}$, $\mathbf{v} = 3\mathbf{i} - 4\mathbf{j}$
9. $\mathbf{u} = 4\mathbf{i} - 3\mathbf{j}$, $\mathbf{v} = -20\mathbf{i} + 15\mathbf{j}$
10. $\mathbf{u} = -5\mathbf{i}$, $\mathbf{v} = 3\mathbf{j}$
11. $\mathbf{u} = 4\mathbf{i} - 3\mathbf{j}$, $\mathbf{v} = -3\mathbf{i} + 4\mathbf{j}$
12. $\mathbf{u} = a\mathbf{i} + b\mathbf{j} \neq \mathbf{0}$, $\mathbf{v} = b\mathbf{i} - a\mathbf{j}$

In Problems 13 through 22 determine the scalar and vector projections of **u** on **v**.

13. $\mathbf{u} = 7\mathbf{j}$, $\mathbf{v} = -6\mathbf{i}$
14. $\mathbf{u} = -6\mathbf{i}$, $\mathbf{v} = 7\mathbf{j}$
15. $\mathbf{u} = 3\mathbf{i} - 4\mathbf{j}$, $\mathbf{v} = 9\mathbf{i} + 12\mathbf{j}$
16. $\mathbf{u} = -3\mathbf{i} + 4\mathbf{j}$, $\mathbf{v} = 12\mathbf{i} + 5\mathbf{j}$
17. $\mathbf{u} = 12\mathbf{i} + 5\mathbf{j}$, $\mathbf{v} = -5\mathbf{i} + 12\mathbf{j}$
18. $\mathbf{u} = 12\mathbf{i} + 5\mathbf{j}$, $\mathbf{v} = -3\mathbf{i} + 4\mathbf{j}$
19. $\mathbf{u} = 4\mathbf{i} - 3\mathbf{j}$, $\mathbf{v} = 4\mathbf{i} - 3\mathbf{j}$
20. $\mathbf{u} = 4\mathbf{i} - 3\mathbf{j}$, $\mathbf{v} = -4\mathbf{i} + 3\mathbf{j}$
21. $\mathbf{u} = 2\mathbf{i} + 10\mathbf{j}$, $\mathbf{v} = 4\mathbf{i} + 3\mathbf{j}$
22. $\mathbf{u} = -4\mathbf{i} + \mathbf{j}$, $\mathbf{v} = 4\mathbf{i} + 3\mathbf{j}$
23. Obtain five vectors $\mathbf{v} = x\mathbf{i} + y\mathbf{j}$ orthogonal to $\mathbf{u} = -5\mathbf{i} + 7\mathbf{j}$.
24. If $ax + by = c$ is an equation of a line L, then for each $k \in R$, $bx - ay = k$ is an equation of a line perpendicular to L. From the forms of these equations obtain a vector orthogonal to $\mathbf{v} = x\mathbf{i} + y\mathbf{j}$.
25. Discuss the scalar projections of $\mathbf{v} = x\mathbf{i} + y\mathbf{j}$ on **i** and **j**.

17

In Problems 26 through 29 prove the assertions.

26. $\mathbf{u} \cdot \mathbf{v} = \mathbf{v} \cdot \mathbf{u}$ 27. $\mathbf{u} \cdot (\mathbf{v} + \mathbf{w}) = \mathbf{u} \cdot \mathbf{v} + \mathbf{u} \cdot \mathbf{w}$

28. $c(\mathbf{u} \cdot \mathbf{v}) = (c\mathbf{u}) \cdot \mathbf{v} = \mathbf{u} \cdot (c\mathbf{v})$ 29. $(c\mathbf{u}) \cdot (d\mathbf{v}) = (cd)(\mathbf{u} \cdot \mathbf{v})$

In each of Problems 30 through 35 determine the area of the triangle with the given vertices.

30. $(0, 0)$, $(5, 0)$, $(0, 8)$ 31. $(3, 2)$, $(8, 2)$, $(8, -4)$

32. $(0, 0)$, $(4, 4)$, $(5, 0)$ 33. $(0, 0)$, $(4, -4)$, $(-4, -4)$

34. $(1, 2)$, $(-3, 4)$, $(3, -5)$ 35. $(-2, 1)$, $(-1, -5)$, $(3, 2)$

36. What can be said of the areas of the parallelograms that have three vertices those of Problems 30 through 35?

In each of Problems 37 through 40 obtain the distance between the indicated line and point.

37. $x + y = 5$, $(0, 0)$ 38. $x + y = 0$, $(3, 4)$

39. $3x + 4y = 12$, $(-2, -3)$ 40. $5x - 2y = 10$, $(1, -1)$

41. Show that an angle inscribed in a semicircle is a right angle.

42. Prove that the median to the base of an isosceles triangle is perpendicular to the base.

43. Prove that $(\mathbf{u} + \mathbf{v}) \cdot (\mathbf{u} + \mathbf{v}) = (\mathbf{u} + \mathbf{v}) \cdot \mathbf{u} + (\mathbf{u} + \mathbf{v}) \cdot \mathbf{v}$.

44. Verify that $(\mathbf{u} - \mathbf{v}) \cdot (\mathbf{u} - \mathbf{v}) = \mathbf{u} \cdot \mathbf{u} - 2\mathbf{u} \cdot \mathbf{v} + \mathbf{v} \cdot \mathbf{v}$.

45. Complete the square on $\mathbf{u} \cdot \mathbf{u} + \mathbf{u} \cdot \mathbf{v}$. (See Problems 43 and 44.)

1-4. LINES IN TWO DIMENSIONS

Let A and B be distinct points neither the origin (see Fig. 1–4.1). Let $\mathbf{OA} = \mathbf{a}$, $\mathbf{OB} = \mathbf{b}$, and $\mathbf{OP} = \mathbf{v}$. Now, P is in the line L con-

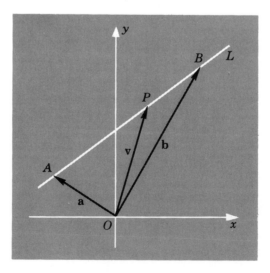

Figure 1–4.1

taining A and B if and only if the vector $\mathbf{AP}$ is a scalar multiple of $\mathbf{AB}$. Thus, $\mathbf{AP} = r\mathbf{AB}$ for some $r \in R$. Since $\mathbf{AP} = \mathbf{v} - \mathbf{a}$ and $\mathbf{AB} = \mathbf{b} - \mathbf{a}$, substitution gives $\mathbf{v} - \mathbf{a} = r(\mathbf{b} - \mathbf{a})$ from which

$$\text{(1-4.1)} \qquad \mathbf{v} = \mathbf{a} + r(\mathbf{b} - \mathbf{a})$$

This equation can be expressed as $\mathbf{v} = (1 - r)\mathbf{a} + r\mathbf{b}$. A more symmetric form for this vector equation of L is

$$\text{(1-4.2)} \qquad \mathbf{v} = q\mathbf{a} + r\mathbf{b}$$

where $q = 1 - r$. If A and B are not at the origin but A, B, and O are collinear, Eq. (1-4.2) still holds. In this case L contains the origin.

Illustration 1

Determine a vector equation and a coordinate equation of the line L that contains the points $A(-2, 3)$ and $B(5, 6)$. Since $\mathbf{a} = (-2, 3)$ and $\mathbf{b} = (5, 6)$, then

$$\mathbf{v} = q(-2, 3) + r(5, 6) = (-2q, 3q) + (5r, 6r) = (-2q + 5r, \ 3q + 6r)$$

where $q = 1 - r$. In terms of r only, $\mathbf{v} = (-2 + 7r, \ 3 + 3r)$. Notice that $r = 0$ gives $\mathbf{v} = \mathbf{a}$ and $r = 1$ gives $\mathbf{v} = \mathbf{b}$ and from these the points A and B are obtained. If we let $\mathbf{v} = (x, y)$, then $(x, y) = (-2 + 7r, \ 3 + 3r)$. Vector equality provides the system of parametric equations

$$\begin{cases} x = -2 + 7r \\ y = 3 + 3r \end{cases}$$

Elimination of r leads to $3x - 7y + 27 = 0$, a coordinate equation of L.

Equation (1-4.1), $\mathbf{v} = \mathbf{a} + r(\mathbf{b} - \mathbf{a})$, can be interpreted as a point of division formula for the line segment AB. The relative positions of the points A, B, and P are easily seen to be:

i. P is between A and B if and only if $0 < r < 1$,
ii. B is between A and P if and only if $r > 1$,
iii. A is between P and B if and only if $r < 0$,
iv. A and P coincide if and only if $r = 0$, and
v. B and P coincide if and only if $r = 1$.

If $r = \frac{1}{2}$, then $\mathbf{v} = \mathbf{a} + r(\mathbf{b} - \mathbf{a})$ reduces to

$$\text{(1-4.3)} \qquad \mathbf{v} = \tfrac{1}{2}(\mathbf{a} + \mathbf{b})$$

the *midpoint formula* for vectors. (See Problem 7, Problem Set 1-1.)

Illustration 2

Obtain the midpoint P of the segment with endpoints $A(-6, 7)$ and $B(10, -9)$. Now, $\mathbf{a} = (-6, 7)$ and $\mathbf{b} = (10, -9)$. By Eq. (1-4.3),

$$\mathbf{v} = \tfrac{1}{2}[\,(-6, 7) + (10, -9)\,] = \tfrac{1}{2}(4, -2) = (2, -1)$$

and the coordinates of P are $(2, -1)$.

19

Illustration 3

Divide the segment between $A(-6, 4)$ and $B(2, -3)$ such that the ratio $|BP|/|AP| = \frac{1}{4}$. Here, the absolute value notation denotes lengths of segments. Now, $|AP|/|BP| = \frac{4}{1}$ implies that $|AP|/|AB| = \frac{4}{3} = r$. Since $1 - r = -\frac{1}{3}$, $\mathbf{a} = (-6, 4)$, and $\mathbf{b} = (2, -3)$, Eq. (1-4.2) gives

$$
\begin{aligned}
\mathbf{v} &= -\tfrac{1}{3}(-6, 4) + \tfrac{4}{3}(2, -3) \\
&= \tfrac{1}{3}[\,(-1)(-6, 4) + 4(2, -3)\,] \\
&= \tfrac{1}{3}[\,(6, -4) + (8, -12)\,] \qquad\qquad \textit{Provide all reasons.} \\
&= \tfrac{1}{3}(14, -16) \\
&= (\tfrac{14}{3}, -\tfrac{16}{3})
\end{aligned}
$$

Thus, the coordinates of P are $(4\frac{2}{3}, -5\frac{1}{3})$.

Problem Set 1–4

In Problems 1 through 6 let $A(2, -3)$ and $B(-4, 6)$ be the given points.

1. Obtain the midpoint of the segment between A and B.
2. Determine a point one-sixth the distance from A to B.
3. Obtain a point P such that $|AP|/|PB| = \frac{1}{4}$.
4. Locate a point P between A and B such that $|BP|/|PA| = \frac{1}{3}$.
5. Obtain points P on the line containing A and B such that P is three times as far from A as from B.
6. Repeat Problem 5 if P is three times as far from B as from A.

In Problems 7 through 15 write vector equations of the lines that contain the given points. Use vector equality to obtain parametric equations of the lines. Finally, eliminate the parameter, when possible, to obtain a co-ordinate equation of each line.

7. $A(0, 0)$, $B(0, 6)$ 8. $A(3, 0)$, $B(0, 7)$
9. $A(-2, 0)$, $B(10, 0)$ 10. $A(3, 4)$, $B(4, 5)$
11. $A(-4, -6)$, $B(2, 7)$ 12. $A(3, 2)$, $B(-4, 6)$
13. $A(a, b)$, $B(c, d)$, for $a = c$ and $b \neq d$
14. $A(a, b)$, $B(c, d)$, for $b = d$ and $a \neq c$
15. $A(a, b)$, $B(c, d)$, for $a \neq c$ and $b \neq d$
16. Prove that the line joining one vertex of a parallelogram to the mid-point of an opposite side trisects the diagonal that it intersects.
17. Prove that the medians of a triangle intersect at a point two-thirds of the distance from each vertex to the opposite side.

1–5. THREE-SPACE VECTORS

Suppose A and B are distinct points in Euclidean three-space. The points A and B determine exactly one line segment with end-points A and B. If the line segment is directed from A to B, then

A is called the initial point and B is called the terminal point of the segment. We will call such a segment a *vector* in three-space and denote it as **AB**. If A and B are not distinct points we still consider **AB** to be a vector. This vector is called a *zero vector* at A (at B) and is denoted by **0**. No particular direction is assigned to a zero vector. We denote the set of all vectors in space by E^3. As with E^2, the vectors of E^3 are considered to be *free vectors*. Two nonzero vectors **AB** and **CD** are equal if and only if $|\mathbf{AB}| = |\mathbf{CD}|$ and **AB** and **CD** are parallel and have the same direction, that is, the arrows are pointed in the same way along the parallel lines that contain them. The absolute value notation denotes the *magnitude* or length of a vector. Any two zero vectors are equal. The sum $\mathbf{AB} + \mathbf{BC} = \mathbf{AC}$, since there is at least one plane that contains A, B, and C, and in this plane the parallelogram law holds. We will use the same addition and scalar multiplication as for E^2. Then, all parts of Definition 1-1.1 except *part* (c) clearly hold. However, you can convince yourself that this part also holds. In fact, *all* algebraic properties of vectors in E^2 also apply to vectors in E^3. The following theorem will hold.

THEOREM 1-5.1.　E^3 *is a vector space over* R.

In order to interpret a three-space vector as a point and as a linear combination of certain unit vectors, we need a coordinate system for three-space. Thus, let three mutually perpendicular lines, called *axes*, intersect in a point called the *origin*. The axes are usually denoted by x, y, and z (see Fig. 1-5.1). The arrowheads indicate the positive directions along the axes while the opposite directions are considered to be negative. As in two-space the same

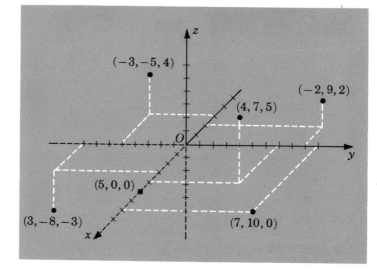

Figure 1-5.1

21

linear unit is usually chosen for measurements along the axes. Since two intersecting lines determine a plane, the three axes determine three planes, called *coordinate planes*. The *xy*, *xz*, and *yz* coordinate planes are those determined by the *x* and *y* axes, the *x* and *z* axes, and the *y* and *z* axes, respectively.

The location of a point is known when the distances between the coordinate planes and the point are known, along with the agreement concerning signed directions. This location is specified by an ordered triple, (x, y, z), of real numbers where $|x|$, $|y|$, and $|z|$ are the distances between the *yz*, *xz*, and *xy* planes, respectively, and the point. The ordered triple (x, y, z) is called the *coordinates of the point* while *x* is the *x* coordinate, *y* is the *y* coordinate, and *z* is the *z* coordinate of the point. The points whose locations are $(4, 7, 5)$, $(-2, 9, 2)$, $(-3, -5, 4)$, $(3, -8, -3)$, $(7, 10, 0)$, and $(5, 0, 0)$ are shown in Fig. 1–5.1. It should be clear that given any ordered triple of real numbers (x, y, z) the procedure described locates a unique point in three-space. If the location of a point in three-space is known and the distances between the coordinate planes and the point can be measured, we can obtain a unique set of coordinates for the point. Thus, there exists a natural pairing between the set of all points in space and the set of all ordered triples of real numbers. The three axes along with the method of locating points is called the *rectangular coordinate system of three-space*. We denote both a point and its location with the ordered triple notation. The system we have described is a *right-handed system*. The *yzx* and *zxy* systems are other right-handed systems, since they can be rotated to an *xyz* system. The *xzy*, *yxz*, and *zyx* coordinate systems are *left-handed systems* because they cannot be rotated to an *xyz* system. Another way to describe right-handed systems and left-handed systems is as follows. Suppose a right-threaded screw with tip at the origin is pointed along the positive *z*-axis. Twist the blade of the screw, through 90°, from the positive *x*-axis to the positive *y*-axis. If the screw advances, the system is a right-handed system; if the screw retreats, the system is a left-handed system.

The distance formula for two-space generalizes readily to three-space. Let d be the distance between two points $A(x_1, y_1, z_1)$ and $B(x_2, y_2, z_2)$. (See Fig. 1–5.2 for the case $z_1 \neq z_2$). Project A and B onto the *xy* plane to obtain the points $A'(x_1, y_1, 0)$ and $B'(x_2, y_2, 0)$. Now, the distance d_1 between A' and B' is $d_1 = \sqrt{(x_2 - x_1)^2 + (y_2 - y_1)^2}$. If AC is taken parallel to $A'B'$, the length of segment AC is d_1. Now, the length of CB is $|z_2 - z_1|$. Since triangle ACB is a right triangle,

$$d^2 = d_1^2 + |z_2 - z_1|^2$$

Since $|z_2 - z_1|^2 = (z_2 - z_1)^2$, the *distance formula for three-space* is

(1-5.1) $\qquad d = \sqrt{(x_2 - x_1)^2 + (y_2 - y_1)^2 + (z_2 - z_1)^2}$

You can easily show that this distance formula holds in case $z_1 = z_2$, and, more generally, for any point $A(x_1, y_1, z_1)$ and any point $B(x_2, y_2, z_2)$. The magnitude of the vector from A to B is then $|\mathbf{AB}| = d$. If A is the origin, then $|\mathbf{AB}| = \sqrt{x_2^2 + y_2^2 + z_2^2}$.

Figure 1-5.2

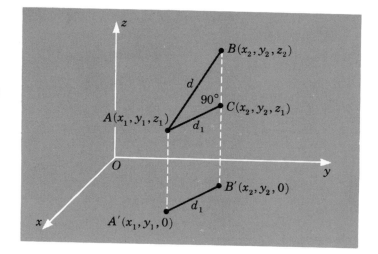

Clearly, there exists a natural pairing between the set of all non-zero vectors from the origin and the set of all points not the origin. If we denote the origin by $\mathbf{0}$, then a point can be used to describe a vector. By the parallelogram law, the vector from $A(x_1, y_1, z_1)$ to $B(x_2, y_2, z_2)$ is equal to $\mathbf{OC}$, a vector in standard position, where the coordinates of C are $(x_2 - x_1, y_2 - y_1, z_2 - z_1)$. (You should show this.) With the following definitions (compare with Definitions 1-2.1 through 1-2.4), the set of all points in three-space (or all ordered triples of real numbers) is a vector space over R. This vector space is denoted by R^3.

DEFINITION 1-5.1. *If x, y, $z \in R$, then $\mathbf{v} = (x, y, z)$ is a vector.*

DEFINITION 1-5.2. *If $\mathbf{u} = (a, b, c)$ and $\mathbf{v} = (x, y, z)$, then $\mathbf{u} = \mathbf{v}$ if and only if $a = x$, $b = y$, and $c = z$.*

DEFINITION 1-5.3. *If $\mathbf{u} = (a, b, c)$ and $\mathbf{v} = (x, y, z)$, then the sum $\mathbf{u} + \mathbf{v} = (a + x, b + y, c + z)$.*

DEFINITION 1-5.4. *If $\mathbf{v} = (x, y, z)$ and $c \in R$, then $c\mathbf{v} = (cx, cy, cz)$.*

If $c = -1$, then $-1\mathbf{v} = (-x, -y, -z)$, which is denoted by $-\mathbf{v}$. As usual, subtraction is defined by $\mathbf{u} - \mathbf{v} = \mathbf{u} + (-\mathbf{v})$.

23

Illustration 1

If $\mathbf{u} = (3, 4, -5)$ and $\mathbf{v} = (3, -6, 2)$, then $\mathbf{u} \neq \mathbf{v}$ since $-5 \neq 2$

$$\mathbf{u} + \mathbf{v} = (3 + 3,\ 4 - 6,\ -5 + 2) = (6, -2, -3)$$

$$4\mathbf{u} = 4(3, 4, -5) = (12, 16, -20)$$

and

$$2\mathbf{u} - 3\mathbf{v} = 2(3, 4, -5) - 3(3, -6, 2) = (6, 8, -10) + (-9, 18, -6)$$
$$= (-3, 26, -16)$$

THEOREM 1-5.2. R^3 *is a vector space over* R.

The vectors $\mathbf{i} = (1, 0, 0)$, $\mathbf{j} = (0, 1, 0)$, and $\mathbf{k} = (0, 0, 1)$ are of particular importance. Since $|\mathbf{i}| = |\mathbf{j}| = |\mathbf{k}| = 1$, $\mathbf{i}$, $\mathbf{j}$, and $\mathbf{k}$ are unit vectors. The directions of these vectors are those of the positive x, y, and z-axes, respectively. By an extension of the argument used to prove Theorem 1-2.1, you can prove our next theorem. Simply apply the parallelogram law twice (see Fig. 1-5.3).

THEOREM 1-5.3. *The vector* $\mathbf{v}$ *in standard position with terminal point* (x, y, z) *is* $\mathbf{v} = x\mathbf{i} + y\mathbf{j} + z\mathbf{k}$, *and the terminal point of* $\mathbf{v} = x\mathbf{i} + y\mathbf{j} + z\mathbf{k}$ *is the point* (x, y, z).

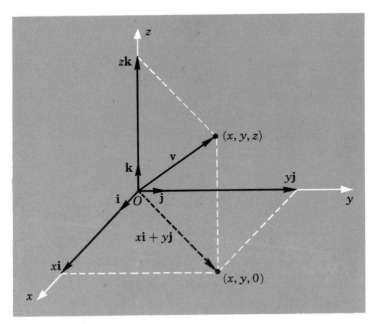

Figure 1-5.3

Thus, any space vector can be expressed as a linear combination of the unit vectors $\mathbf{i}$, $\mathbf{j}$, and $\mathbf{k}$. The vector from the origin to the point $A(x, y, z)$ can be expressed in any of the three ways: $\mathbf{OA}$, the point or ordered triple (x, y, z), or the linear combination $x\mathbf{i} + y\mathbf{j} + z\mathbf{k}$. You can easily show that the various operations on vectors as linear combinations of $\mathbf{i}$, $\mathbf{j}$, and $\mathbf{k}$ can be performed by treating them as polynomials in $\mathbf{i}$, $\mathbf{j}$, and $\mathbf{k}$. For example,

$$(3\mathbf{i} + 5\mathbf{j} - 4\mathbf{k}) + (\mathbf{i} - 7\mathbf{j} + 6\mathbf{k}) = 4\mathbf{i} - 2\mathbf{j} + 2\mathbf{k}$$

$$4(3\mathbf{i} - \mathbf{j} + 2\mathbf{k}) = 12\mathbf{i} - 4\mathbf{j} + 8\mathbf{k}$$

and

$$(5\mathbf{i} - \mathbf{j}) - (3\mathbf{i} + 2\mathbf{j} - 3\mathbf{k}) = (5\mathbf{i} - \mathbf{j} + 0\mathbf{k}) + (-3\mathbf{i} - 2\mathbf{j} + 3\mathbf{k})$$
$$= 2\mathbf{i} - 3\mathbf{j} + 3\mathbf{k}$$

We define the dot product of three-space vectors as an extension of the dot product for planar vectors (see Definition 1–3.1).

DEFINITION 1-5.5. *If* $\mathbf{u} = a\mathbf{i} + b\mathbf{j} + c\mathbf{k}$ *and* $\mathbf{v} = x\mathbf{i} + y\mathbf{j} + z\mathbf{k}$, *the dot product* $\mathbf{u} \cdot \mathbf{v} = ax + by + cz.$

As with planar vectors, the dot product yields a scalar. With this definition, Eqq. (1–3.1), (1–3.2), and (1–3.3), with $\mathbf{u}$ and $\mathbf{v}$ three-space vectors, give the angle between three-space vectors, the vector projection of $\mathbf{u}$ onto $\mathbf{v}$, and the scalar projection of $\mathbf{u}$ onto $\mathbf{v}$. The derivations of these equations for space vectors can be patterned after the derivations given for planar vectors.

Illustration 2

Obtain the angle θ between $\mathbf{u} = 6\mathbf{i} - 3\mathbf{j} + 2\mathbf{k}$ and $\mathbf{v} = -7\mathbf{i} + 4\mathbf{j} + 4\mathbf{k}$. Also, determine the projections of $\mathbf{u}$ onto $\mathbf{v}$. Since

$$\mathbf{u} \cdot \mathbf{v} = 6(-7) + (-3)(4) + 2(4) = -46$$

$$|\mathbf{u}| = \sqrt{36 + 9 + 4} = 7$$

and

$$|\mathbf{v}| = \sqrt{49 + 16 + 16} = 9$$

then

$$\cos \theta = \frac{-46}{7(9)} = -0.730$$

Thus, $\theta = 136.9°$. The vector projection, $\mathbf{OC}$, of $\mathbf{u}$ onto $\mathbf{v}$ is, by Eq. (1–3.2),

$$\mathbf{OC} = \frac{-46}{9^2}(-7\mathbf{i} + 4\mathbf{j} + 4\mathbf{k}) = (\tfrac{322}{81})\mathbf{i} - (\tfrac{184}{81})\mathbf{j} - (\tfrac{184}{81})\mathbf{k}$$

By Eq. (1–3.3), the scalar projection, $|\mathbf{OC}|$, is

$$|\mathbf{OC}| = \frac{|-46|}{9} = \frac{46}{9} = 5\tfrac{1}{9}$$

So far we have treated R^3 as a generalization of R^2. There is one concept that holds for R^3 but does not hold for R^2. This is the *cross product*, a certain product that yields a vector rather than a scalar.

DEFINITION 1–5.6. *If* $\mathbf{u} = a\mathbf{i} + b\mathbf{j} + c\mathbf{k}$ *and* $\mathbf{v} = x\mathbf{i} + y\mathbf{j} + z\mathbf{k}$, *the cross product* $\mathbf{u} \times \mathbf{v} = (bz - cy)\mathbf{i} + (cx - az)\mathbf{j} + (ay - bx)\mathbf{k}$.

There are many interesting algebraic properties that concern the cross product. Our main purpose for introducing the cross product is to use it to obtain a vector orthogonal to two given vectors. If $\mathbf{u} = a\mathbf{i} + b\mathbf{j} + c\mathbf{k}$ and $\mathbf{v} = x\mathbf{i} + y\mathbf{j} + z\mathbf{k}$, then

$$\mathbf{u} \cdot (\mathbf{u} \times \mathbf{v}) = a(bz - cy) + b(cx - az) + c(ay - bx) = 0$$

and

$$\mathbf{v} \cdot (\mathbf{u} \times \mathbf{v}) = x(bz - cy) + y(cx - az) + z(ay - bx) = 0$$

Thus, $\mathbf{u} \times \mathbf{v}$ is a vector orthogonal to both $\mathbf{u}$ and $\mathbf{v}$. If $\mathbf{u}$ and $\mathbf{v}$ determine a plane, then $\mathbf{u} \times \mathbf{v}$ is orthogonal to this plane. If $\mathbf{u} \neq \mathbf{0}$ and $\mathbf{v} = \mathbf{0}$, what is the direction of $\mathbf{u} \times \mathbf{v}$? You can easily show that $\mathbf{i} \times \mathbf{j} = \mathbf{k}$. Since $\mathbf{i}$, $\mathbf{j}$, and $\mathbf{k}$ determine a right-handed system (the xyz system), we agree that the direction of $\mathbf{u} \times \mathbf{v}$ is such that $\mathbf{u}$, $\mathbf{v}$, and $\mathbf{u} \times \mathbf{v}$ form a right-handed system. Notice that $\mathbf{u}$, $\mathbf{v}$, and $\mathbf{v} \times \mathbf{u}$ form a left-handed system.

Illustration 3

Obtain a vector orthogonal to both $\mathbf{u} = 2\mathbf{i} - \mathbf{j} - 3\mathbf{k}$ and $\mathbf{v} = \mathbf{i} + 2\mathbf{j} - \mathbf{k}$. One such vector is

$$\mathbf{u} \times \mathbf{v} = [\,(-1)(-1) - (-3)(2)\,]\mathbf{i} + [\,(-3)(1) - 2(-1)\,]\mathbf{j}$$
$$+ [\,2(2) - (-1)(1)\,]\mathbf{k} = 7\mathbf{i} - \mathbf{j} + 5\mathbf{k}$$

Problem Set 1–5

1. Plot the following points. Sketch the vectors from the origin to the points.
   (a) $(4, 6, 5)$ (b) $(2, 7, -3)$ (c) $(-3, 5, 4)$
   (d) $(-5, -8, -6)$ (e) $(5, -7, 8)$ (f) $(6, -3, -2)$

2. Sketch the following vectors. Describe each vector as a vector in standard position.

	Initial point	Terminal point
(a)	$(0, 0, 0)$	$(3, 4, 7)$
(b)	$(1, -2, 3)$	$(6, 5, -8)$
(c)	$(-4, -3, 7)$	$(-5, 8, 3)$
(d)	$(3, 4, 7)$	$(0, 0, 0)$
(e)	$(-5, 8, 3)$	$(-4, -3, 7)$

3. If $\mathbf{u} = (4, -3, 5)$, $\mathbf{v} = (-3, 5, -2)$, $\mathbf{w} = (0, -1, -4)$, and $\mathbf{0} = (0, 0, 0)$, evaluate:
   (a) $\mathbf{u} + \mathbf{v}$ (b) $\mathbf{u} - \mathbf{w}$ (c) $\mathbf{v} + \mathbf{0}$
   (d) $5\mathbf{v}$ (e) $-4\mathbf{w}$ (f) $3\mathbf{u} + 2\mathbf{v}$
   (g) $4\mathbf{v} - 6\mathbf{w}$ (h) $3\mathbf{u} - 4\mathbf{v} + 2\mathbf{w}$

4. Repeat Problem 3 with $\mathbf{u} = 4\mathbf{i} - 3\mathbf{j} + 5\mathbf{k}$, $\mathbf{v} = -3\mathbf{i} + 5\mathbf{j} - 2\mathbf{k}$, and $\mathbf{w} = -\mathbf{j} - 4\mathbf{k} = 0\mathbf{i} - \mathbf{j} - 4\mathbf{k}$.

5. For the vectors of Problem 4, evaluate:

(a) $\mathbf{u} \cdot \mathbf{v}$	(b) $\mathbf{v} \cdot \mathbf{w}$	(c) $\mathbf{u} \cdot \mathbf{w}$
(d) $\mathbf{u} \cdot (\mathbf{v} + \mathbf{w})$	(e) $(4\mathbf{u}) \cdot \mathbf{v}$	(f) $\mathbf{v} \cdot \mathbf{0}$
(g) $\mathbf{w} \cdot \mathbf{i}$	(h) $\mathbf{j} \cdot \mathbf{v}$	(i) $\mathbf{u} \cdot (-\mathbf{v})$
(j) $\mathbf{v} \cdot \mathbf{v}$	(k) $(\mathbf{u} - 3\mathbf{v}) \cdot \mathbf{w}$	(l) $\mathbf{u} \cdot \mathbf{w} - 3(\mathbf{v} \cdot \mathbf{w})$

In each of Problems 6 through 13 obtain the angle between the given vectors.

6. $\mathbf{i}$ and $\mathbf{k}$

7. $\mathbf{j}$ and $5\mathbf{i} - 7\mathbf{k}$

8. $\mathbf{k}$ and $a\mathbf{i} + b\mathbf{j}$, a and b not both zero

9. $\mathbf{i}$ and $a\mathbf{i} + b\mathbf{k}$, a and b not both zero

10. $4\mathbf{i} - 7\mathbf{j} - 4\mathbf{k}$ and $3\mathbf{i} - 6\mathbf{j} + 2\mathbf{k}$ (Compare results with Problems 11, 12, 13.)

11. $4\mathbf{i} - 7\mathbf{j} - 4\mathbf{k}$ and $-3\mathbf{i} + 6\mathbf{j} - 2\mathbf{k}$

12. $-4\mathbf{i} + 7\mathbf{j} + 4\mathbf{k}$ and $3\mathbf{i} - 6\mathbf{j} + 2\mathbf{k}$

13. $-4\mathbf{i} + 7\mathbf{j} + 4\mathbf{k}$ and $-3\mathbf{i} + 6\mathbf{j} - 2\mathbf{k}$

In Problems 14 through 21 determine the scalar and vector projections of $\mathbf{u}$ on $\mathbf{v}$.

14. $\mathbf{u} = 7\mathbf{i} - 4\mathbf{j} - 4\mathbf{k}$, $\mathbf{v} = 3\mathbf{i} + 2\mathbf{j} - 6\mathbf{k}$

15. $\mathbf{u} = 7\mathbf{i} - 4\mathbf{j} - 4\mathbf{k}$, $\mathbf{v} = -3\mathbf{i} - 2\mathbf{j} + 6\mathbf{k}$

16. $\mathbf{u} = 3\mathbf{i} + 2\mathbf{j} - 6\mathbf{k}$, $\mathbf{v} = 7\mathbf{i} - 4\mathbf{j} - 4\mathbf{k}$

17. $\mathbf{u} = 3\mathbf{i} + 2\mathbf{j} - 6\mathbf{k}$, $\mathbf{v} = -7\mathbf{i} + 4\mathbf{j} + 4\mathbf{k}$

18. $\mathbf{u} = -7\mathbf{i} + 4\mathbf{j} + 4\mathbf{k}$, $\mathbf{v} = -3\mathbf{i} - 2\mathbf{j} + 6\mathbf{k}$

19. $\mathbf{u} = -3\mathbf{i} - 2\mathbf{j} + 6\mathbf{k}$, $\mathbf{v} = -7\mathbf{i} + 4\mathbf{j} + 4\mathbf{k}$

20. $\mathbf{u} = \mathbf{0}$, $\mathbf{v} = 8\mathbf{i} + 2\mathbf{j} - 7\mathbf{k}$

21. $\mathbf{u} = 5\mathbf{i} - 3\mathbf{j} + 4\mathbf{k}$, $\mathbf{v} = 4\mathbf{i} + 8\mathbf{j} + \mathbf{k}$

22. If $|\mathbf{OC}|$ and $\mathbf{OC}$ are the scalar and vector projections of $\mathbf{u}$ on $\mathbf{v}$, what are the projections of $\mathbf{u}$ on $3\mathbf{v}$? on $\mathbf{v}/5$? on $-7\mathbf{v}$?

In Problems 23 through 31 let $\mathbf{u} = 3\mathbf{i} - 2\mathbf{j} + 4\mathbf{k}$, $\mathbf{v} = \mathbf{i} - \mathbf{j} - 3\mathbf{k}$, $\mathbf{w} = -2\mathbf{i} + 5\mathbf{j} + 6\mathbf{k}$, and $\mathbf{0} = 0\mathbf{i} + 0\mathbf{j} + 0\mathbf{k}$. Evaluate the expressions.

23. $\mathbf{u} \times \mathbf{v}$	24. $\mathbf{v} \times \mathbf{u}$	25. $\mathbf{i} \times \mathbf{j}$
26. $\mathbf{u} \times (\mathbf{v} + \mathbf{w})$	27. $(\mathbf{u} \times \mathbf{v}) + (\mathbf{u} \times \mathbf{w})$	28. $\mathbf{u} \times \mathbf{u}$
29. $\mathbf{u} \times \mathbf{0}$	30. $(3\mathbf{u}) \times (2\mathbf{v})$	31. $6(\mathbf{u} \times \mathbf{v})$

Problems 32 and 33 involve important concepts and should be solved by everyone.

32. Show that $a\mathbf{i} + b\mathbf{j} + c\mathbf{k} = \mathbf{0}$ if and only if $a = b = c = 0$. Thus, $\mathbf{i}$, $\mathbf{j}$, and $\mathbf{k}$ are *linearly independent*. Since these three vectors *span* space (by Theorem 1-5.3) and are linearly independent, they form a *basis* for space.

33. If $\mathbf{u} = a\mathbf{i} + b\mathbf{j} + c\mathbf{k} \neq \mathbf{0}$, show that $\mathbf{u}/|\mathbf{u}|$ is a unit vector.

34. Argue that R^3 is a vector space over R.

35. Show that Definitions 1-5.1 through 1-5.4 agree with the directed line segment interpretation of vectors.

36. Argue that the vector from $A(x_1, y_1, z_1)$ to $B(x_2, y_2, z_2)$ is equal to the vector $\mathbf{OC}$ where the coordinates of C are $(x_2 - x_1, y_2 - y_1, z_2 - z_1)$.

1-6. LINES IN THREE-SPACE

Up to this point, we have not emphasized the direction of a vector (the orientation of a vector with respect to the coordinate axes). Suppose $\mathbf{v} = x\mathbf{i} + y\mathbf{j} + z\mathbf{k}$ is a nonzero vector. Then $\mathbf{v}$ is in standard position and not all of x, y, and z are zero (see Fig. 1-6.1.). Let α, β, and γ denote the angles between $\mathbf{v}$ and $\mathbf{i}$, $\mathbf{j}$, and $\mathbf{k}$, respectively. Now, α, β, and γ can be uniquely determined from

$$\cos \alpha = \frac{\mathbf{v} \cdot \mathbf{i}}{|\mathbf{v}||\mathbf{i}|} = \frac{x}{\sqrt{x^2 + y^2 + z^2}}$$

(1-6.1) $$\cos \beta = \frac{\mathbf{v} \cdot \mathbf{j}}{|\mathbf{v}||\mathbf{j}|} = \frac{y}{\sqrt{x^2 + y^2 + z^2}}$$

$$\cos \gamma = \frac{\mathbf{v} \cdot \mathbf{k}}{|\mathbf{v}||\mathbf{k}|} = \frac{z}{\sqrt{x^2 + y^2 + z^2}}$$

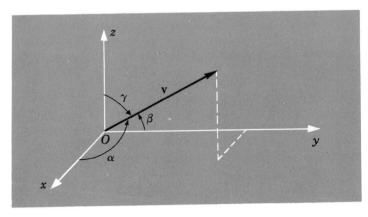

Figure 1-6.1

The three cosines of Eqq. (1-6.1) are called the *direction cosines* of $\mathbf{v} \neq \mathbf{0}$. No direction is assigned the zero vector. However, the zero vector is considered parallel to and orthogonal to every vector. The three direction cosines are not independent, since $\cos^2 \alpha + \cos^2 \beta + \cos^2 \gamma = 1$. Clearly, not all direction cosines can be zero. Notice that $(\cos \alpha)\mathbf{i} + (\cos \beta)\mathbf{j} + (\cos \gamma)\mathbf{k}$ is a unit vector with the same direction as $\mathbf{v}$. In fact, if $h > 0$, the vector $(h \cos \alpha)\mathbf{i} + (h \cos \beta)\mathbf{j} + (h \cos \gamma)\mathbf{k}$ has the same direction as $\mathbf{v}$. For $\mathbf{v} \neq \mathbf{0}$, any ordered triple of real numbers a, b, and c such that for $h > 0$,

(1-6.2)
$$\begin{cases} a = h \cos \alpha \\ b = h \cos \beta \\ c = h \cos \gamma \end{cases}$$

are called *direction numbers* of $\mathbf{v}$ and are denoted by $[a, b, c]$. With $h = 1$, system (1-6.2) gives $a = \cos \alpha$, $b = \cos \beta$, and $c = \cos \gamma$. Thus, direction cosines of a vector are direction numbers of the vector. However, direction numbers of a vector may not be direction cosines of the vector.

Illustration 1

If $\mathbf{v} = 7\mathbf{i} - 4\mathbf{j} + 4\mathbf{k}$, the direction cosines of $\mathbf{v}$ are $\cos \alpha = \frac{7}{9}$, $\cos \beta = -\frac{4}{9}$, and $\cos \gamma = \frac{4}{9}$. Direction numbers of $\mathbf{v}$ are $[7, -4, 4]$, $[14, -8, 8]$, $[\frac{7}{2}, -2, 2]$, or any triple $[(\frac{7}{9})h, (-\frac{4}{9})h, (\frac{4}{9})h]$ with $h > 0$.

If $\mathbf{v} \neq \mathbf{0}$ has direction cosines $\cos \alpha$, $\cos \beta$, and $\cos \gamma$, then by Eqq. (1-6.1) direction cosines of $-\mathbf{v}$ are $-\cos \alpha$, $-\cos \beta$, and $-\cos \gamma$. The line L determined by $\mathbf{v}$ is also determined by $-\mathbf{v}$ (see Fig. 1-6.2). Thus, if we relax $h > 0$ to $h \neq 0$, system (1-6.2) provides *direction numbers of* L.

Figure 1-6.2

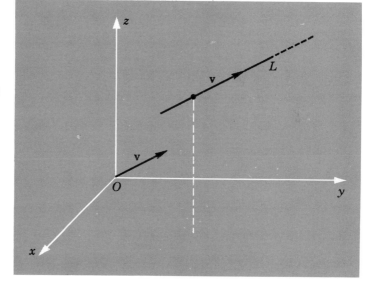

Illustration 2

Direction numbers of the line L determined by $\mathbf{v} = 7\mathbf{i} - 4\mathbf{j} + 4\mathbf{k}$ are $[-7, 4, -4]$ and $[(\frac{7}{9})h, (-\frac{4}{9})h, (\frac{4}{9})h]$ for $h < 0$, as well as those given in Illustration 1.

We know that a point (x_1, y_1, z_1) and a direction determine a unique line L. Suppose (x_1, y_1, z_1) is in the line L, which is parallel to a vector with direction numbers $[a, b, c]$. Then, the point (x, y, z) is in L if and only if $[x - x_1, y - y_1, z - z_1] = t[a, b, c]$ for some $t \in R$ (see Fig. 1-6.3). We interpret this equation to mean that

(1-6.3)
$$\begin{cases} x - x_1 = ta \\ y - y_1 = tb \\ z - z_1 = tc \end{cases}$$

or

(1-6.3a)
$$\begin{cases} x = x_1 + ta \\ y = y_1 + tb \\ z = z_1 + tc \end{cases}$$

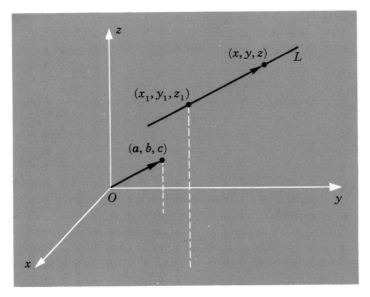

Figure 1-6.3

Illustration 3

Obtain the line L_1 that contains the point $(-5, 3, 2)$ and is parallel to $\mathbf{v} = \mathbf{i} - 4\mathbf{j} + 3\mathbf{k}$. Since $[1, -4, 3]$ are direction numbers of $\mathbf{v}$ (and of L_1), L_1 is immediately obtained as $L_1 = \{ (x, y, z) \mid x = -5 + t, y = 3 - 4t, \text{ and } z = 2 + 3t, \text{ for } t \in R \}$. (See Appendix for set notation.)

If two distinct points (x_1, y_1, z_1) and (x_2, y_2, z_2) are in L, then $[x_2 - x_1, y_2 - y_1, z_2 - z_1]$ are direction numbers of L and system (1-6.3a) can be expressed as

(1-6.4)
$$\begin{cases} x = x_1 + t(x_2 - x_1) \\ y = y_1 + t(y_2 - y_1) \\ z = z_1 + t(z_2 - z_1) \end{cases}$$

If $t = 0$, then system (1-6.4) reduces to $x = x_1$, $y = y_1$, and $z = z_1$ while if $t = 1$ the system reduces to $x = x_2$, $y = y_2$, and $z = z_2$. Therefore, the points (x_1, y_1, z_1) and (x_2, y_2, z_2) are in L. Each equation in system (1-6.3), (1-6.3a), or (1-6.4) is a *system of parametric equations* of L with parameter $t \in R$. Notice that if we let $\mathbf{v} = x\mathbf{i} + y\mathbf{j} + z\mathbf{k}$, $\mathbf{a} = x_1\mathbf{i} + y_1\mathbf{j} + z_1\mathbf{k}$, and $\mathbf{b} = (x_2 - x_1)\mathbf{i} + (y_2 - y_1)\mathbf{j} + (z_2 - z_1)\mathbf{k}$, system (1-6.4) can be written in *vector form* as

(1-6.5) $$\mathbf{v} = \mathbf{a} + t\mathbf{b}$$

(See Fig. 1-6.4.)

Figure 1-6.4

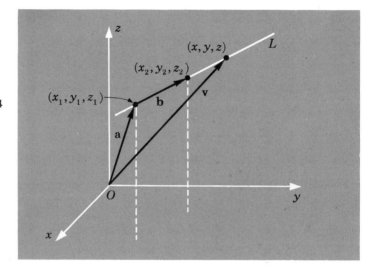

Illustration 4

Determine the line L_2 that contains the points $(3, -2, -1)$ and $(5, 3, -4)$. Since $[5 - 3, 3 - (-2), -4 - (-1)]$ or $[2, 5, -3]$ are direction numbers of L_2, then

$$L_2 = \{ (x, y, z) \mid x = 3 + 2t, y = -2 + 5t, \text{and } z = -1 - 3t, \text{for } t \in R \}$$

Either point can be taken as (x_1, y_1, z_1). Thus, another description of L_2 is

$$L_2 = \{ (x, y, z) \mid x = 5 + 2t', y = 3 + 5t', \text{and } z = -4 - 3t', \text{for } t' \in R \}$$

Of course, $t' \neq t$. The relationship between t' and t is easily obtained from $5 + 2t' = 3 + 2t$ to be $t' = t - 1$. Notice that each of $3 + 5t' = -2 + 5t$ and $-4 - 3t' = -1 - 3t$ also give $t' = t - 1$.

If $abc \neq 0$, Eq. (1-6.3) can be expressed in the *symmetric form*

(1-6.6) $$\frac{x - x_1}{a} = \frac{y - y_1}{b} = \frac{z - z_1}{c}$$

If one or two of a, b, or c is zero, Eq. (1-6.6) cannot be used. In this case, one of the systems of parametric equations must be used.

31

Illustration 5

Use Eq. (1–6.6) to describe the lines of Illustrations 3 and 4. From Illustration 3, we have $L_1 = \left\{ (x, y, z) \left| \dfrac{x + 5}{1} = \dfrac{y - 3}{-4} = \dfrac{z - 2}{3} \right. \right\}$.

From Illustration 4, $L_2 = \left\{ (x, y, z) \left| \dfrac{x - 3}{2} = \dfrac{y + 2}{5} = \dfrac{z + 1}{-3} \right. \right\}$ or $L_2 = \left\{ (x, y, z) \left| \dfrac{x - 5}{2} = \dfrac{y - 3}{5} = \dfrac{z + 4}{-3} \right. \right\}$.

Problem Set 1–6

In Problems 1 through 12 determine the direction cosines of the vector.

1. $4\mathbf{i} - 7\mathbf{j} - 4\mathbf{k}$
2. $-4\mathbf{i} + 7\mathbf{j} + 4\mathbf{k}$
3. $\mathbf{i} - 2\mathbf{j} + 2\mathbf{k}$
4. $a\mathbf{i} - 2a\mathbf{j} + 2a\mathbf{k},\ a > 0$
5. $a\mathbf{i} - 2a\mathbf{j} + 2a\mathbf{k},\ a < 0$
6. $\mathbf{i}$
7. $\mathbf{j}$
8. $\mathbf{k}$
9. $4\mathbf{i} - 3\mathbf{k}$
10. $3\mathbf{j} + 4\mathbf{k}$
11. $3\mathbf{i} + 2\mathbf{j} - 6\mathbf{k}$
12. $-6\mathbf{i} + 2\mathbf{j} - 3\mathbf{k}$

In Problems 13 through 18 obtain the direction cosines that are not given.

13. $\cos \alpha = \frac{2}{3},\ \cos \beta = -\frac{1}{3}$
14. $\cos \alpha = -\frac{2}{3},\ \cos \gamma = \frac{2}{3}$
15. $\cos \beta = -\frac{2}{3},\ \cos \gamma = -\frac{2}{3}$
16. $\cos \alpha = \frac{7}{9},\ \cos \beta = \frac{4}{9}$
17. $\cos \alpha = -\frac{7}{9},\ \cos \gamma = \frac{4}{9}$
18. $\cos \beta = -\frac{4}{9},\ \cos \gamma = -\frac{7}{9}$

In Problems 19 through 28 locate three other points in the line determined by the given points and direction numbers.

19. $(0, 0, 0),\ [5, 7, 2]$
20. $(3, 4, 0),\ [1, -3, 6]$
21. $(5, 0, 3),\ [0, 3, 0]$
22. $(5, 8, 7),\ [2, 0, 0]$
23. $(5, 8, 7),\ [0, 2, 0]$
24. $(5, 8, 7),\ [0, 0, 2]$
25. $(5, 8, 7),\ [1, 2, 0]$
26. $(5, 8, 7),\ [1, 0, 2]$
27. $(5, 8, 7),\ [0, 1, 2]$
28. $(-6, -3, 2),\ [-4, -7, 6]$

29. Obtain direction numbers of the line that contains the given points.
    - (a) $(4, 5, 2),\ (3, -7, -8)$
    - (b) $(-3, -5, 2),\ (6, -5, -2)$
    - (c) $(1, 0, 0),\ (1, 4, -3)$
    - (d) $(0, 0, 0),\ (-4, 3, -5)$
    - (e) $(7, -5, -10),\ (-3, -6, -2)$
    - (f) $(3, -6, 7),\ (-3, 6, -7)$
    - (g) $(0, 0, 4),\ (3, 0, 0)$
    - (h) $(4, 3, 0),\ (0, 2, 3)$

In each of Problems 30 through 37 describe the line that contains the points in the problems referred to using parametric equations and the symmetric form, where possible.

30. Problem 29a
31. Problem 29b
32. Problem 29c
33. Problem 29d
34. Problem 29e
35. Problem 29f
36. Problem 29g
37. Problem 29h

In Problems 38 through 47 describe the lines that contain the points and have the given direction numbers. Use parametric equations and the symmetric form, where possible.

38. Problem 19	39. Problem 20
40. Problem 21	41. Problem 22
42. Problem 23	43. Problem 24
44. Problem 25	45. Problem 26
46. Problem·27	47. Problem 28

48. If $\mathbf{u} = a\mathbf{i} + b\mathbf{j} + c\mathbf{k} \neq \mathbf{0}$ has direction cosines $\cos\alpha$, $\cos\beta$, and $\cos\gamma$, prove that $\mathbf{v} = (\cos\alpha)\mathbf{i} + (\cos\beta)\mathbf{j} + (\cos\gamma)\mathbf{k}$ is a unit vector with the same direction as $\mathbf{u}$.

49. If $\mathbf{u} = a\mathbf{i} + b\mathbf{j} + c\mathbf{k} \neq \mathbf{0}$ has direction cosines $\cos\alpha$, $\cos\beta$, and $\cos\gamma$, prove that if $h > 0$, then $\mathbf{v} = (h\cos\alpha)\mathbf{i} + (h\cos\beta)\mathbf{j} + (h\cos\gamma)\mathbf{k}$ is a vector with the same direction as $\mathbf{u}$.

1-7. PLANES

In the previous section, we used direction numbers of a vector parallel to a line. Here, we need direction numbers of a vector orthogonal to a plane. A vector $\mathbf{a}$ is *orthogonal to a plane* Π if and only if $\mathbf{a}$ is orthogonal to every vector in Π.

Suppose (x_1, y_1, z_1) is a point in a plane Π. Let $\mathbf{a} = a\mathbf{i} + b\mathbf{j} + c\mathbf{k} \neq \mathbf{0}$ be orthogonal to Π (see Fig. 1-7.1). The point (x, y, z) will

Figure 1-7.1

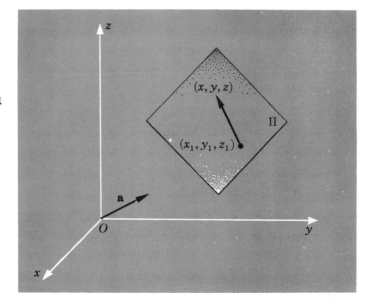

be in Π if and only if $\mathbf{v} = (x - x_1)\mathbf{i} + (y - y_1)\mathbf{j} + (z - z_1)\mathbf{k}$ and $\mathbf{a}$ are orthogonal, that is, if and only if

(1-7.1) $\mathbf{a} \cdot \mathbf{v} = 0$

This equation can be expressed as

(1-7.2) $a(x - x_1) + b(y - y_1) + c(z - z_1) = 0$

which is called the *point, direction number form* of the equation of a plane. If we set $ax_1 + by_1 + cz_1 = -d$, Eq. (1-7.2) becomes

(1-7.3) $ax + by + cz + d = 0$

the *general equation* of a plane. Notice the similarity of Eq. (1-7.3) and the general form of an equation of a line in two-space.

Illustration 1

Determine the plane Π that contains the point $(4, -3, -5)$ and is orthogonal to $\mathbf{a} = -2\mathbf{i} + \mathbf{j} - 7\mathbf{k}$. If we let $\mathbf{v} = (x - 4)\mathbf{i} + (y + 3)\mathbf{j} + (z + 5)\mathbf{k}$, then $\mathbf{a} \cdot \mathbf{v} = 0$ or

$$-2(x - 4) + 1(y + 3) - 7(z + 5) = 0$$

This last equation simplifies to $2x - y + 7z + 24 = 0$, and the plane is

$$\Pi = \{ (x, y, z) \mid 2x - y + 7z + 24 = 0 \}$$

Illustration 2

Obtain the plane Π that contains the three points $A(2, 3, 0)$, $B(-1, -2, 3)$, and $C(4, 1, -2)$. The cross product is useful here. The vector $\mathbf{AB} \times \mathbf{AC}$ is orthogonal to both $\mathbf{AB}$ and $\mathbf{AC}$, and consequently, to Π. Now,

$$\mathbf{AB} \times \mathbf{AC} = (-3\mathbf{i} - 5\mathbf{j} + 3\mathbf{k}) \times (2\mathbf{i} - 2\mathbf{j} - 2\mathbf{k}) = 16\mathbf{i} + 16\mathbf{k}$$

Notice that $\frac{1}{16}(\mathbf{AB} \times \mathbf{AC}) = \mathbf{i} + \mathbf{k}$ is also orthogonal to Π. Using point A, we have $1(x - 2) + 0(y - 3) + 1(z - 0) = 0$ from which $\Pi = \{ (x, y, z) \mid x + z = 2 \}$. The same result is obtained if either point B or point C is used.

Although the distance between a point and a plane and the distance between two parallel planes can be evaluated in other ways, we will use projections to obtain them. Suppose $ax + by + cz + d = 0$ is an equation of a plane Π and $P_1(x_1, y_1, z_1)$ is a point. Let $P_2(x_2, y_2, z_2)$ be a point in Π. Since $\mathbf{a} = a\mathbf{i} + b\mathbf{j} + c\mathbf{k}$ is orthogonal to Π, the scalar projection of $\mathbf{P_1P_2}$ onto $\mathbf{a}$ is the distance between $\mathbf{P}_1$ and Π (see Fig. 1-7.2).

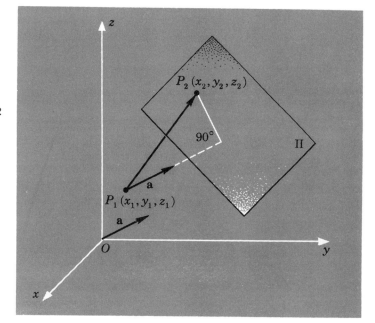

Figure 1-7.2

Illustration 3

What is the distance ρ between the point $P_1(-3, 2, 5)$ and the plane $\Pi = \{ (x, y, z) \mid 4x - 3y - z + 6 = 0 \}$? First, we need a point in Π. Let $x = 2$, $y = 1$ and solve for $z = 4(2) - 3(1) + 6 = 11$. Thus, $P_2(2, 1, 11)$ is in Π. Now, ρ is the scalar projection of $P_1P_2 = 5i - j + 6k$ on $a = 4i - 3j - k$. Therefore,

$$\rho = \frac{|5(4) - 1(-3) + 6(-1)|}{\sqrt{16 + 9 + 1}} = \frac{17}{\sqrt{26}} = 17\sqrt{26}/26$$

Illustration 4

What is the distance ρ between the origin and $\Pi = \{ (x, y, z) \mid 4x - 3y - z + 6 = 0 \}$? Again, $P_2(2, 1, 11)$ is in Π and $a = 4i - 3j - k$. Project $OP_2 = 2i + j + 11k$ onto a to obtain

$$\rho = \frac{|2(4) + 1(-3) + 11(-1)|}{\sqrt{26}} = 3\sqrt{26}/13$$

Suppose $P_1(x_1, y_1, z_1)$ is in $\Pi_1 = \{ (x, y, z) \mid ax + by + cz + d_1 = 0 \}$ and $P_2(x_2, y_2, z_2)$ is a point in $\Pi_2 = \{ (x, y, z) \mid ax + by + cz + d_2 = 0 \}$ (see Fig. 1-7.3). Notice that Π_1 and Π_2 are parallel planes. The distance ρ_1 between the origin and Π_1 is the scalar projection

35

of $\mathbf{v}_1 = x_1\mathbf{i} + y_1\mathbf{j} + z_1\mathbf{k}$ onto $\mathbf{a} = a\mathbf{i} + b\mathbf{j} + c\mathbf{k}$, while the distance ρ_2 between the origin and Π_2 is the scalar projection of $\mathbf{v}_2 = x_2\mathbf{i} + y_2\mathbf{j} + z_2\mathbf{k}$ onto $\mathbf{a}$. Now, if Π_1 and Π_2 are on the same side of the origin, the distance between them is $\rho = |\rho_2 - \rho_1|$. However, if Π_1 and Π_2 are on opposite sides of the origin, then $\rho = \rho_1 + \rho_2$. Notice that Π_1 and Π_2 are on the same side of the origin provided $\mathbf{v}_1 \cdot \mathbf{a}$ and $\mathbf{v}_2 \cdot \mathbf{a}$ have like signs and they are on opposite sides of the origin if $\mathbf{v}_1 \cdot \mathbf{a}$ and $\mathbf{v}_2 \cdot \mathbf{a}$ have different signs. (You should verify these statements.) Of course, if Π_1 contains the origin, then $\rho = \rho_2$ and if Π_2 contains the origin, then $\rho = \rho_1$.

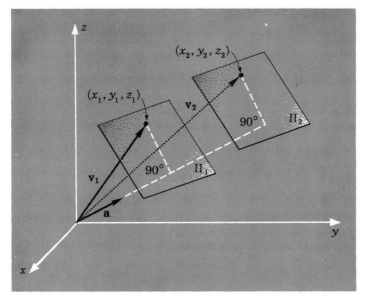

Figure 1–7.3

Illustration 5

Obtain the distance between $\Pi_1 = \{ (x, y, z) \mid 6x - 3y - 2z + 8 = 0 \}$ and (a) $\Pi_2 = \{ (x, y, z) \mid 6x - 3y - 2z + 4 = 0 \}$, (b) $\Pi_3 = \{ (x, y, z) \mid 6x - 3y - 2z = 0 \}$, and (c) $\Pi_4 = \{ (x, y, z) \mid 6x - 3y - 2z - 6 = 0 \}$. Let ρ_i denote the distance between the origin and Π_i for $i = 1, 2, 3, 4$. Now, $(0, 0, 4)$ is a point in Π_1, $(0, 0, 2)$ is a point in Π_2, the origin is in Π_3, and $(0, 0, -3)$ is a point in Π_4. Then,

$$\rho_1 = \frac{|4\mathbf{k} \cdot (6\mathbf{i} - 3\mathbf{j} - 2\mathbf{k})|}{|6\mathbf{i} - 3\mathbf{j} - 2\mathbf{k}|} = \frac{|-8|}{7} = \frac{8}{7}$$

$$\rho_2 = \frac{|2\mathbf{k} \cdot (6\mathbf{i} - 3\mathbf{j} - 2\mathbf{k})|}{7} = \frac{|-4|}{7} = \frac{4}{7}$$

$$\rho_3 = 0$$

and

$$p_4 = \frac{|-3\mathbf{k} \cdot (6\mathbf{i} - 3\mathbf{j} - 2\mathbf{k})|}{7} = \frac{|6|}{7} = \frac{6}{7}$$

Since Π_1 and Π_2 are on the same side of the origin, Π_3 contains the origin, and Π_1 and Π_4 are on opposite sides of the origin,

for (a), $\rho = |\frac{4}{7} - \frac{8}{7}| = |-\frac{4}{7}| = \frac{4}{7}$
for (b), $\rho = \frac{8}{7}$
and for (c), $\rho = \frac{8}{7} + \frac{6}{7} = 2$

Problem Set 1-7

In each of Problems 1 through 13 obtain an equation of a plane Π for the given conditions.

1. The point $(5, -3, -7)$ is in Π and $\mathbf{a} = 2\mathbf{i} + \mathbf{j} - 6\mathbf{k}$ is orthogonal to Π.

2. The point $(-4, 2, -6)$ is in Π and $\mathbf{a} = -4\mathbf{i} + 2\mathbf{j} - 6\mathbf{k}$ is orthogonal to Π.

3. The point $(-4, 2, -6)$ is in Π and $\mathbf{a} = 4\mathbf{i} - 2\mathbf{j} + 6\mathbf{k}$ is orthogonal to Π.

4. The point $(3, -2, 1)$ is in Π and a line perpendicular to Π contains the points $(0, 4, -7)$ and $(5, 2, 3)$.

5. The line containing $(-3, 2, -4)$ and $(1, 0, 3)$ is perpendicular to Π at the point $(5, -2, 10)$.

6. The point $(0, 0, 0)$ is in Π and $L = \{(x, y, z) \mid (x - 2)/3 = (y + 1)/-4 = z/1\}$ is perpendicular to Π.

7. The point $(-5, 2, 4)$ is in Π and $L = \{(x, y, z) \mid (x + 5)/(-6) = (y - 3)/4 = (z + 7)/(-8)\}$ is perpendicular to Π.

8. The point $(-5, 2, 4)$ is in Π and $L = \{(x, y, z) \mid x = 2 + 4t, y = 7t,$ and $z = -3 + t$ for $t \in R\}$ is perpendicular to Π.

9. Solve Problem 8 for $L = \{(x, y, z) \mid x = -5 + t, y = 4 - 3t,$ and $z = 2 - 7t$ for $t \in R\}$.

10. The points $(3, 0, 0)$, $(0, 4, 0)$, and $(0, 0, 5)$ are in Π.

11. The points $(3, 0, 0)$, $(0, 0, 0)$, and $(0, 4, 3)$ are in Π.

12. The points $(5, 0, 0)$, $(5, 3, 0)$, and $(5, 0, 7)$ are in Π.

13. The points $(7, -3, 2)$, $(1, 2, -6)$, and $(-3, 4, 8)$ are in Π.

In each of Problems 14 through 22 determine the distance between the point and plane or the parallel planes.

14. $(5, -2, 3)$, $\{(x, y, z) \mid 6x + 3y - 2z = 10\}$
15. $(0, 0, 0)$, $\{(x, y, z) \mid 6x + 3y + 2z = 12\}$
16. $(6, -3, 2)$, $\{(x, y, z) \mid 4x - 7y + 4z = 20\}$
17. $(-3, 2, 7)$, $\{(x, y, z) \mid 2x + y - 2z = 0\}$
18. $(1, -4, -1)$, $\{(x, y, z) \mid 2x - y - 2z = 8\}$
19. $\{(x, y, z) \mid x + y + z = 4\}$, $\{(x, y, z) \mid x + y + z = 10\}$
20. $\{(x, y, z) \mid 2x - y + 2z = 10\}$, $\{(x, y, z) \mid 2x - y + 2z + 6 = 0\}$

37

21. $\{(x, y, z) \mid 6x + 3y - 2z = 10\}$, $\{(x, y, z) \mid 6x + 3y - 2z + 12 = 0\}$

22. $\{(x, y, z) \mid 6x - 3y - 2z = 0\}$, $\{(x, y, z) \mid 6x - 3y - 2z = 6\}$

23. Obtain an equation of a plane that contains $(4, -3, 2)$ and is parallel to $\Pi = \{(x, y, z) \mid 7x - 3y + z = 10\}$.

24. Obtain an equation of a plane that contains $(0, 0, 0)$ and is parallel to $\Pi = \{(x, y, z) \mid 3x - 2y + z = 6\}$.

In each of Problems 25 through 28 locate the point of intersection of the line and plane.

25. $\{(x, y, z) \mid x = 4$ and $(y - 3)/2 = (z + 5)/3\}$,
    $\{(x, y, z) \mid 2x - 3y + z = 7\}$

26. $\{(x, y, z) \mid x = 3$ and $z = 4\}$, $\{(x, y, z) \mid x + y + z = 8\}$

27. $\{(x, y, z) \mid (x - 2)/2 = (y + 1)/3 = (z - 3)/1\}$,
    $\{(x, y, z) \mid x - 2y + 3z = 6\}$

28. $\{(x, y, z) \mid (x + 7)/(-3) = (y - 5)/4 = (z + 3)/(-2)\}$,
    $\{(x, y, z) \mid 2x - y + z = 7\}$

In Problems 29 through 32 first obtain two points on the line of intersection of the planes then write equations of the line of intersection.

29. $\{(x, y, z) \mid x + y + z = 3\}$, $\{(x, y, z) \mid 2x - y + z = 5\}$

30. $\{(x, y, z) \mid 2x - y - 2z = 4\}$, $\{(x, y, z) \mid x + y + z = 1\}$

31. $\{(x, y, z) \mid 3x - 5y + z = 15\}$, $\{(x, y, z) \mid 6x + 2y - 3z = 4\}$

32. $\{(x, y, z) \mid 2x + y - 3z = 6\}$, $\{(x, y, z) \mid x - y + z = 2\}$

33. If $abcd \neq 0$, express $ax + by + cz + d = 0$ in the form $x/A + y/B + z/C = 1$. This form is called the intercept form of the equation of a plane. The numbers A, B, and C are the x, y, and z-intercepts of the plane.

34. Express the following equations in the intercept form. (See Problem 33.)

(a) $x + y + z = 4$ (b) $4x - 2y + 3z = 12$

(c) $5x + 2y - 3z + 30 = 0$ (d) $3x - 5y + 2z = 7$

(e) $5x - y - 3z = 4$ (f) $-7x + 2y - 8z = 51$

$$2$$

Introduction to Matrices

You will recall that a solution of the equation $3x - 2y = 5$ is an ordered pair of real numbers or a point (x, y) whose coordinates satisfy the equation. We have considered each such ordered pair as a vector in R^2. Also, a solution of $2x - 3y - 5z = 2$ is an ordered triple of real numbers or a point (x, y, z) whose coordinates satisfy this equation. Here, each such ordered triple is considered as a vector in R^3. It is natural to consider a solution of $x + 2y - 3z + w = 8$ as an ordered quadruple of real numbers or a point (x, y, z, w) in four-space whose coordinates satisfy the equation. More generally, a solution of $a_1x_1 + a_2x_2 + \cdots + a_nx_n = b_1$ can be considered as an ordered n-tuple of real numbers or a point $(x_1, x_2, \ldots, x_n)$ in n-space whose coordinates $x_1, x_2, \ldots, x_n$ satisfy the equation. Just as we called (x, y) a vector in R^2 and (x, y, z) a vector in R^3, we will call $(x_1, x_2, \ldots, x_n)$ a vector in n-space. The set of all vectors in n-space is denoted by R^n.

DEFINITION 2-1.1. *If $x_1, x_2, \ldots, x_n \in R$, then $\mathbf{v} = (x_1, x_2, \ldots, x_n)$ is a vector with magnitude $|\mathbf{v}| = \sqrt{x_1^2 + x_2^2 + \cdots + x_n^2}$. The zero vector is $\mathbf{0} = (0, 0, \ldots, 0)$.*

39

DEFINITION 2-1.2. *If* $\mathbf{u} = (a_1, a_2, \ldots, a_n)$ *and* $\mathbf{v} = (x_1, x_2, \ldots, x_n)$, *then* $\mathbf{u} = \mathbf{v}$ *if and only if* $a_1 = x_1, a_2 = x_2, \ldots,$ *and* $a_n = x_n$.

Notice that equality for R^n is an *equivalence relation* since the following properties of an equivalence relation hold.

i.   If $\mathbf{u} \in R^n$, then $\mathbf{u} = \mathbf{u}$ *Reflexive Property*

ii. If $\mathbf{u}, \mathbf{v} \in R^n$ and $\mathbf{u} = \mathbf{v}$, then $\mathbf{v} = \mathbf{u}$ *Symmetric Property*

iii. If $\mathbf{u}, \mathbf{v}, \mathbf{w} \in R^n$, $\mathbf{u} = \mathbf{v}$, and $\mathbf{v} = \mathbf{w}$,   *Transitive Property*
     then $\mathbf{u} = \mathbf{w}$

DEFINITION 2-1.3. *If* $\mathbf{u} = (a_1, a_2, \ldots, a_n)$ *and* $\mathbf{v} = (x_1, x_2, \ldots, x_n)$, *then the sum*

$$\mathbf{u} + \mathbf{v} = (a_1 + x_1, a_2 + x_2, \ldots, a_n + x_n)$$

DEFINITION 2-1.4. *If* $\mathbf{v} = (x_1, x_2, \ldots, x_n)$ *and* $c \in R$, *then* $c\mathbf{v} = (cx_1, cx_2, \ldots, cx_n)$.

If $c = -1$, then $-1\mathbf{v} = (-x_1, -x_2, \ldots, -x_n)$, which is denoted by $-\mathbf{v}$. Also, subtraction is defined by $\mathbf{u} - \mathbf{v} = \mathbf{u} + (-\mathbf{v})$.

With the above definitions, which are similar to Definitions 1-2.1 through 1-2.4, the following theorem is easily proved. (See Definition 1-1.1.) Refer to Definition 5-1.1, if needed, for information concerning R.

THEOREM 2-1.1. *For each positive integer* n, R^n *is a vector space over* R.

Notice that when $n = 1$, we have that R^1 or the set of all (ordered) 1-tuples of real numbers is a vector space over R. Why can we then say that R is a vector space over R?

With the concept of vectors in n-space we are prepared to define a mathematical object called a *matrix*. A matrix is simply a rectangular array with rows from the same n-space if the rows are considered as vectors. To see that the n in n-space need not be large, let $n = 2$. Since $(1, 4)$, $(-3, 2)$, $(0, 0)$, and $(6, -5)$ are in R^2, some examples of matrices are

$$\begin{pmatrix} 1 & 4 \\ -3 & 2 \end{pmatrix}, \quad (1 \quad 4), \quad \begin{pmatrix} -3 & 2 \\ 0 & 0 \\ 6 & -5 \end{pmatrix}, \quad \begin{pmatrix} 0 & 0 \\ 0 & 0 \end{pmatrix}, \quad \text{and} \quad \begin{pmatrix} 6 & -5 \\ 1 & 4 \\ -3 & 2 \\ 0 & 0 \end{pmatrix}$$

If $n = 3$, some examples of matrices are

$$\begin{pmatrix} 1 & 0 & 0 \\ 0 & 1 & 0 \end{pmatrix}, \quad (1 \quad 0 \quad 0), \quad \begin{pmatrix} -3 & 0 & 1 \\ 0 & 1 & 0 \\ 0 & 0 & 0 \end{pmatrix}, \quad \text{and} \quad \begin{pmatrix} 0 & 1 & 0 \\ -3 & 0 & 1 \\ 0 & 0 & 0 \\ 1 & 0 & 0 \end{pmatrix}$$

since $(1, 0, 0)$, $(0, 1, 0)$, $(-3, 0, 1)$, and $(0, 0, 0)$ are vectors in R^3.

As we will see, matrices are basic to the study of linear algebra. The symbol Z^+, first used in the next definition, denotes the set of all positive integers.

DEFINITION 2-1.5. *The rectangular array*

$$A = \begin{pmatrix} a_{11} & a_{12} & \cdots & a_{1n} \\ a_{21} & a_{22} & \cdots & a_{2n} \\ \vdots & \vdots & \ddots & \vdots \\ a_{m1} & a_{m2} & \cdots & a_{mn} \end{pmatrix}$$

with m, $n \in Z^+$ is a matrix.

The notation (a_{ij}), where $1 \leq i \leq m$ and $1 \leq j \leq n$, will sometimes be used to denote the matrix of Definition 2-1.5. The ijth *entry*, a_{ij}, of A is that entry in the ith row and jth column of A, the mn entries of A will be real numbers, unless otherwise specified. A is called an $m \times n$ (read m by n) dimension matrix, since A has m rows and n columns. If $m = n$, then A is a *square* matrix. The double subscript notation gives the position of an entry. The first subscript identifies the row while the second identifies the column that contains the entry. If $m \geq 6$ and $n \geq 4$, then a_{34} is the entry in the third row and fourth column, a_{64} is the entry in the sixth row and fourth column, and a_{ij} is the entry in the ith row and jth column. We will consider the rows to be *row vectors* and the columns to be *column vectors*. Since the ith row consists of the entries $a_{i1}, a_{i2}, \ldots, a_{in}$, the ith row vector is $(a_{i1}, a_{i2}, \ldots, a_{in})$. The jth column consists of the entries $a_{1j}, a_{2j}, \ldots, a_{mj}$, consequently, the jth column vector is

$$\begin{pmatrix} a_{1j} \\ a_{2j} \\ \vdots \\ a_{mj} \end{pmatrix}$$

Illustration 1

The matrices

$$A = \begin{pmatrix} 2 & -3 & 0 \\ 5 & 1 & 3 \end{pmatrix}, \qquad B = (4 \ -2 \ \ 3), \qquad \text{and} \qquad C = \begin{pmatrix} 2 \\ -3 \end{pmatrix}$$

are examples of 2×3, 1×3, and 2×1 dimension matrices. The row vectors of A are $(2, -3, 0)$ and $(5, 1, 3)$ while the column vectors are $\begin{pmatrix} 2 \\ 5 \end{pmatrix}$, $\begin{pmatrix} -3 \\ 1 \end{pmatrix}$, and $\begin{pmatrix} 0 \\ 3 \end{pmatrix}$. Notice that B has one row vector and three column vectors while C has two row vectors and one column vector.

The definitions that follow are motivated from our knowledge of vectors. Since we want to consider the matrix $(a_{i1} \ a_{i2} \ldots a_{in})$

in the same way as the row vector $(a_{i1}, a_{i2}, \ldots, a_{in})$, we define equality and operations on matrices as the equality and operations on corresponding row (or column) vectors.

DEFINITION 2-1.6. *If $A = (a_{ij})$ and $B = (b_{ij})$ are $m \times n$ dimension matrices, then $A = B$ if and only if $a_{ij} = b_{ij}$ for all $i \in \{1, 2, \ldots, m\}$ and $j \in \{1, 2, \ldots, n\}$.*

Thus, two matrices of the same dimension are equal if and only if corresponding entries (corresponding with respect to position) are equal. An equivalent definition is: two matrices of the same dimension are equal if and only if corresponding row (column) vectors are equal. The equality of matrices can be easily shown to be an equivalence relation.

Illustration 2

If $A = \begin{pmatrix} 3 & -2 & 1 \\ 4 & a & b \end{pmatrix}$, $B = \begin{pmatrix} c & -2 & d \\ 4 & 5 & -2 \end{pmatrix}$ and $A = B$, then by Definition 2-1.6, $a = 5$, $b = -2$, $c = 3$, and $d = 1$.

DEFINITION 2-1.7. *If $A = (a_{ij})$ and $B = (b_{ij})$ are $m \times n$ dimension matrices, the sum $A + B = (a_{ij} + b_{ij})$.*

The sum $A + B$ is that $m \times n$ dimension matrix obtained by adding corresponding entries of A and B. Notice that the ith row vector (jth column vector) is the sum of the ith row vectors (jth column vectors) of A and B.

Illustration 3

If $A = \begin{pmatrix} 1 & 3 \\ 2 & -4 \end{pmatrix}$, $B = \begin{pmatrix} 0 & 1 \\ -1 & 2 \end{pmatrix}$, $C = (2 \quad 1)$, and $D = (-5 \quad 7)$,

then $A + B = \begin{pmatrix} 1+0 & 3+1 \\ 2-1 & -4+2 \end{pmatrix} = \begin{pmatrix} 1 & 4 \\ 1 & -2 \end{pmatrix}$,

$$C + D = (2 - 5 \quad 1 + 7) = (-3 \quad 8)$$

and

$$B + A = \begin{pmatrix} 1 & 4 \\ 1 & -2 \end{pmatrix}$$

Notice that $A + C$, $A + D$, $B + C$, and $B + D$ are not defined since A and B are 2×2, while C and D are 1×2.

DEFINITION 2-1.8. *If c is a scalar (real number) and $A = (a_{ij})$ is an $m \times n$ dimension matrix, the scalar product $cA = (ca_{ij})$.*

If A is $m \times n$, then cA is also $m \times n$. Furthermore, cA is obtained from A by multiplying each entry of A by c.

Illustration 4

If $A = (2 \ -5 \ 3)$ and $B = \begin{pmatrix} 1 & 0 \\ 2 & -3 \\ -1 & 0 \end{pmatrix}$, then $2A = (4 \ -10 \ 6)$,

$3A = (6 \ -15 \ 9)$, $-2A = (-4 \ 10 \ -6)$, $0A = (0 \ 0 \ 0)$, $4B = \begin{pmatrix} 4 & 0 \\ 8 & -12 \\ -4 & 0 \end{pmatrix}$, $-5B = \begin{pmatrix} -5 & 0 \\ -10 & 15 \\ 5 & 0 \end{pmatrix}$, $0B = \begin{pmatrix} 0 & 0 \\ 0 & 0 \\ 0 & 0 \end{pmatrix}$, and $\frac{1}{2}B = \begin{pmatrix} \frac{1}{2} & 0 \\ 1 & -\frac{3}{2} \\ -\frac{1}{2} & 0 \end{pmatrix}$.

DEFINITION 2-1.9. *If $A = (a_{ij})$ is an $m \times n$ dimension matrix, then $-A = (-a_{ij})$.*

By this definition and Definition 2-1.8, $-A = -1A$. Furthermore, subtraction can now be defined, as usual, in terms of addition.

DEFINITION 2-1.10. *If $A = (a_{ij})$ and $B = (b_{ij})$ are $m \times n$ dimension matrices, the difference $A - B = A + (-B)$.*

DEFINITION 2-1.11. *Any matrix each of whose entries is zero is a zero matrix and is denoted by O.*

Thus, $(0 \ 0)$, $\begin{pmatrix} 0 & 0 \\ 0 & 0 \end{pmatrix}$, and $\begin{pmatrix} 0 & 0 & 0 \\ 0 & 0 & 0 \end{pmatrix}$ are the zero 1×2, 2×2, and 2×3 dimension matrices, respectively. Any of these will be denoted by O, provided the dimension is clear from the context.

With the definitions that we have made, each requirement of a vector space over R (see Definition 1-1.1) is easily shown to hold for the set of all $m \times n$ dimension matrices.

THEOREM 2-1.2. *For each pair of numbers m, $n \in Z^+$, the set of all $m \times n$ dimension matrices is a vector space over R.*

COROLLARY 2-1.1. *For each $n \in Z^+$, the set of all $n \times n$ dimension matrices is a vector space over R.*

Illustration 5

If $r, t \in R$ and $A = \begin{pmatrix} a & b & c \\ x & y & z \end{pmatrix}$, prove that $(r + t)A = rA + tA$. Now,

$$(r + t)A = (r + t) \begin{pmatrix} a & b & c \\ x & y & z \end{pmatrix}$$

$$= \begin{pmatrix} (r + t)a & (r + t)b & (r + t)c \\ (r + t)x & (r + t)y & (r + t)z \end{pmatrix}$$

$$= \begin{pmatrix} ra + ta & rb + tb & rc + tc \\ rx + tx & ry + ty & rz + tz \end{pmatrix} \qquad \textit{Provide all reasons.}$$

$$= \begin{pmatrix} ra & rb & rc \\ rx & ry & rz \end{pmatrix} + \begin{pmatrix} ta & tb & tc \\ tx & ty & tz \end{pmatrix}$$

$$= rA + tA$$

By the transitive property of equality of matrices, $(r + t)A = rA + tA$.

43

Problem Set 2-1

1. If $\begin{pmatrix} 3 & -5 & d \\ a & c & e \\ b & 7 & f \end{pmatrix} = \begin{pmatrix} x & y & -2 \\ 5 & 0 & -1 \\ 1 & z & 3 \end{pmatrix}$, what numbers do the letters represent?

2. Let $A = \begin{pmatrix} 3 & -5 & 2 & -4 \\ 0 & 1 & -1 & 7 \end{pmatrix}$.
   (a) What is the dimension of A?
   (b) List the row vectors of A.
   (c) What are the column vectors of A?
   (d) List the entry in: first row, third column; second row, fourth column; second row, second column; first row, second column.

3. Perform the indicated operations for $\mathbf{u} = (2, -1, 3, 5)$, $\mathbf{v} = (1, 4, 0, -3)$, $\mathbf{w} = (-4, 0, 0, 2)$, and $\mathbf{0} = (0, 0, 0, 0)$.
   (a) $\mathbf{u} + \mathbf{v}$ (b) $\mathbf{u} + \mathbf{0}$ (c) $\mathbf{u} + (\mathbf{v} + \mathbf{w})$
   (d) $(\mathbf{u} + \mathbf{v}) + \mathbf{w}$ (e) $4\mathbf{v}$ (f) $-3\mathbf{w}$
   (g) $4\mathbf{v} - 3\mathbf{w}$ (h) $\mathbf{w} - \mathbf{w}$ (i) $3\mathbf{u} - 5\mathbf{v} + 2\mathbf{w}$
   (j) $-5\mathbf{u} + 2\mathbf{v} - \mathbf{w}$ (k) $-\frac{1}{2}\mathbf{w}$

In Problems 4 through 20, let $A = \begin{pmatrix} -1 & 2 & 3 \\ 0 & -5 & 4 \\ 4 & -2 & 1 \end{pmatrix}$, $B = \begin{pmatrix} 5 & -2 \\ 3 & 0 \\ -4 & 2 \end{pmatrix}$,

$C = \begin{pmatrix} 5 & -3 & 1 \\ 0 & 6 & -4 \\ 1 & -2 & 7 \end{pmatrix}$, and $D = \begin{pmatrix} 10 & -4 \\ 6 & 0 \\ -8 & 4 \end{pmatrix}$. Answer the questions and perform the indicated operations.

4. Is it possible to add A and B? If not, why?

5. Is it possible to add C and D? If not, why?

6. $A + C$ 7. $B + D$ 8. $D + B$

9. $C + A$ 10. $2B$ 11. $-5C$

12. $2B - D$ 13. $0A$ 14. $C - C$

15. $5A + 2C$ 16. $3A - 2C$ 17. $B - 3D$

18. $3D - B$ 19. $-2B + D$ 20. $6B - 5D$

In Problems 21 through 30 let $\mathbf{u}$, $\mathbf{v}$, $\mathbf{w}$, and $\mathbf{0}$ be vectors in R^n and let $a, b \in R$. Prove each statement.

21. Argue that equality for R^n is an equivalence relation.

22. $\mathbf{u} + \mathbf{v} = \mathbf{v} + \mathbf{u}$ 23. $(\mathbf{u} + \mathbf{v}) + \mathbf{w} = \mathbf{u} + (\mathbf{v} + \mathbf{w})$

24. $\mathbf{u} + \mathbf{0} = \mathbf{u}$ 25. $\mathbf{u} + (-\mathbf{u}) = \mathbf{0}$

26. $a\mathbf{u} \in R^n$ 27. $(ab)\mathbf{u} = a(b\mathbf{u})$

28. $(a + b)\mathbf{u} = a\mathbf{u} + b\mathbf{u}$ 29. $a(\mathbf{u} + \mathbf{v}) = a\mathbf{u} + a\mathbf{v}$

30. $1\mathbf{u} = \mathbf{u}$

31. If s is a scalar, $A = \begin{pmatrix} a & b & c \\ d & e & f \end{pmatrix}$, and $B = \begin{pmatrix} x & y & z \\ t & u & v \end{pmatrix}$, prove that $s(A + B) = sA + sB$.

32. For A and B of Problem 31 and $C = \begin{pmatrix} g & h & i \\ j & k & l \end{pmatrix}$, prove that $(A + B) + C = A + (B + C)$.

In Problems 33 through 42 let A, B, C, and O be $m \times n$ dimension matrices and let $c, d \in R$. Prove each assertion.

33. Argue that equality for the set of all $m \times n$ dimension matrices is an equivalence relation. (See Problem 21.)

34. $A + B = B + A$ 35. $(A + B) + C = A + (B + C)$

36. $A + O = A$ 37. $A + (-A) = O$

38. cA is an $m \times n$ matrix   39. $(cd)A = c(dA)$

40. $(c + d)A = cA + dA$ 41. $c(A + B) = cA + cB$

42. $1A = A$

43. Extend the definitions of the dot product for R^2 and R^3 to R^4, then to R^n.

44. For the vectors of Problem 3, evaluate:

    (a) $\mathbf{u} \cdot \mathbf{v}$ (b) $\mathbf{v} \cdot \mathbf{u}$ (c) $\mathbf{u} \cdot (\mathbf{v} + \mathbf{w})$

    (d) $(\mathbf{u} \cdot \mathbf{v}) + (\mathbf{u} \cdot \mathbf{w})$ (e) $\mathbf{u} \cdot \mathbf{u}$ (f) $\mathbf{u} \cdot (\mathbf{v} - \mathbf{w})$

    (g) $\mathbf{u} \cdot \mathbf{v} - \mathbf{u} \cdot \mathbf{w}$ (h) $\mathbf{w} \cdot \mathbf{0}$ (i) $|\mathbf{u}|$

    (j) $|\mathbf{v}|$ (k) $|\mathbf{w}|$ (l) $(4\mathbf{v}) \cdot (-3\mathbf{w})$

45. Prove Theorem 2-1.2.

2-2. MATRIX MULTIPLICATION

Since addition of matrices was motivated from addition of vectors, you would expect that matrix multiplication could be motivated from multiplication of vectors. Now, the cross product of vectors is defined for R^3 but not for R^2 or R^1, however, the dot product is defined in R^n for each $n \in Z^+$. (See Problem 43 of Problem Set 2-1.)

Thus, if $A = (a_1\, a_2 \ldots a_n)$ and $B = \begin{pmatrix} b_1 \\ b_2 \\ \vdots \\ b_n \end{pmatrix}$, we will define AB to be

that 1×1 matrix whose entry is the dot product of the row vector $(a_1, a_2, \ldots, a_n)$ of A and the column vector $(b_1, b_2, \ldots, b_n)$ of B. Therefore, $AB = (a_1b_1 + a_2b_2 + \cdots + a_nb_n)$.

The Greek letter sigma ($\sum$) provides a concise notation for a sum. For example, $3 + 6 + 9 + 12$ is written $\sum_{k=1}^{k=4} 3k$ where k is given the values 1, 2, 3, and 4 and the resulting numbers are added. Some other examples are:

$$5 + 10 + 15 + \cdots + 50 = \sum_{k=1}^{k=10} 5k$$

$$4 + 4 + 4 + 4 = \sum_{k=1}^{k=4} 4$$

$$a_1 + a_2 + \cdots + a_n = \sum_{k=1}^{k=n} a_k$$

$$b_{i1} + b_{i2} + \cdots + b_{in} = \sum_{k=1}^{k=n} b_{ik}$$

45

and

$$a_{i1}b_{1j} + a_{i2}b_{2j} + \cdots + a_{in}b_{nj} = \sum_{k=1}^{k=n} a_{ik}b_{kj}$$

We are now ready to define multiplication of matrices.

DEFINITION 2-2.1. *If $A = (a_{ij})$ has dimension $m \times n$ and $B = (b_{ij})$ has dimension $n \times t$, then the product*

$$AB = (c_{ij}) = \left(\sum_{k=1}^{k=n} a_{ik}b_{kj} \right)$$

for $1 \le i \le m$ and $1 \le j \le t$.

To understand this definition better, we express A, B, and AB in the equivalent forms

$$A = \begin{pmatrix} a_{11} & a_{12} & \cdots & a_{1n} \\ a_{21} & a_{22} & \cdots & a_{2n} \\ \vdots & \vdots & \ddots & \vdots \\ a_{i1} & a_{i2} & \cdots & a_{in} \\ \vdots & \vdots & \ddots & \vdots \\ a_{m1} & a_{m2} & \cdots & a_{mn} \end{pmatrix} \text{ith row,} \qquad B = \begin{pmatrix} b_{11} & b_{12} & \cdots & b_{1j} & \cdots & b_{1t} \\ b_{21} & b_{22} & \cdots & b_{2j} & \cdots & b_{2t} \\ \vdots & \vdots & \ddots & \vdots & \ddots & \vdots \\ b_{n1} & b_{n2} & \cdots & b_{nj} & \cdots & b_{nt} \end{pmatrix}$$

(*j*th column, above B)

and

$$AB = \begin{pmatrix} \sum_{k=1}^{k=n} a_{1k}b_{k1} & \sum_{k=1}^{k=n} a_{1k}b_{k2} & \cdots & \sum_{k=1}^{k=n} a_{1k}b_{kj} & \cdots & \sum_{k=1}^{k=n} a_{1k}b_{kt} \\ \sum_{k=1}^{k=n} a_{2k}b_{k1} & \sum_{k=1}^{k=n} a_{2k}b_{k2} & \cdots & \sum_{k=1}^{k=n} a_{2k}b_{kj} & \cdots & \sum_{k=1}^{k=n} a_{2k}b_{kt} \\ \vdots & \vdots & \ddots & \vdots & \ddots & \vdots \\ \sum_{k=1}^{k=n} a_{ik}b_{k1} & \sum_{k=1}^{k=n} a_{ik}b_{k2} & \cdots & \sum_{k=1}^{k=n} a_{ik}b_{kj} & \cdots & \sum_{k=1}^{k=n} a_{ik}b_{kt} \\ \vdots & \vdots & \ddots & \vdots & \ddots & \vdots \\ \sum_{k=1}^{k=n} a_{mk}b_{k1} & \sum_{k=1}^{k=n} a_{mk}b_{k2} & \cdots & \sum_{k=1}^{k=n} a_{mk}b_{kj} & \cdots & \sum_{k=1}^{k=n} a_{mk}b_{kt} \end{pmatrix} \text{ith row}$$

(*j*th column, above AB)

Notice that AB has dimension $m \times t$. Furthermore, each entry of AB is the dot product of a row vector of A and a column vector of B. The ijth entry of AB is the dot product of the ith row vector of A and the jth column vector of B. Another important result to notice is that each row vector of AB is a linear combination of the row vectors of B. This result will be more clearly seen from the following illustration.

Illustration 1

Obtain AB if $A = \begin{pmatrix} a & b \\ c & d \end{pmatrix}$ and $B = \begin{pmatrix} x & y & z \\ u & v & w \end{pmatrix}$. From the definition

of the product AB, we have $AB = \begin{pmatrix} ax + bu & ay + bv & az + bw \\ cx + du & cy + dv & cz + dw \end{pmatrix}$.

Since A is 2×2 and B is 2×3, AB is 2×3. The two row vectors of AB as linear combinations of the row vectors of B are

$$\mathbf{v}_1 = a(x, y, z) + b(u, v, w)$$

and

$$\mathbf{v}_2 = c(x, y, z) + d(u, v, w)$$

Thus,

$$\mathbf{v}_1 = (ax + bu, \; ay + bv, \; az + bw)$$
$$\mathbf{v}_2 = (cx + du, \; cy + dv, \; cz + dw)$$

and the product AB is as given above.

Theorem 2-2.1. *If $A = (a_{ij})$ has dimension $m \times n$, $B = (b_{ij})$ has dimension $n \times t$, and the row vectors of B are $\mathbf{b}_1, \mathbf{b}_2, \ldots, \mathbf{b}_n$, then the ith row vector, $\mathbf{v}_i$, of AB is $\mathbf{v}_i = a_{i1}\mathbf{b}_1 + a_{i2}\mathbf{b}_2 + \cdots + a_{in}\mathbf{b}_n$.*

Illustration 2

If $A = \begin{pmatrix} 3 & 4 & -2 \\ 0 & 1 & 5 \\ 1 & -3 & 0 \end{pmatrix}$ and $B = \begin{pmatrix} 4 & -2 \\ 1 & 3 \\ 0 & 5 \end{pmatrix}$, determine AB in two ways.

The three row vectors $\mathbf{v}_1$, $\mathbf{v}_2$, and $\mathbf{v}_3$ of AB are

$$\mathbf{v}_1 = 3(4, -2) + 4(1, 3) + (-2)(0, 5) = (16, -4)$$
$$\mathbf{v}_2 = 0(4, -2) + 1(1, 3) + 5(0, 5) = (1, 28)$$
$$\mathbf{v}_3 = 1(4, -2) + (-3)(1, 3) + 0(0, 5) = (1, -11)$$

Therefore,

$$AB = \begin{pmatrix} 16 & -4 \\ 1 & 28 \\ 1 & -11 \end{pmatrix}$$

Using Definition 2-2.1,

$$AB = \begin{pmatrix} 3(4) + 4(1) + (-2)0 & 3(-2) + 4(3) + (-2)5 \\ 0(4) + 1(1) + 5(0) & 0(-2) + 1(3) + 5(5) \\ 1(4) + (-3)1 + 0(0) & 1(-2) + (-3)(3) + 0(5) \end{pmatrix} = \begin{pmatrix} 16 & -4 \\ 1 & 28 \\ 1 & -11 \end{pmatrix}$$

as before.

The product BA for the matrices A and B of Illustration 2 is not defined since B is 3×2 and A is 3×3. Thus, matrix multiplication is not commutative. Even if AB and BA both exist they may not be equal, as the next illustration shows.

47

Illustration 3

If $A = \begin{pmatrix} 0 & 2 \\ 2 & 0 \end{pmatrix}$ and $B = \begin{pmatrix} 2 & 0 \\ 2 & 0 \end{pmatrix}$, then $AB \neq BA$ for $AB = \begin{pmatrix} 4 & 0 \\ 4 & 0 \end{pmatrix}$
while $BA = \begin{pmatrix} 0 & 4 \\ 0 & 4 \end{pmatrix}$.

We close this section with some theorems concerning matrix multiplication. Some of the theorems are easily proved while others are not so easily proved.

THEOREM 2-2.2. *If $A = (a_{ij})$ is $m \times n$, $B = (b_{ij})$ is $n \times t$, and $c \in R$, then*

$$c(AB) = (cA)B = A(cB)$$

THEOREM 2-2.3. *If $A = B$, and*

a. *if CA exists, then $CA = CB$*   *Premultiplicative Property*
b. *if AC exists, then $AC = BC$*   *Postmultiplicative Property*

THEOREM 2-2.4. *If A has dimension $m \times n$, B and C have dimension $n \times t$, and D has dimension $t \times s$, then*

a. $A(B + C) = AB + AC$ *Left Distributive Property*
b. $(B + C)D = BD + CD$ *Right Distributive Property*

THEOREM 2-2.5. *If A has dimension $m \times n$, B dimension $n \times t$, and C dimension $t \times s$, then*

$$A(BC) = (AB)C \qquad \text{Associative Property}$$

Proof of Theorem 2-2.4, Part a: The ijth entry of $A(B + C)$ is the dot product of the ith row vector, $(a_{i1}, a_{i2}, \ldots, a_{in})$, of A and the jth column vector, $(b_{1j} + c_{1j}, b_{2j} + c_{2j}, \ldots, b_{nj} + c_{nj})$, of $B + C$. Now,

$(a_{i1}, a_{i2}, \ldots, a_{in}) \cdot (b_{1j} + c_{1j}, b_{2j} + c_{2j}, \ldots, b_{nj} + c_{nj})$

$= a_{i1}(b_{1j} + c_{1j}) + a_{i2}(b_{2j} + c_{2j}) + \cdots + a_{in}(b_{nj} + c_{nj})$

$= (a_{i1}b_{1j} + a_{i2}b_{2j} + \cdots + a_{in}b_{nj}) + (a_{i1}c_{1j} + a_{i2}c_{2j} + \cdots + a_{in}c_{nj})$

$= (a_{i1}, a_{i2}, \ldots, a_{in}) \cdot (b_{1j}, b_{2j}, \ldots, b_{nj})$

$\quad + (a_{i1}, a_{i2}, \ldots, a_{in}) \cdot (c_{1j}, c_{2j}, \ldots, c_{nj})$

which is the sum of the dot products of the ith row vector of A with the jth column vectors of B and C. Thus, the ijth entry of $A(B + C)$ is the sum of the ijth entries of AB and BC. Therefore, $A(B + C) = AB + AC$.

Problem Set 2-2

1. Write out the indicated summations.

(a) $\sum\limits_{k=1}^{k=4} 8k$ (b) $\sum\limits_{k=1}^{k=5} -3k$ (c) $\sum\limits_{k=1}^{k=3} 6$

(d) $\sum\limits_{k=0}^{k=n-1} ar^k, \qquad r \neq 0$ (e) $\sum\limits_{k=0}^{k=n} \dfrac{x^k}{k!}, \qquad x \neq 0$

(f) $\sum\limits_{k=1}^{k=n} \dfrac{(-1)^{k-1}x^{2k-1}}{(2k-1)!}$ (g) $\sum\limits_{k=0}^{k=n} \dfrac{(-1)^k x^{2k}}{(2k)!}, \qquad x \neq 0$

In Problems 2 through 16 perform the indicated operations, where possible, if $A = \begin{pmatrix} 3 \\ -5 \end{pmatrix}$, $B = \begin{pmatrix} 1 & -4 \\ 2 & 0 \\ 3 & -2 \end{pmatrix}$, $C = \begin{pmatrix} -1 & 0 & 2 \\ 2 & 1 & 3 \\ 0 & 1 & -1 \end{pmatrix}$, $D = (2 \ -1)$, $E = \begin{pmatrix} 2 & 0 \\ 0 & 2 \end{pmatrix}$, and $F = \begin{pmatrix} 3 & -2 \\ 1 & 0 \\ 0 & -4 \end{pmatrix}$.

2. AD	3. DA	4. BE	5. EB
6. DE	7. FE	8. CF	9. CB
10. EE	11. BB	12. CC	13. $C(B+F)$
14. $CB + CF$	15. $(B+F)E$	16. $BE + FE$	

In Problems 17 through 25 use the same matrices as for Problems 2 through 16. Express the row vectors of the indicated product matrix as linear combinations of the row vectors of the second matrix in each product.

17. AD	18. DA	19. BE	20. DE
21. FE	22. CF	23. CB	24. EE
25. CC			

26. If $AC = BC$, is it true that $A = B$? If not, why?

27. If $CA = CB$, is it true that $A = B$? If not, why?

28. If A is $m \times n$, B is $n \times t$, and C is $t \times s$, what is the dimension of $(AB)C$? of $A(BC)$?

29. Prove part b of Theorem 2-2.4. (*Hint:* Pattern a proof after that of part a.)

30. Prove Theorem 2-2.2.

31. Prove Theorem 2-2.3.

32. If A is 2×3, B is 3×3, and C is 3×2, prove that $(AB)C = A(BC)$.

2-3. SOME SPECIAL MATRICES

Square matrices, zero matrices, and the additive inverse, $-A$, of a matrix A have already been described. Some other matrices that have certain forms or affect other matrices in certain ways under addition or multiplication are now introduced. Other special matrices will be discussed when they are needed.

In the first four definitions we use the *main diagonal* of a square matrix. The main diagonal is the line connecting the entry in the upper left-hand corner with the entry in the lower right-hand corner. If $A = (a_{ij})$ is $n \times n$, the entries on the main diagonal are $a_{11}, a_{22}, \ldots, a_{nn}$.

DEFINITION 2-3.1. *A diagonal matrix is a square matrix with zeros everywhere off the main diagonal.*

Thus, $A = (a_{ij})$ is a diagonal matrix if and only if $a_{ij} = 0$ for $i \neq j$. The next two illustrations show how a diagonal matrix affects other matrices under multiplication.

Illustration 1

If $A = \begin{pmatrix} a & 0 \\ 0 & b \end{pmatrix}$ and $B = \begin{pmatrix} r & s & t & u \\ x & y & z & w \end{pmatrix}$, obtain AB. The product is easily obtained as

$$AB = \begin{pmatrix} ar & as & at & au \\ bx & by & bz & bw \end{pmatrix}$$

Thus, AB is the matrix formed from B by multiplying each entry in the first row of B by a and each entry in the second row of B by b. In terms of row vectors, the row vectors of AB are those of B multiplied by a and b, respectively. More generally, if $A = (a_{ij})$ is a diagonal $n \times n$ matrix and B is an $n \times t$ matrix, the row vectors of AB are those of B multiplied by $a_{11}, a_{22}, \ldots, a_{nn}$, respectively.

Illustration 2

Obtain BA if $A = \begin{pmatrix} a & 0 \\ 0 & b \end{pmatrix}$ and $B = \begin{pmatrix} r & x \\ s & y \\ t & z \\ u & w \end{pmatrix}$

Clearly,

$$BA = \begin{pmatrix} ar & bx \\ as & by \\ at & bz \\ au & bw \end{pmatrix}$$

Now, BA, is the matrix formed from B by multiplying each entry in the first column of B by a and each entry in the second column by b. Using column vectors, the column vectors of BA are those of B multiplied by a and b, respectively. In general, if $A = (a_{ij})$ is a diagonal $n \times n$ matrix and B is an $m \times n$ matrix, the column vectors of BA are those of B multiplied by $a_{11}, a_{22}, \ldots, a_{nn}$, respectively.

DEFINITION 2-3.2. *For an* $n \in Z^+$, *if* $IA = AI = A$ *for all matrices A of dimension* $n \times n$, *then I is the multiplicative identity for the set of all* $n \times n$ *matrices.*

Illustration 3

The matrix $I = \begin{pmatrix} 1 & 0 \\ 0 & 1 \end{pmatrix}$ is the multiplicative identity for the set of all

2 × 2 matrices. If $A = \begin{pmatrix} a & b \\ c & d \end{pmatrix}$, then $IA = AI = A$. The matrix $I = \begin{pmatrix} 1 & 0 & 0 \\ 0 & 1 & 0 \\ 0 & 0 & 1 \end{pmatrix}$ is the multiplicative identity matrix for the set of all 3 × 3

matrices. More generally, notice that the identity matrix I for the set of all $n \times n$ matrices is that $n \times n$ diagonal matrix with ones everywhere on the main diagonal. As indicated, I is used to denote an identity matrix of any dimension.

Illustration 4

Obtain AB if $A = \begin{pmatrix} 1 & 0 \\ 0 & 1 \end{pmatrix}$ and $B = \begin{pmatrix} 4 & -2 & 0 & 3 \\ 3 & 1 & 5 & -1 \end{pmatrix}$. Now,

$$AB = \begin{pmatrix} 1 & 0 \\ 0 & 1 \end{pmatrix} \begin{pmatrix} 4 & -2 & 0 & 3 \\ 3 & 1 & 5 & -1 \end{pmatrix} = \begin{pmatrix} 4 & -2 & 0 & 3 \\ 3 & 1 & 5 & -1 \end{pmatrix} = B$$

Since $AB = B$, A is called a *left identity* for B. Furthermore, A is a left identity for the set of all 2 × n matrices. Since BA is not defined, A is not a right identity for B. Can you guess a right identity for B?

DEFINITION 2-3.3. *A scalar matrix is a diagonal matrix with the same scalar a everywhere on the main diagonal.*

An identity matrix is a scalar matrix with $a = 1$. Our knowledge of matrix multiplication provides the following information. If A is an $n \times n$ scalar matrix with a on the main diagonal and B is an $n \times t$ matrix, then $AB = aB$. Thus, A as a left multiplier of B reproduces B multiplied by the scalar a. If C is an $m \times n$ matrix, then $CA = aC$. Notice that $A = aI$.

DEFINITION 2-3.4. *A triangular matrix is a square matrix such that*

a. *all entries above the main diagonal are zero, or*
b. *all entries below the main diagonal are zero.*

Triangular matrices will be useful in solving systems of linear equations. As we will see, the determinant (number) associated with a triangular matrix is easily evaluated.

The last special matrix considered here is one that is formed from a given matrix by changing the row (column) vectors to corresponding numbered column (row) vectors.

51

DEFINITION 2-3.5. *If $A = (a_{ij})$ is an $m \times n$ matrix, the transpose of A (or A transpose) is the $n \times m$ matrix $A^t = (a_{ji})$.*

Illustration 5

If $A = \begin{pmatrix} 1 & 5 \\ 3 & -2 \end{pmatrix}$, then $A^t = \begin{pmatrix} 1 & 3 \\ 5 & -2 \end{pmatrix}$. If $B = \begin{pmatrix} 3 & 2 & -5 & 4 \\ 0 & 2 & 1 & -2 \\ 1 & 7 & 0 & 1 \end{pmatrix}$,

then $B^t = \begin{pmatrix} 3 & 0 & 1 \\ 2 & 2 & 7 \\ -5 & 1 & 0 \\ 4 & -2 & 1 \end{pmatrix}$.

More generally, if

$$C = \begin{pmatrix} c_{11} & c_{12} & \cdots & c_{1n} \\ c_{21} & c_{22} & \cdots & c_{2n} \\ \vdots & \vdots & \ddots & \vdots \\ c_{m1} & c_{m2} & \cdots & c_{mn} \end{pmatrix}, \text{ then } C^t = \begin{pmatrix} c_{11} & c_{21} & \cdots & c_{m1} \\ c_{12} & c_{22} & \cdots & c_{m2} \\ \vdots & \vdots & \ddots & \vdots \\ c_{1n} & c_{2n} & \cdots & c_{mn} \end{pmatrix}$$

The following three theorems are easily proved. Furthermore, you will see the mathematical patterns repeated in other areas of mathematics.

THEOREM 2-3.1. *If A is a matrix, $(A^t)^t = A$.*

THEOREM 2-3.2. *If B and C are $m \times n$ matrices and $A = B + C$, then,*

$$A^t = B^t + C^t$$

THEOREM 2-3.3. *If B is an $m \times n$ matrix, C is $n \times t$, and $A = BC$, then*

$$A^t = C^t B^t$$

Proof of Theorem 2-3.2: The ijth entry of A^t is the jith entry of A. Since $A = B + C$, the jith entry of A is the sum of the jith entries of B and C. Further, the jith entries of B and C are the ijth entries of B^t and C^t. Therefore, the ijth entry of A^t is the sum of the ijth entries of B^t and C^t. Consequently, $A^t = B^t + C^t$.

Problem Set 2-3

In Problems 1 through 6 let $A = \begin{pmatrix} 3 & -5 \\ -2 & 4 \end{pmatrix}$.

1. If $I = \begin{pmatrix} 1 & 0 \\ 0 & 1 \end{pmatrix}$, then $AI = ?$ $IA = ?$

2. If $B = \begin{pmatrix} 5 & 0 \\ 0 & 5 \end{pmatrix}$, compute AB and BA.

3. If $B = \begin{pmatrix} -3 & 0 \\ 0 & -3 \end{pmatrix}$, compute AB and BA.

4. If $B = \begin{pmatrix} 0 & 1 \\ 1 & 0 \end{pmatrix}$, then $AB = ?$ $BA = ?$

5. Determine AB and BA if $B = \begin{pmatrix} 4 & 0 \\ 0 & 1 \end{pmatrix}$.

6. If $B = \begin{pmatrix} 1 & 0 \\ 3 & 1 \end{pmatrix}$, then $AB = ?$ $BA = ?$

In Problems 7 through 15 let $A = \begin{pmatrix} 3 & -4 & 2 \\ -2 & 1 & 0 \\ 1 & 2 & -3 \end{pmatrix}$ and determine the products AB and BA for the given matrices B.

7. $B = \begin{pmatrix} 5 & 0 & 0 \\ 0 & 5 & 0 \\ 0 & 0 & 5 \end{pmatrix}$
8. $B = \begin{pmatrix} -3 & 0 & 0 \\ 0 & -3 & 0 \\ 0 & 0 & -3 \end{pmatrix}$

9. $B = \begin{pmatrix} 5 & 0 & 0 \\ 0 & -3 & 0 \\ 0 & 0 & 2 \end{pmatrix}$
10. $B = \begin{pmatrix} 0 & 0 & 1 \\ 0 & 1 & 0 \\ 1 & 0 & 0 \end{pmatrix}$

11. $B = \begin{pmatrix} 1 & 0 & 0 \\ 0 & 3 & 0 \\ 0 & 0 & 1 \end{pmatrix}$
12. $B = \begin{pmatrix} 1 & 0 & 0 \\ 0 & 1 & 0 \\ 1 & 0 & 1 \end{pmatrix}$

13. $B = \begin{pmatrix} 1 & 0 & 2 \\ 0 & 1 & 0 \\ 0 & 0 & 1 \end{pmatrix}$
14. $B = \begin{pmatrix} 1 & 0 & 0 \\ 0 & 3 & 0 \\ 5 & 0 & 1 \end{pmatrix}$

15. $B = \begin{pmatrix} 1 & 0 & 0 \\ -3, & 1 & 0 \\ 0 & 0 & -5 \end{pmatrix}$

16. If $A = \begin{pmatrix} 4 & 0 \\ 0 & 4 \end{pmatrix}$ and $B = \begin{pmatrix} 2 & -3 & 5 \\ 4 & 0 & -2 \end{pmatrix}$, obtain AB.

17. If $A = \begin{pmatrix} -2 & 0 \\ 0 & -2 \end{pmatrix}$ and $B = \begin{pmatrix} 2 & -3 & 5 \\ 4 & 0 & -2 \end{pmatrix}$, then $AB = ?$

18. Obtain AB if $A = \begin{pmatrix} 3 & 0 \\ 0 & -2 \end{pmatrix}$ and $B = \begin{pmatrix} 2 & -3 & 5 \\ 4 & 0 & -2 \end{pmatrix}$.

19. Determine AB if $A = \begin{pmatrix} 3 & 0 \\ 4 & -2 \end{pmatrix}$ and $B = \begin{pmatrix} 2 & -3 & 5 \\ 4 & 0 & -2 \end{pmatrix}$.

20. Obtain the transpose of each of the following matrices.

(a) $\begin{pmatrix} 1 & 0 \\ 0 & 1 \end{pmatrix}$
(b) $\begin{pmatrix} a & 0 \\ 0 & b \end{pmatrix}$
(c) $\begin{pmatrix} 0 & a \\ b & 0 \end{pmatrix}$

(d) $\begin{pmatrix} 2 & -3 & 5 \\ 4 & 0 & -2 \end{pmatrix}$
(e) $\begin{pmatrix} a & 0 & 0 \\ 0 & b & 0 \\ 0 & 0 & c \end{pmatrix}$

(f) $\begin{pmatrix} 3 & 2 & -1 \\ 0 & -4 & 2 \\ 1 & 0 & 5 \end{pmatrix}$
(g) $\begin{pmatrix} 2 & -3 & 0 & 1 & -6 \\ 1 & 0 & 2 & 5 & 4 \\ 0 & 3 & 1 & -2 & 1 \end{pmatrix}$

(h) $\begin{pmatrix} a & b & c \\ b & d & e \\ c & e & f \end{pmatrix}$
(i) $\begin{pmatrix} a & b & c & d \\ b & e & f & g \\ c & f & h & i \\ d & g & i & j \end{pmatrix}$

21. Prove that $I = \begin{pmatrix} 1 & 0 & 0 \\ 0 & 1 & 0 \\ 0 & 0 & 1 \end{pmatrix}$ is the identity 3×3 matrix.

22. Prove that the $n \times n$ diagonal matrix with 1s everywhere on the main diagonal is the identity $n \times n$ matrix.

23. If A is a diagonal matrix, prove that $A^t = A$.

24. If A is a triangular matrix, prove that A^t is triangular.

25. Prove Theorem 2–3.1.

26. Prove Theorem 2–3.3.

Systems of Linear Equations

3-1. HOMOGENEOUS SYSTEMS OF LINEAR EQUATIONS

Matrices provide several methods of solving systems of linear equations. In this chapter, two such methods are discussed. The first method is essentially the same as the algebraic method of elimination except that the operations are performed on certain matrices rather than on equations. In this section we consider systems of homogeneous equations (homogeneous systems), then, in the next section, systems of nonhomogeneous equations (nonhomogeneous systems).

The general homogeneous system of m linear equations in n unknowns is

(3-1.1)
$$\begin{cases} a_{11}x_1 + a_{12}x_2 + \cdots + a_{1n}x_n = 0 \\ a_{21}x_1 + a_{22}x_2 + \cdots + a_{2n}x_n = 0 \\ \vdots \qquad \vdots \qquad \ddots \qquad \vdots \qquad \vdots \\ a_{m1}x_1 + a_{m2}x_2 + \cdots + a_{mn}x_n = 0 \end{cases}$$

where $x_1, x_2, \ldots, x_n$ are the unknowns. In this study the coefficients a_{ij} for $1 \leq i \leq m$, $1 \leq j \leq n$, and $i, j \in Z^+$ are real numbers. Since each term on one side of each equation involves an unknown while the term on the other side is zero, each equation is *homogeneous* and the system is called a *homogeneous system*. A solution of system (3–1.1) is an ordered n-tuple $(x_1, x_2, \ldots, x_n) \in R^n$ that satisfies each equation in the system, while the *solution set S* of the system is the set of all such solutions. *Two homogeneous systems are equivalent if and only if each equation in each system is a linear combination of the equations in the other system.* For example, the systems

$$\begin{cases} 2x - 3y = 0 \\ x + 2y = 0 \end{cases} \quad \text{and} \quad \begin{cases} -7y = 0 \\ x + 2y = 0 \end{cases}$$

are equivalent since

$$2x - 3y = 1(-7y) + 2(x + 2y)$$

$$x + 2y = 0(-7y) + 1(x + 2y)$$

and

$$-7y = 1(2x - 3y) - 2(x + 2y)$$

$$x + 2y = 0(2x - 3y) + 1(x + 2y)$$

Notice that equivalence of systems is an equivalence relation. (See Section 2–1.) If two homogeneous systems of m linear equations in n unknowns are equivalent, then each solution of either system is a solution of the other system. This result is stated as a theorem. (Refer to Appendix for equality of sets.)

THEOREM 3–1.1. *If two homogeneous systems H_1 and H_2 of m linear equations in n unknowns are equivalent and have solution sets S_1 and S_2, respectively, then $S_1 = S_2$.*

The homogeneous system (3–1.1) may have many solutions and always has the *trivial solution* $(0, 0, \ldots, 0)$. The matrix form of system (3–1.1) is $AX = B$, where

$$A = \begin{pmatrix} a_{11} & a_{12} & \cdots & a_{1n} \\ a_{21} & a_{22} & \cdots & a_{2n} \\ \vdots & \vdots & \ddots & \vdots \\ a_{m1} & a_{m2} & \cdots & a_{mn} \end{pmatrix}, \quad X = \begin{pmatrix} x_1 \\ x_2 \\ \vdots \\ x_n \end{pmatrix}, \quad \text{and} \quad B = \begin{pmatrix} 0 \\ 0 \\ \vdots \\ 0 \end{pmatrix}$$

The matrix A is the *matrix of coefficients* or the *coefficient matrix* for the system. As we shall see, the method of elimination applied to system (3–1.1) is equivalent to using certain row operations on the matrix A (see Illustrations 1 and 2).

Illustration 1

Use elimination to solve the system

$$\begin{cases} 2x - 3y = 0 \\ x + 2y = 0 \end{cases}$$

The elimination method can be applied as follows to yield a sequence of systems each equivalent to the given system.

$$\begin{cases} x + 2y = 0 \\ 2x - 3y = 0 \end{cases}$$ *Interchange the two equations.*

$$\begin{cases} x + 2y = 0 \\ - 7y = 0 \end{cases}$$ *Multiply the first equation by -2 and add*
to the second equation.

$$\begin{cases} x + 2y = 0 \\ y = 0 \end{cases}$$ *Multiply the second equation by $-\frac{1}{7}$.*

$$\begin{cases} x = 0 \\ y = 0 \end{cases}$$ *Multiply the second equation by -2 and*
add to the first equation.

Therefore, the solution set $S = \{ (0, 0) \}$. Geometrically, the lines in R^2 defined by the equations of the system intersect only at the origin.

In the above illustration notice the operations on equations that were used to obtain systems equivalent to the preceding systems. These operations are called *elementary operations on equations*, and are

i. multiplying an equation by a nonzero scalar,
ii. interchanging two equations, and
iii. adding the product of a scalar and an equation to another equation.

It should be clear that if any one of these three operations is performed on a system of homogeneous linear equations, an equivalent system is obtained. More actually holds, as the following theorem states.

THEOREM 3–1.2.   *Two homogeneous systems of m linear equations in n unknowns are equivalent if and only if each system is the result of a finite sequence of elementary operations on equations applied to the other system.*

In matrix form, the system of Illustration 1 is $AX = B$, where

$$A = \begin{pmatrix} 2 & -3 \\ 1 & 2 \end{pmatrix}, \qquad X = \begin{pmatrix} x \\ y \end{pmatrix}, \qquad \text{and} \qquad B = \begin{pmatrix} 0 \\ 0 \end{pmatrix}$$

The operations on the equations can be performed using A and elementary row operations. The *elementary row operations* on a matrix are

i. multiplying a row by a nonzero scalar,
ii. interchanging two rows, and
iii. adding the product of a scalar and a row to another row.

In the next illustration elementary row operations are used to solve the system of Illustration 1. In fact, the operations on rows will be exactly those operations on equations that were used in Illustration 1. Notice that row operations are operations on row vectors. The word vector will not be used because we do not want to always consider a vector as an n-tuple.

Illustration 2

Solve the system $\begin{cases} 2x - 3y = 0 \\ x + 2y = 0 \end{cases}$ using elementary row operations on

the coefficient matrix $A = \begin{pmatrix} 2 & -3 \\ 1 & 2 \end{pmatrix}$. From A, we have

$\begin{pmatrix} 1 & 2 \\ 2 & -3 \end{pmatrix}$ *Interchange the two rows of A.*

$\begin{pmatrix} 1 & 2 \\ 0 & -7 \end{pmatrix}$ *Add -2 times the first row to the second row.*

$\begin{pmatrix} 1 & 2 \\ 0 & 1 \end{pmatrix}$ *Multiply the second row by $-\frac{1}{7}$.*

$\begin{pmatrix} 1 & 0 \\ 0 & 1 \end{pmatrix}$ *Add -2 times the second row to the first row.*

This last matrix is the coefficient matrix of the system $\begin{cases} x = 0 \\ y = 0 \end{cases}$, since

$\begin{pmatrix} 1 & 0 \\ 0 & 1 \end{pmatrix} \begin{pmatrix} x \\ y \end{pmatrix} = \begin{pmatrix} 0 \\ 0 \end{pmatrix}$. Therefore, $S = \{ (0, 0) \}$, as before.

The conclusion that $S = \{ (0, 0) \}$ in the above illustration is valid since the following theorem holds. This theorem is simply a restatement of Theorem 3-1.2 in terms of elementary row operations.

THEOREM 3-1.3. *Two homogeneous systems of m linear equations in n unknowns are equivalent if and only if each coefficient matrix is the result of a finite sequence of elementary row operations on the other coefficient matrix.*

Next, we define the concept of row-equivalence for matrices, then restate Theorem 3-1.3 in terms of this concept.

DEFINITION 3-1.1. *If A and B are m × n matrices over R, then A is row-equivalent to B if and only if B is the result of a finite sequence of elementary row operations on A.*

You can easily show that *is row-equivalent to* is an equivalence relation on the set of all $m \times n$ matrices. Thus, if A is row-equivalent to B, then B is row-equivalent to A and we sometimes say that A and B are row-equivalent.

THEOREM 3-1.4. *Two homogeneous systems of m linear equations in n unknowns are equivalent if and only if their coefficient matrices are row-equivalent.*

In the next illustration we use different sequences of row operations on a coefficient matrix to solve a system. The point to notice here is that equal solution sets are obtained. Thus, the order in which the row operations are applied is not important.

Illustration 3

Solve the system $\begin{cases} 2x - 3y + z = 0 \\ x + 2y - z = 0 \\ 6x - 9y + 3z = 0 \end{cases}$. The matrix of coefficients is

$A = \begin{pmatrix} 2 & -3 & 1 \\ 1 & 2 & -1 \\ 6 & -9 & 3 \end{pmatrix}$. One sequence of row operations on A is

$\begin{pmatrix} 1 & 2 & -1 \\ 2 & -3 & 1 \\ 6 & -9 & 3 \end{pmatrix}$ *Interchange the first and second rows.*

$\begin{pmatrix} 1 & 2 & -1 \\ 0 & -7 & 3 \\ 0 & -21 & 9 \end{pmatrix}$ *Add -2 times the first row to the second row.*

$\begin{pmatrix} 1 & 2 & -1 \\ 0 & -7 & 3 \\ 0 & 0 & 0 \end{pmatrix}$ *Why?*

This last matrix is the coefficient matrix of the system $\begin{cases} x + 2y - z = 0 \\ 0x - 7y + 3z = 0 \\ 0x + 0y + 0z = 0 \end{cases}$.

If we let $z = k$, then $y = (\frac{3}{7})k$, and $x = (\frac{1}{7})k$. Therefore, $S_1 = \{ ((\frac{1}{7})k,$ $(\frac{3}{7})k, k) \mid k \in R \}$. Notice that A can be changed immediately to

$\begin{pmatrix} 2 & -3 & 1 \\ 3 & -1 & 0 \\ 0 & 0 & 0 \end{pmatrix}$ *Why?*

which is the coefficient matrix of the system $\begin{cases} 2x - 3y + z = 0 \\ 3x - y + 0z = 0 \\ 0x + 0y + 0z = 0 \end{cases}$. Here,

if we let $x = K$, then $y = 3K$ and $z = 7K$. Therefore, $S_2 = \{ (K, 3K,$ $7K) \mid K \in R \}$. Clearly, $S_1 = S_2$ since the relationship between k and K is $k = 7K$. Geometrically, the solution set is the line of intersection of the planes (there are only two planes) in R^2 defined by the equations of the original system.

Problem Set 3–1A

1. List the coefficient matrices for the following systems.

(a) $\begin{cases} 5x - y = 0 \\ 3x + 7y = 0 \end{cases}$ (b) $\begin{cases} x + 3y - z = 0 \\ 2x - y + 4z = 0 \end{cases}$

(c) $\begin{cases} x = 0 \\ y = 0 \end{cases}$ (d) $\begin{cases} 5x + y = 0 \\ 0x + 0y = 0 \\ 2x - 3y = 0 \end{cases}$

(e) $\begin{cases} 2x - 7y = 0 \\ x + 5y = 0 \\ -4x + y = 0 \end{cases}$ (f) $\begin{cases} x + 5y = 0 \\ 2x - 7y = 0 \\ -4x + y = 0 \end{cases}$

(g) $\begin{cases} -4x + y = 0 \\ 2x - 7y = 0 \\ x + 5y = 0 \end{cases}$ (h) $\begin{cases} 3x - 2y = 0 \\ 5y + 2x = 0 \end{cases}$

59

(i) $\quad x - 5y + z + 7w = 0$ (j) $\begin{cases} 2x_1 - 7x_2 \qquad\quad + 3x_4 = 0 \\ x_1 \qquad\quad + 5x_3 - \quad x_4 = 0 \\ -4x_1 + 3x_2 \qquad\qquad\qquad = 0 \\ \qquad\quad x_2 - \quad x_3 + 5x_4 = 0 \\ x_1 - \quad x_2 + \quad x_3 - \quad x_4 = 0 \end{cases}$

In Problems 2 through 7 show that the systems are equivalent by expressing each equation in each system as a linear combination of the equations in the other system.

2. $\begin{cases} 6x - 2y = 0 \\ x + 3y = 0 \end{cases}$, $\begin{cases} 3x - y = 0 \\ x + 3y = 0 \end{cases}$

3. $\begin{cases} 3x - y = 0 \\ x + 3y = 0 \end{cases}$, $\begin{cases} x + 3y = 0 \\ 3x - y = 0 \end{cases}$

4. $\begin{cases} 3x - y = 0 \\ x + 3y = 0 \end{cases}$, $\begin{cases} 3x - y = 0 \\ 10x \qquad\; = 0 \end{cases}$

5. $\begin{cases} 3x - y = 0 \\ x + 3y = 0 \end{cases}$, $\begin{cases} -10y = 0 \\ x + 3y = 0 \end{cases}$

6. $\begin{cases} 3x - y = 0 \\ x + 3y = 0 \end{cases}$, $\begin{cases} 3x - y = 0 \\ x + 3y = 0 \\ 6x - 2y = 0 \end{cases}$

7. $\begin{cases} 3x - y = 0 \\ x + 3y = 0 \end{cases}$, $\begin{cases} 3x - y = 0 \\ 0x + 0y = 0 \\ x + 3y = 0 \end{cases}$

8. Which of the following are row-equivalent to $A = \begin{pmatrix} 3 & -1 \\ 1 & 3 \end{pmatrix}$?

(a) $\begin{pmatrix} 1 & 3 \\ 3 & -1 \end{pmatrix}$ (b) $\begin{pmatrix} 3 & -1 \\ 10 & 0 \end{pmatrix}$ (c) $\begin{pmatrix} 0 & -10 \\ 1 & 3 \end{pmatrix}$

(d) $\begin{pmatrix} 3 & -1 \\ 1 & 3 \\ 6 & -2 \end{pmatrix}$ (e) $\begin{pmatrix} 3 & -1 \\ 0 & 0 \\ 1 & 3 \end{pmatrix}$ (f) $\begin{pmatrix} 3 & -1 & 0 \\ 1 & 3 & 0 \end{pmatrix}$

9. Which of the following are row-equivalent to $A = \begin{pmatrix} 1 & 0 & -2 \\ 3 & -5 & 1 \\ 0 & 2 & -4 \end{pmatrix}$?

(a) $\begin{pmatrix} 3 & -5 & 1 \\ 0 & 2 & -4 \\ 1 & 0 & -2 \end{pmatrix}$ (b) $\begin{pmatrix} 1 & 0 & -2 \\ 6 & -10 & 2 \\ 0 & 1 & -2 \end{pmatrix}$ (c) $\begin{pmatrix} 1 & 0 & -2 \\ 0 & -5 & -5 \\ 0 & 2 & -4 \end{pmatrix}$

(d) $\begin{pmatrix} 1 & 0 & -2 \\ 0 & 2 & -4 \\ 0 & -5 & 7 \end{pmatrix}$ (e) $\begin{pmatrix} 1 & 0 & -2 \\ 0 & 1 & -2 \\ 0 & 5 & -7 \end{pmatrix}$ (f) $\begin{pmatrix} 1 & 0 & -2 \\ 0 & 1 & -2 \\ 0 & 0 & 3 \end{pmatrix}$

In Problems 10 through 19 use the two methods involving elimination and elementary row operations, where possible, to obtain the solution sets of the systems.

10. $\begin{cases} x - 5y = 0 \\ 3x + y = 0 \end{cases}$

11. $\begin{cases} 5x - 3y = 0 \\ 2x + y = 0 \end{cases}$

12. $\begin{cases} 3x + \frac{1}{3}y = 0 \\ 9x + y = 0 \end{cases}$

13. $\begin{cases} 2x - 3y + 5z = 0 \\ 2x + 3y - 5z = 0 \end{cases}$

14. $4x + 3y - z = 0$

15. $\begin{cases} 4x + 3y - z = 0 \\ -4x - 3y + z = 0 \end{cases}$

16. $\begin{cases} 3x + y = 0 \\ x - 2y = 0 \\ 2x - y = 0 \end{cases}$

17. $\begin{cases} 4x + 3y - z = 0 \\ x - 2y + 3z = 0 \end{cases}$

18. $\begin{cases} 2x - y + 3z = 0 \\ x + 2y - 4z = 0 \\ y + z = 0 \end{cases}$ 19. $\begin{cases} 3x + 2y - 5z = 0 \\ x + 2y = 0 \\ 2x - y + z = 0 \end{cases}$

20. Show that the solutions of Problem 17 depend on z. Show that the solutions also depend on each of x and y.

21. Argue that equivalence of systems is an equivalence relation.

22. Show that any one elementary operation on equations applied to a system yields an equivalent system.

23. Argue that *is row-equivalent to* is an equivalence relation on the set of all $m \times n$ matrices.

24. Show that if two homogeneous systems of linear equations in two unknowns have equal solution sets, then the systems are equivalent.

25. Discuss equivalence for the systems

$$\begin{cases} x + 2y = 0 \\ 3x - y = 0 \end{cases} \quad \text{and} \quad \begin{cases} x + 2y + 0z = 0 \\ x - 5y + 0z = 0 \end{cases}$$

Are the solution sets equal?

In order to provide a more systematic way of solving a system of linear equations, we introduce the concept of a *row reduced echelon matrix*, or more simply, a *reduced matrix*.

DEFINITION 3–1.1. *A matrix is a reduced matrix if and only if*

a. *the first nonzero entry in each row is one and the column in which the first one occurs has zero for all other entries,*

b. *the first nonzero entry in each row is to the right of the first nonzero entry of each preceding row, and*

c. *all rows consisting of only zeros are below those that contain a non-zero entry.*

The matrices $\begin{pmatrix} 1 & -2 \\ 0 & 1 \end{pmatrix}$, $\begin{pmatrix} 0 & 1 & 0 \\ 1 & 0 & 2 \\ 0 & 0 & 0 \end{pmatrix}$, and $\begin{pmatrix} 0 & 1 & 0 & 0 \\ 0 & 0 & 0 & 0 \\ 0 & 0 & 1 & 0 \end{pmatrix}$ are not reduced since *part (a)* of Definition 3–1.1 does not hold for the first matrix, *part (b)* does not hold for the second matrix, and *part (c)* does not hold for the third matrix. These three matrices can be reduced by elementary row operations to $\begin{pmatrix} 1 & 0 \\ 0 & 1 \end{pmatrix}$, $\begin{pmatrix} 1 & 0 & 2 \\ 0 & 1 & 0 \\ 0 & 0 & 0 \end{pmatrix}$, and $\begin{pmatrix} 0 & 1 & 0 & 0 \\ 0 & 0 & 1 & 0 \\ 0 & 0 & 0 & 0 \end{pmatrix}$, respectively. The next theorem shows a rela-tionship between a matrix A and a reduced matrix obtained from A.

THEOREM 3–1.5. *If A is an $m \times n$ matrix, then A is row-equivalent to a reduced matrix.*

61

The next illustration involves a system having more unknowns than equations. As expected, there are many solutions for such a system (see Theorem 3-1.6). In all following illustrations we use reduced matrices.

Illustration 4

Solve the system $\begin{cases} 3x + 2y - 4z = 0 \\ 5x - 7y + 3z = 0 \end{cases}$. The coefficient matrix is $A = \begin{pmatrix} 3 & 2 & -4 \\ 5 & -7 & 3 \end{pmatrix}$, which we reduce as follows

$$\begin{pmatrix} 6 & 4 & -8 \\ 5 & -7 & 3 \end{pmatrix} \qquad \text{Multiply the first row by 2.}$$

$$\begin{pmatrix} 1 & 11 & -11 \\ 5 & -7 & 3 \end{pmatrix} \qquad \text{Add } -1 \text{ times the second row to the first row.}$$

$$\begin{pmatrix} 1 & 11 & -11 \\ 0 & -62 & 58 \end{pmatrix} \qquad \text{Why?}$$

$$\begin{pmatrix} 1 & 11 & -11 \\ 0 & 1 & -\frac{29}{31} \end{pmatrix} \qquad \text{Why?}$$

$$\begin{pmatrix} 1 & 0 & -\frac{22}{31} \\ 0 & 1 & -\frac{29}{31} \end{pmatrix} \qquad \text{Why?}$$

This last matrix is the coefficient matrix of the system

$$\begin{cases} x + 0y - (\frac{22}{31})z = 0 \\ 0x + y - (\frac{29}{31})z = 0 \end{cases}$$

To avoid fractions, we set $z = 31k$. Then, $y = 29k$, $x = 22k$, and the solution set $S = \{ (22k, 29k, 31k) \mid k \in R \}$. Geometrically, the two planes in R^3 intersect in a line that contains the origin.

Before we state and prove the next theorem we consider an example that will help us understand the proof. Suppose we want to show that the system

$$\begin{cases} x + y + z + u + v + w & = 0 \\ x - y + z - u + v - 2w & = 0 \\ x + y + z - u - v + 2w & = 0 \\ 5x + 3y + 5z + 3u + 5v + 2w & = 0 \end{cases}$$

of four linear equations in six unknowns has a nontrivial solution. In matrix form the system is $AX = O$, where

$$A = \begin{pmatrix} 1 & 1 & 1 & 1 & 1 & 1 \\ 1 & -1 & 1 & -1 & 1 & -2 \\ 1 & 1 & 1 & -1 & -1 & 2 \\ 5 & 3 & 5 & 3 & 5 & 2 \end{pmatrix} \qquad \text{and} \qquad X = \begin{pmatrix} x \\ y \\ z \\ u \\ v \\ w \end{pmatrix}$$

By the usual method we reduce A to

$$B = \begin{pmatrix} 1 & 0 & 1 & 0 & 1 & -\frac{1}{2} \\ 0 & 1 & 0 & 0 & -1 & 2 \\ 0 & 0 & 0 & 1 & 1 & -\frac{1}{2} \\ 0 & 0 & 0 & 0 & 0 & 0 \end{pmatrix}$$

Now $AX = O$ and $BX = O$ are equivalent (by Theorem 3-1.4) and so have equal solution sets (by Theorem 3-1.1). From $BX = O$ we have

$$\begin{cases} x + (z + v - w/2) = 0 \\ y + (-v + 2w) = 0 \\ u + (v - w/2) = 0 \end{cases}$$

Here, any values can be assigned to z, v, w, and the values of x, y, u can be obtained. By assigning a nonzero value to z, v, or w, we see that a nontrivial solution exists for $BX = O$ and, consequently, for $AX = O$.

THEOREM 3-1.6. *If a homogeneous system of linear equations has coefficient matrix A of dimension $m \times n$ and $m < n$, then the system has a nontrivial solution.*

Proof: In matrix form the system is $AX = O$. Let B be a reduced matrix row-equivalent to A. The systems $AX = O$ and $BX = O$ are equivalent, by Theorem 3-1.4. Then, by Theorem 3-1.1, $AX = O$ and $BX = O$ have equal solution sets. Let p be the number of nonzero rows in B. Then, $p \leq m$. Since $m < n$, then $p < n$. Suppose the first nonzero entry in row i is in column k_i. The system $BX = O$ has p nontrivial equations and the unknown x_{k_i} (with coefficient 1) occurs only in the ith equation. Let $y_1, y_2, \ldots, y_{n-p}$ denote the $n - p$ unknowns different from $x_{k_1}, x_{k_2}, \ldots, x_{k_p}$. The p nontrivial equations of $BX = O$ are then

$$\begin{cases} x_{k_1} + \sum_{j=1}^{j=n-p} c_{1j}y_j = 0 \\ x_{k_2} + \sum_{j=1}^{j=n-p} c_{2j}y_j = 0 \\ \vdots \qquad \vdots \qquad \vdots \\ x_{k_p} + \sum_{j=1}^{j=n-p} c_{pj}y_j = 0 \end{cases}$$

Here, we can assign any values to $y_1, y_2, \ldots, y_{n-p}$ and solve for $x_{k_1}, x_{k_2}, \ldots, x_{k_p}$. By assigning a nonzero value to some y_j, we obtain a nontrivial solution of $BX = O$, and consequently, of $AX = O$.

If a homogeneous system has one nontrivial solution, then the system has many solutions. You can easily show that if $(x_1, x_2, \ldots, x_n)$ is a solution of a homogeneous system, then $(cx_1, cx_2, \ldots, cx_n)$ is a solution for $c \in R$.

The next illustration involves a homogeneous system with more equations than unknowns. Although you might expect only the trivial solution, there may be others as well.

Illustration 5

Solve the system $\begin{cases} x + 3y = 0 \\ 2x - 5y = 0 \\ -3x + 2y = 0 \end{cases}$. The coefficient matrix $A = \begin{pmatrix} 1 & 3 \\ 2 & -5 \\ -3 & 2 \end{pmatrix}$ is reduced as follows.

$\begin{pmatrix} 1 & 3 \\ 0 & -11 \\ 0 & 11 \end{pmatrix}$ *Add -2 times the first row to the second row. Other?*

$\begin{pmatrix} 1 & 3 \\ 0 & 1 \\ 0 & 11 \end{pmatrix}$ *Why?*

$\begin{pmatrix} 1 & 0 \\ 0 & 1 \\ 0 & 0 \end{pmatrix}$ *Add -11 times the second row to the third row. Other?*

The original system is then equivalent to $\begin{cases} x + 0y = 0 \\ 0x + y = 0 \\ 0x + 0y = 0 \end{cases}$, from which $x = 0$ and $y = 0$. Consequently, the solution set $S = \{\, (0, 0) \,\}$.

To see that a system with more equations than unknowns may have solutions other than the trivial one, consider $\begin{cases} x + 3y = 0 \\ 2x + 6y = 0 \\ -5x - 15y = 0 \end{cases}$. The coefficient matrix $A = \begin{pmatrix} 1 & 3 \\ 2 & 6 \\ -5 & 15 \end{pmatrix}$ can be reduced to $\begin{pmatrix} 1 & 3 \\ 0 & 0 \\ 0 & 0 \end{pmatrix}$, which leads to the solution set $S = \{\, (x, y) \mid x = -3y \,\}$. Thus, in R^2 the lines of the system coincide. Consider the system consisting of the first two equations here and the system consisting of the first two equations of Illustration 5. The next theorem tells why these systems have different solutions.

THEOREM 3–1.7. *If the coefficient matrix A of a homogeneous system of linear equations is square, then the system has only the trivial solution if and only if A is row-equivalent to an identity matrix.*

Problem Set 3–1B

1. Which of the following matrices are reduced matrices? For those not reduced explain why they are not reduced, then reduce them.

(a) $(1 \ -5 \ 3)$ (b) $(0 \ 2 \ 1)$

(c) $\begin{pmatrix} 0 & 0 & 0 \\ 0 & 0 & 0 \end{pmatrix}$ (d) $\begin{pmatrix} 1 & 0 & 1 \\ 0 & 1 & 0 \end{pmatrix}$

(e) $\begin{pmatrix} 0 & 0 & 0 \\ 0 & 0 & 1 \end{pmatrix}$

(f) $\begin{pmatrix} 0 & 0 & 1 \\ 1 & 0 & 1 \end{pmatrix}$

(g) $\begin{pmatrix} 1 & 0 & 0 & 1 \\ 0 & 1 & 0 & 0 \\ 0 & 0 & 0 & 1 \end{pmatrix}$

(h) $\begin{pmatrix} 1 & 5 & 0 & 0 \\ 0 & 0 & 1 & 0 \\ 0 & 0 & 0 & 0 \\ 0 & 0 & 0 & 1 \end{pmatrix}$

Solve Problems 2 through 12 by changing the coefficient matrices to reduced matrices. List the reduced matrices. The problems referred to are from Problem Set 3–1A.

2. Problem 10   3. Problem 11   4. Problem 12
5. Problem 13   6. Problem 14   7. Problem 15
8. Problem 16   9. Problem 17   10. Problem 18
11. Problem 1(j)

12. $\begin{cases} x - y + z - w = 0 \\ x + y - z + w = 0 \\ x - y - z - w = 0 \\ x + y + z - w = 0 \end{cases}$

13. If $ad - bc \neq 0$, show that $A = \begin{pmatrix} a & b \\ c & d \end{pmatrix}$ reduces to $\begin{pmatrix} 1 & 0 \\ 0 & 1 \end{pmatrix}$. If $ad - bc = 0$, describe the reduced matrix.

14. If $ad - bc \neq 0$, reduce $A = \begin{pmatrix} a & b \\ c & d \end{pmatrix}$ and solve $\begin{cases} ax + by = 0 \\ cx + dy = 0 \end{cases}$.

15. List all possible 2×2 reduced matrices.

16. List all possible 2×3 reduced matrices.

17. List all possible 3×3 reduced matrices.

18. Argue that if the third row of A is a sum of multiples of the first and second rows of A, then A can be reduced to a matrix with a row of zeros.

19. State and prove a more general result than that of Problem 18.

20. Argue that if A can be reduced to B, then B can be reduced to A.

21. If $a + bx = 0$ for all $x \in R$, argue that $a = b = 0$. (*Hint:* Let $x = 0, 1$ to obtain a system of equations in a and b.)

22. If $a + bx + cx^2 = 0$ for all $x \in R$, prove that $a = b = c = 0$. (See Problem 21.)

23. If $a + bx + cx^2 + dx^3 = 0$ for all $x \in R$, argue that $a = b = c = d = 0$.

24. If $a \sin x + b \sin 2x = 0$ for all $x \in R$, argue that $a = b = 0$.

25. If $a \cos x + b \cos 2x = 0$ for all $x \in R$, prove that $a = b = 0$.

26. If $a \sin x + b \cos x = 0$ for all $x \in R$, prove that $a = b = 0$.

27. Prove Theorem 3–1.5 for the special case $m = 2$ and $n = 3$.

3-2. NONHOMOGENEOUS SYSTEMS OF LINEAR EQUATIONS

If the zero on the right side of one (or more) equation in system (3–1.1) is replaced with a nonzero real number, the result is a

65

nonhomogeneous system of m linear equations in n unknowns

(3-2.1)
$$\begin{cases} a_{11}x_1 + a_{12}x_2 + \cdots + a_{1n}x_n = b_1 \\ a_{21}x_1 + a_{22}x_2 + \cdots + a_{2n}x_n = b_2 \\ \vdots \qquad \vdots \qquad \ddots \qquad \vdots \qquad \vdots \\ a_{m1}x_1 + a_{m2}x_2 + \cdots + a_{mn}x_n = b_m \end{cases}$$

If $b_i \neq 0$ for some $i \in \{1, 2, \ldots, m\}$, then $a_{i1}x_1 + a_{i2}x_2 + \cdots + a_{in}x_n = b_i$ is a *nonhomogeneous* linear equation and any system of linear equations that contains this equation is *a nonhomogeneous system*. The definitions of a solution and the solution set of a non-homogeneous system are the same as those for a homogeneous system. Two nonhomogeneous systems of linear equations are *equivalent* if and only if each equation in either system is a linear combination of the equations in the other system. For example, the systems

$$\begin{cases} 2x - 3y = 8 \\ x + 2y = -3 \end{cases} \quad \text{and} \quad \begin{cases} -7y = 14 \\ x + 2y = -3 \end{cases}$$

are equivalent for

$2x - 3y = 8$ is the linear combination
$$1(-7y) + 2(x + 2y) = 1(14) + 2(-3)$$

$x + 2y = -3$ is the linear combination
$$0(-7y) + 1(x + 2y) = 0(14) + 1(-3)$$

$-7y = 14$ is the linear combination
$$1(2x - 3y) - 2(x + 2y) = 1(8) - 2(-3)$$

$x + 2y = -3$ is the linear combination
$$0(2x - 3y) + 1(x + 2y) = 0(8) + 1(-3)$$

As with homogeneous systems, equivalence for nonhomogeneous systems is an equivalence relation. Also, Theorem 3-1.1 holds for *homogeneous* replaced with *nonhomogeneous*.

THEOREM 3-2.1. *If two nonhomogeneous systems of m linear equations in n unknowns are equivalent and have solution sets S_1 and S_2, then $S_1 = S_2$.*

The coefficient matrix A for the system (3-2.1) is the same as for the homogeneous system (3-1.1). The system (3-2.1) can be solved much as was system (3-1.1) if we use the *augmented coefficient matrix*

$$aug\ A = \begin{pmatrix} a_{11} & a_{12} & \cdots & a_{1n} & b_1 \\ a_{21} & a_{22} & \cdots & a_{2n} & b_2 \\ \vdots & \vdots & \ddots & \vdots & \vdots \\ a_{m1} & a_{m2} & \cdots & a_{mn} & b_m \end{pmatrix}$$

and elementary row operations on this matrix. The technique is emphasized in the following illustrations.

Illustration 1

Solve the system $\begin{cases} 4x - 3y = 5 \\ -x + (\frac{3}{4})y = 3 \end{cases}$. Using elementary row operations

on the augmented matrix $aug\ A = \begin{pmatrix} 4 & -3 & 5 \\ -1 & \frac{3}{4} & 3 \end{pmatrix}$, gives

$\begin{pmatrix} -1 & \frac{3}{4} & 3 \\ 4 & -3 & 5 \end{pmatrix}$ *Interchange the rows.*

$\begin{pmatrix} 1 & -\frac{3}{4} & -3 \\ 4 & -3 & 5 \end{pmatrix}$ *Why?*

$\begin{pmatrix} 1 & -\frac{3}{4} & -3 \\ 0 & 0 & 17 \end{pmatrix}$ *Add -4 times the first row to the second row.*

$\begin{pmatrix} 1 & -\frac{3}{4} & -3 \\ 0 & 0 & 1 \end{pmatrix}$ *Multiply the second row by $\frac{1}{17}$.*

$\begin{pmatrix} 1 & -\frac{3}{4} & 0 \\ 0 & 0 & 1 \end{pmatrix}$ *Why?*

This last matrix is the augmented matrix of the system $\begin{cases} x - (\frac{3}{4})y = 0 \\ 0x + 0y = 1 \end{cases}$.
Since $0 \neq 1$, the solution set $S = \emptyset$ (the empty set). Geometrically, this
means that the lines in R^2, defined by the equations, are parallel. Notice
that the same operations performed on the equations of the system rather
than on the augmented matrix produces the same computations and the
same solution set. It should be clear that $S = \emptyset$ for any nonhomogeneous
system for which the augmented matrix can be reduced to a matrix such
that all entries except the last in some row are zero.

The next two theorems, which are similar to Theorems 3-1.3 and
3-1.4, verify that the method used in Illustration 1 produces the
solution set of a nonhomogeneous system.

THEOREM 3-2.2. *Two nonhomogeneous systems of m linear equations
in n unknowns are equivalent if and only if each augmented matrix is
the result of a finite sequence of elementary row operations on the other
augmented matrix.*

THEOREM 3-2.3. *Two nonhomogeneous systems of m linear equations
in n unknowns are equivalent if and only if their augmented matrices
are row-equivalent.*

Illustration 2

Solve the system $\begin{cases} x + 2y - z = 3 \\ -3x + y + 5z = -22 \\ 4x - 3y + z = 8 \end{cases}$. We use elementary row

operations on

$$aug\ A = \begin{pmatrix} 1 & 2 & -1 & 3 \\ -3 & 1 & 5 & -22 \\ 4 & -3 & 1 & 8 \end{pmatrix}$$

67

as follows.

$$\begin{pmatrix} 1 & 2 & -1 & 3 \\ 0 & 7 & 2 & -13 \\ 0 & -11 & 5 & -4 \end{pmatrix}$$
Add 3 times the first row to the second row. Other?

$$\begin{pmatrix} 1 & 2 & -1 & 3 \\ 0 & 1 & \frac{2}{7} & -\frac{13}{7} \\ 0 & -11 & 5 & -4 \end{pmatrix}$$
Why?

$$\begin{pmatrix} 1 & 2 & -1 & 3 \\ 0 & 1 & \frac{2}{7} & -\frac{13}{7} \\ 0 & 0 & \frac{57}{7} & -\frac{171}{7} \end{pmatrix}$$
Why?

$$\begin{pmatrix} 1 & 2 & -1 & 3 \\ 0 & 1 & \frac{2}{7} & -\frac{13}{7} \\ 0 & 0 & 1 & -3 \end{pmatrix}$$
Why?

$$\begin{pmatrix} 1 & 2 & 0 & 0 \\ 0 & 1 & 0 & -1 \\ 0 & 0 & 1 & -3 \end{pmatrix}$$
Add 1 times the third row to the first row. Other?

$$\begin{pmatrix} 1 & 0 & 0 & 2 \\ 0 & 1 & 0 & -1 \\ 0 & 0 & 1 & -3 \end{pmatrix}$$
Why?

This last matrix is the augmented matrix of the system

$$\begin{cases} x + 0y + 0z = 2 \\ 0x + y + 0z = -1 \\ 0x + 0y + z = -3 \end{cases}$$

Therefore, $x = 2$, $y = -1$, $z = -3$, and the solution set $S = \{ (2, -1, -3) \}$. Notice that since the coefficient matrix reduced to an identity matrix, this system will have exactly one solution for any values in place of 3, -22, and 8. (*What does this mean geometrically?*)

THEOREM 3–2.4. *If the coefficient matrix A is a nonhomogeneous system of linear equations is square, then the system has exactly one solution if and only if A is row-equivalent to an identity matrix.*

For our last illustration, we show that a nonhomogeneous system with more unknowns than equations may have many solutions.

Illustration 3

Solve the system $\begin{cases} x + 2y - z = 3 \\ -3x + y + 5z = -22 \end{cases}$.

Since

$$aug\, A = \begin{pmatrix} 1 & 2 & -1 & 3 \\ -3 & 1 & 5 & -22 \end{pmatrix}$$

we have

$$\begin{pmatrix} 1 & 2 & -1 & 3 \\ 0 & 7 & 2 & -13 \end{pmatrix} \qquad Why?$$

$$\begin{pmatrix} 1 & 2 & -1 & 3 \\ 0 & 1 & \frac{2}{7} & -\frac{13}{7} \end{pmatrix} \qquad \textit{Why?}$$

$$\begin{pmatrix} 1 & 0 & -\frac{11}{7} & \frac{47}{7} \\ 0 & 1 & \frac{2}{7} & -\frac{13}{7} \end{pmatrix} \qquad \textit{Why?}$$

This last matrix is the augmented matrix of the system

$$\begin{cases} x + 0y - \frac{11}{7}z = \frac{47}{7} \\ 0x + y + \frac{2}{7}z = -\frac{13}{7} \end{cases}$$

If we choose $z = 7k$, then $y = -(14k + 13)/7$ and $x = (77k + 47)/7$.

Therefore, the solution set $S = \left\{ \left(\dfrac{77k + 47}{7}, \ -\dfrac{14k + 13}{7}, 7k \right) \Big| k \in R \right\}$.

Problem Set 3-2

In Problems 1 through 11 solve the systems by reducing the augmented matrices.

1. $\begin{cases} x - 5y = 2 \\ 3x + y = 3 \end{cases}$

2. $\begin{cases} 5x - 3y = -2 \\ 2x + y = 5 \end{cases}$

3. $\begin{cases} 3x + \frac{1}{3}y = 4 \\ 9x + y = 5 \end{cases}$

4. $\begin{cases} 2x - 3y + 5z = -3 \\ 2x + 3y - 5z = 4 \end{cases}$

5. $\begin{cases} 4x + 3y - z = 1 \\ -4x - 3y + z = -2 \end{cases}$

6. $\begin{cases} 3x + y = 1 \\ x - 2y = 0 \\ 2x - y = 3 \end{cases}$

7. $\begin{cases} 4x + 3y - z = 5 \\ x - 2y + 3z = -3 \end{cases}$

8. $\begin{cases} 2x - y + 3z = 4 \\ x + 2y - 4z = 1 \\ y + z = -2 \end{cases}$

9. $\begin{cases} 3x + 2y - 5z = 2 \\ x + 2y = 1 \\ 2x - y + z = -3 \end{cases}$

10. $\begin{cases} x - y + z - w = 1 \\ x + y - z + w = 2 \\ x - y - z - w = -1 \\ x + y + z - w = -3 \end{cases}$

11. $\begin{cases} 2x_1 - 7x_2 + 3x_4 = 1 \\ x_1 + 5x_3 - x_4 = -2 \\ -4x_1 + 3x_2 = 1 \\ x_2 - x_3 + 5x_4 = 0 \\ x_1 - x_2 + x_3 - x_4 = 3 \end{cases}$

12. Solve the system $\begin{cases} x + y + z = 0 \\ 2x - y + z = 0 \\ x + y - z = 0 \end{cases}$. Use the same row operations to solve the system $\begin{cases} x + y + z = 5 \\ 2x - y + z = -2 \\ x + y - z = 3 \end{cases}$. Notice that this second system will have exactly one solution for any triple of numbers on the right sides of the equations.

13. If the following are coefficient matrices of nonhomogeneous systems, decide which solution sets have exactly one element.

(a) $\begin{pmatrix} 1 & 0 & 1 \\ 0 & 1 & 1 \\ 0 & 0 & 1 \end{pmatrix}$

(b) $\begin{pmatrix} 1 & -3 & 4 \\ 0 & 1 & 1 \\ 0 & 0 & 0 \end{pmatrix}$

(c) $\begin{pmatrix} 1 & -3 & 0 & 0 \\ 0 & 0 & 1 & 2 \\ 0 & 0 & 0 & 1 \end{pmatrix}$
(d) $\begin{pmatrix} 1 & -2 & 3 \\ 0 & 1 & 5 \\ 0 & 0 & 4 \\ 0 & 0 & 0 \end{pmatrix}$

14. Repeat Problem 13 if the given matrices are augmented matrices of systems of equations.

In Problems 15 through 19 refer to Problems 21 through 26 of Problem Set 3–1B. The derivative can be used to advantage through Problem 21.

15. Prove that no a and b exist such that $x^2 = ax + b$ for all $x \in R$.

16. Prove that no a, b, and c exist such that $x^3 = ax^2 + bx + c$ for all $x \in R$.

17. Show that no a, b, c, and d exist such that $x^4 = ax^3 + bx^2 + cx + d$ for all $x \in R$.

18. Show that no a and b exist such that $\sin 3x = a \sin x + b \sin 2x$ for all $x \in R$.

19. Argue that no a and b exist such that $\cos 3x = a \cos x + b \cos 2x$ for all $x \in R$.

20. Show that no a and b exist such that $e^{3x} = ae^x + be^{2x}$ for all $x \in R$.

21. Prove that no a, b, and c exist such that $e^{4x} = \dot{a}e^x + be^{2x} + ce^{3x}$ for all $x \in R$.

22. If the solution set of the system $\begin{cases} ax + by = 0 \\ cx + dy = 0 \end{cases}$ has exactly one element, what must $\begin{pmatrix} a & b \\ c & d \end{pmatrix}$ reduce to? In this case, show that the solution set of the system $\begin{cases} ax + by = e \\ cx + dy = f \end{cases}$ has exactly one element for particular values of e and f.

3–3. ELEMENTARY MATRICES

The elementary row operations on a matrix A can be considered as the result of multiplying A on the left by certain *elementary matrices*. These elementary matrices are obtained from an identity matrix I in particular ways. Recall that if I is $n \times n$ and A is $n \times t$, then $IA = A$, while if B is $m \times n$, then $BI = B$. The elementary matrices also have interesting properties. Furthermore, they will be used to determine the multiplicative inverse of a nonsingular matrix and to solve systems of linear equations.

DEFINITION 3–3.1. *If I is the $n \times n$ identity matrix, then*

a. *a matrix obtained from I by replacing exactly one entry on the main diagonal by a, where $a \neq 0$, is an nth order elementary matrix of the first kind,*

b. *a matrix obtained from I by interchanging two rows (or columns) is an nth order elementary matrix of the second kind, and*

c. *a matrix obtained from I by replacing exactly one zero entry by $a \neq 0$ is an nth order elementary matrix of the third kind.*

The notations D_{ii}, P_{ij}, and S_{ij} for $i \neq j$ are used for elementary matrices of the first kind, second kind, and third kind, respectively. The subscripts on D indicate the position of the one in I that is altered, the subscripts on P indicate the two rows (columns) of I that are interchanged, and the subscripts on S indicate the position of the zero that is replaced with a.

Illustration 1

If I is 2×2, the second order elementary matrices are:

First kind

$$D_{11} = \begin{pmatrix} a & 0 \\ 0 & 1 \end{pmatrix}, \qquad D_{22} = \begin{pmatrix} 1 & 0 \\ 0 & a \end{pmatrix}$$

Second kind

$$P_{12} = \begin{pmatrix} 0 & 1 \\ 1 & 0 \end{pmatrix}$$

Third kind

$$S_{12} = \begin{pmatrix} 1 & a \\ 0 & 1 \end{pmatrix}, \qquad S_{21} = \begin{pmatrix} 1 & 0 \\ a & 1 \end{pmatrix}$$

Illustration 2

If I is 3×3, the third order elementary matrices are:

First kind

$$D_{11} = \begin{pmatrix} a & 0 & 0 \\ 0 & 1 & 0 \\ 0 & 0 & 1 \end{pmatrix}, \quad D_{22} = \begin{pmatrix} 1 & 0 & 0 \\ 0 & a & 0 \\ 0 & 0 & 1 \end{pmatrix}, \quad D_{33} = \begin{pmatrix} 1 & 0 & 0 \\ 0 & 1 & 0 \\ 0 & 0 & a \end{pmatrix}$$

Second kind

$$P_{12} = \begin{pmatrix} 0 & 1 & 0 \\ 1 & 0 & 0 \\ 0 & 0 & 1 \end{pmatrix}, \quad P_{13} = \begin{pmatrix} 0 & 0 & 1 \\ 0 & 1 & 0 \\ 1 & 0 & 0 \end{pmatrix}, \quad P_{23} = \begin{pmatrix} 1 & 0 & 0 \\ 0 & 0 & 1 \\ 0 & 1 & 0 \end{pmatrix}$$

Third kind

$$S_{12} = \begin{pmatrix} 1 & a & 0 \\ 0 & 1 & 0 \\ 0 & 0 & 1 \end{pmatrix}, \quad S_{13} = \begin{pmatrix} 1 & 0 & a \\ 0 & 1 & 0 \\ 0 & 0 & 1 \end{pmatrix}, \quad S_{21} = \begin{pmatrix} 1 & 0 & 0 \\ a & 1 & 0 \\ 0 & 0 & 1 \end{pmatrix}$$

$$S_{23} = \begin{pmatrix} 1 & 0 & 0 \\ 0 & 1 & a \\ 0 & 0 & 1 \end{pmatrix}, \quad S_{31} = \begin{pmatrix} 1 & 0 & 0 \\ 0 & 1 & 0 \\ a & 0 & 1 \end{pmatrix}, \quad S_{32} = \begin{pmatrix} 1 & 0 & 0 \\ 0 & 1 & 0 \\ 0 & a & 1 \end{pmatrix}$$

If A is $n \times t$, how does left multiplication by an nth order elementary matrix affect A? Clearly, $D_{ii}A$ is obtained from A by multiplying the ith row of A by a, $P_{ij}A$ is obtained from A by interchanging the ith and jth rows, and $S_{ij}A$ is obtained from A by adding a times the jth row to the ith row.

71

Illustration 3

If $A = \begin{pmatrix} 2 & 1 & 0 & -3 \\ 1 & -2 & -1 & 5 \\ 0 & 3 & -4 & 2 \end{pmatrix}$, $D_{22} = \begin{pmatrix} 1 & 0 & 0 \\ 0 & 3 & 0 \\ 0 & 0 & 1 \end{pmatrix}$, $P_{23} = \begin{pmatrix} 1 & 0 & 0 \\ 0 & 0 & 1 \\ 0 & 1 & 0 \end{pmatrix}$, and

$S_{13} = \begin{pmatrix} 1 & 0 & -2 \\ 0 & 1 & 0 \\ 0 & 0 & 1 \end{pmatrix}$, obtain $D_{22}A$, $D_{23}A$, and $S_{13}A$.

From A, we have

$$D_{22}A = \begin{pmatrix} 2 & 1 & 0 & -3 \\ 3 & -6 & -3 & 15 \\ 0 & 3 & -4 & 2 \end{pmatrix} \qquad \textit{Multiply the second row of A by 3.}$$

$$P_{23}A = \begin{pmatrix} 2 & 1 & 0 & -3 \\ 0 & 3 & -4 & 2 \\ 1 & -2 & -1 & 5 \end{pmatrix} \qquad \textit{Interchange the second and third rows of A.}$$

$$S_{13}A = \begin{pmatrix} 2 & -5 & 8 & -7 \\ 1 & -2 & -1 & 5 \\ 0 & 3 & -4 & 2 \end{pmatrix} \qquad \textit{Add} -2 \textit{ times the third row of A to the first row of A.}$$

Illustration 4

If $A = \begin{pmatrix} 2 & 1 & 0 & -3 \\ 1 & -2 & -1 & 5 \\ 0 & 3 & -4 & 2 \end{pmatrix}$, what elementary matrix is E if

(a) $EA = \begin{pmatrix} 0 & 3 & -4 & 2 \\ 1 & -2 & -1 & 5 \\ 2 & 1 & 0 & -3 \end{pmatrix}$

(b) $EA = \begin{pmatrix} 2 & 1 & 0 & -3 \\ 1 & -2 & -1 & 5 \\ 0 & -6 & 8 & -4 \end{pmatrix}$

(c) $EA = \begin{pmatrix} 2 & 1 & 0 & -3 \\ 1 & 13 & -21 & 15 \\ 0 & 3 & -4 & 2 \end{pmatrix}$

For (a), since EA is obtained from A by interchanging the first and third rows,

$$E = P_{13} = \begin{pmatrix} 0 & 0 & 1 \\ 0 & 1 & 0 \\ 1 & 0 & 0 \end{pmatrix}$$

For (b), EA is obtained from A by multiplying the third row by -2. Thus,

$$E = D_{33} = \begin{pmatrix} 1 & 0 & 0 \\ 0 & 1 & 0 \\ 0 & 0 & -2 \end{pmatrix}$$

In case (c), close inspection reveals that EA is obtained from A by adding 5 times the third row to the second row. Hence,

$$E = S_{23} = \begin{pmatrix} 1 & 0 & 0 \\ 0 & 1 & 5 \\ 0 & 0 & 1 \end{pmatrix}$$

Since left multiplications of a matrix A produce the same effect as elementary row operations the following theorem follows immediately from Definition 3–1.1.

THEOREM 3–3.1. *If A and B are $m \times n$ matrices over R, then A is row-equivalent to B if and only if there exists a finite sequence, E_1, $E_2, \ldots, E_s$, of elementary matrices such that $B = E_s E_{s-1} \cdots E_2 E_1 A$.*

Many times the multiplicative inverse of a matrix is needed. Sometimes just knowing that the inverse exists provides useful information.

DEFINITION 3–3.2. *If A and B are matrices and $AB = BA = I$, then B is a multiplicative inverse of A.*

You will prove that if B and C are multiplicative inverses of A, then $B = C$. (See Problem 22 of Problem Set 3–3B.) Thus, there is at most one inverse of a matrix A. This inverse, if it exists, is denoted by A^{-1}. The notation A^{-1} is read *the inverse of A* or A *inverse*. If B is an inverse of A, then A and B must each be square and have the same dimension. (Why?) From the definition, A is a multiplicative inverse of B. A matrix that has an inverse is called a *nonsingular* (or *invertible*) matrix; otherwise the matrix is *singular* (or *noninvertible*).

We already know several matrices that can be classified as singular or nonsingular. If I is any identity matrix, then $I^{-1} = I$. Each elementary matrix is nonsingular. The inverse of D_{ii} is obtained from D_{ii} by replacing a with $1/a$, the inverse of P_{ij} is P_{ij}, and the inverse of S_{ij} is obtained from S_{ij} by replacing a with $-a$. As already noted, if A has an inverse then A must be a square matrix. Therefore, any nonsquare matrix is singular. As we will see, many square matrices are also singular.

Illustration 5

The matrix $A = \begin{pmatrix} 1 & 2 \\ -4 & 3 \end{pmatrix}$ is nonsingular, for

$$A^{-1} = \frac{1}{11} \begin{pmatrix} 3 & -2 \\ 4 & 1 \end{pmatrix}$$

To verify this, let $B = \frac{1}{11} \begin{pmatrix} 3 & -2 \\ 4 & 1 \end{pmatrix}$ and compute $AB = BA = I$, where $I = \begin{pmatrix} 1 & 0 \\ 0 & 1 \end{pmatrix}$.

Illustration 6

If I is 3×3, then $D_{22}^{-1} = \begin{pmatrix} 1 & 0 & 0 \\ 0 & 1/a & 0 \\ 0 & 0 & 1 \end{pmatrix}$, $P_{23}^{-1} = P_{23}$, and $S_{31}^{-1} = \begin{pmatrix} 1 & 0 & 0 \\ 0 & 1 & 0 \\ -a & 0 & 1 \end{pmatrix}$. The multiplications that verify these are left for the reader.

Problem Set 3–3A

1. Verify for 3×3 matrices that D_{ii}^{-1} is obtained from D_{ii} by replacing a with $1/a$.

2. Verify for 3×3 matrices that $P_{ij}^{-1} = P_{ij}$.

3. Verify for 3×3 matrices that S_{ij}^{-1} is obtained from S_{ij} by replacing a with $-a$.

4. Repeat Problem 1 for $n \times n$ matrices.
5. Repeat Problem 2 for $n \times n$ matrices.
6. Repeat Problem 3 for $n \times n$ matrices.

In each of Problems 7 through 20 determine the elementary matrix E that satisfies the given equation.

7. $E \begin{pmatrix} 1 & -3 \\ 4 & 2 \end{pmatrix} = \begin{pmatrix} 3 & -9 \\ 4 & 2 \end{pmatrix}$

8. $E \begin{pmatrix} 1 & -3 \\ 4 & 2 \end{pmatrix} = \begin{pmatrix} 1 & -3 \\ -20 & -10 \end{pmatrix}$

9. $E \begin{pmatrix} 1 & -3 \\ 4 & 2 \end{pmatrix} = \begin{pmatrix} 4 & 2 \\ 1 & -3 \end{pmatrix}$

10. $E \begin{pmatrix} 1 & -3 \\ 4 & 2 \end{pmatrix} = \begin{pmatrix} 1 & -3 \\ 5 & -1 \end{pmatrix}$

11. $E \begin{pmatrix} 1 & -3 \\ 4 & 2 \end{pmatrix} = \begin{pmatrix} 1 & -3 \\ 2 & 8 \end{pmatrix}$

12. $E \begin{pmatrix} 1 & -3 \\ 4 & 2 \end{pmatrix} = \begin{pmatrix} 9 & 1 \\ 4 & 2 \end{pmatrix}$

13. $E \begin{pmatrix} 4 & 2 & -3 \\ 1 & 0 & 2 \end{pmatrix} = \begin{pmatrix} 16 & 8 & -12 \\ 1 & 0 & 2 \end{pmatrix}$

14. $E \begin{pmatrix} 4 & 2 & -3 \\ 1 & 0 & 2 \end{pmatrix} = \begin{pmatrix} 4 & 2 & -3 \\ -11 & -6 & 11 \end{pmatrix}$

15. $E \begin{pmatrix} 3 & -2 & 4 \\ 0 & 1 & 5 \\ 2 & -3 & -1 \end{pmatrix} = \begin{pmatrix} 3 & -2 & 4 \\ 0 & -3 & -15 \\ 2 & -3 & -1 \end{pmatrix}$

16. $E \begin{pmatrix} 3 & -2 & 4 \\ 0 & 1 & 5 \\ 2 & -3 & -1 \end{pmatrix} = \begin{pmatrix} 2 & -3 & -1 \\ 0 & 1 & 5 \\ 3 & -2 & 4 \end{pmatrix}$

17. $E \begin{pmatrix} 3 & -2 & 4 \\ 0 & 1 & 5 \\ 2 & -3 & -1 \end{pmatrix} = \begin{pmatrix} 1 & 1 & 5 \\ 0 & 1 & 5 \\ 2 & -3 & -1 \end{pmatrix}$

18. $E \begin{pmatrix} 1 & 2 & 0 & -3 \\ -2 & 1 & 5 & 0 \\ 3 & 0 & -4 & 2 \end{pmatrix} = \begin{pmatrix} 1 & 2 & 0 & -3 \\ 3 & 0 & -4 & 2 \\ -2 & 1 & 5 & 0 \end{pmatrix}$

19. $E \begin{pmatrix} 1 & 2 & 0 & -3 \\ -2 & 1 & 5 & 0 \\ 3 & 0 & -4 & 2 \end{pmatrix} = \begin{pmatrix} 1 & 2 & 0 & -3 \\ -2 & 1 & 5 & 0 \\ -6 & 0 & 8 & -4 \end{pmatrix}$

20. $E \begin{pmatrix} 1 & 2 & 0 & -3 \\ -2 & 1 & 5 & 0 \\ 3 & 0 & -4 & 2 \end{pmatrix} = \begin{pmatrix} 1 & 2 & 0 & -3 \\ -2 & 1 & 5 & 0 \\ 0 & -6 & -4 & 11 \end{pmatrix}$

21. If A is $n \times 3$ explain how right multiplication of A by elementary third order matrices affects A.

In each of Problems 22 through 33 obtain the inverse of the given matrix, if an inverse exists.

22. $\begin{pmatrix} 2 & 1 \\ 3 & 5 \end{pmatrix}$

23. $\begin{pmatrix} 1 & 2 \\ -5 & 3 \end{pmatrix}$

24. $\begin{pmatrix} 1 & 5 \\ 0 & 1 \end{pmatrix}$

25. $\begin{pmatrix} 3 & 0 & 0 \\ 0 & 1 & 0 \\ 0 & 0 & 1 \end{pmatrix}$ 26. $\begin{pmatrix} 1 & 0 & 0 \\ 0 & 1 & 0 \\ -4 & 0 & 1 \end{pmatrix}$ 27. $\begin{pmatrix} 1 & 0 & 0 \\ 0 & 0 & 1 \\ 0 & 1 & 0 \end{pmatrix}$

28. $\begin{pmatrix} 3 & 0 & 1 \\ 0 & 1 & 0 \\ 0 & 0 & 1 \end{pmatrix}$ 29. $\begin{pmatrix} 2 & 0 & 0 \\ 0 & 0 & 1 \\ 0 & 1 & 0 \end{pmatrix}$ 30. $\begin{pmatrix} 2 & 0 & 0 \\ 0 & 1 & 1 \\ 0 & 0 & 1 \end{pmatrix}$

31. $\begin{pmatrix} 1 & 1 \\ 1 & 1 \end{pmatrix}$ 32. $\begin{pmatrix} 3 & -6 \\ 2 & -4 \end{pmatrix}$ 33. $\begin{pmatrix} 3 & -2 & 4 \\ 0 & 1 & 2 \end{pmatrix}$

We next use elementary matrices to obtain the inverse of a non-singular matrix. Thus, suppose A is a nonsingular $n \times n$ matrix, $E_1, E_2, \ldots, E_{n-1}, E_n$ are elementary $n \times n$ matrices, and

(3-3.1) $$E_n E_{n-1} \cdots E_2 E_1 A = I$$

Multiply this equation by A^{-1} to obtain $(E_n E_{n-1} \cdots E_2 E_1 A) A^{-1} = I A^{-1}$, from which

(3-3.2) $$E_n E_{n-1} \cdots E_2 E_1 I = A^{-1}$$

From Eqq. (3-3.1) and (3-3.2) we reason that if the elementary matrices $E_1, E_2, \ldots, E_n$ multiplied on the left of A produce I, then the same elementary matrices multiplied in the same order on the left of I produce A^{-1}. The elementary matrices used here are not important—their effect under left multiplication is the important feature. In the illustration to follow we list the elementary matrices.

Illustration 7

If $A = \begin{pmatrix} 1 & 2 & 1 \\ -1 & -3 & 5 \\ 2 & 1 & 21 \end{pmatrix}$ obtain A^{-1}. Here, we change A to I and I to A^{-1} by left multiplications of A and I by elementary matrices. Now,

$$A = \begin{pmatrix} 1 & 2 & 1 \\ -1 & -3 & 5 \\ 2 & 1 & 21 \end{pmatrix} \quad \text{and} \quad I = \begin{pmatrix} 1 & 0 & 0 \\ 0 & 1 & 0 \\ 0 & 0 & 1 \end{pmatrix}$$

Then,

$\begin{pmatrix} 1 & 2 & 1 \\ 0 & -1 & 6 \\ 2 & 1 & 21 \end{pmatrix}$ $\begin{pmatrix} 1 & 0 & 0 \\ 1 & 1 & 0 \\ 0 & 0 & 1 \end{pmatrix}$ $E_1 = S_{21} = \begin{pmatrix} 1 & 0 & 0 \\ 1 & 1 & 0 \\ 0 & 0 & 1 \end{pmatrix}$

$\begin{pmatrix} 1 & 2 & 1 \\ 0 & -1 & 6 \\ 0 & -3 & 19 \end{pmatrix}$ $\begin{pmatrix} 1 & 0 & 0 \\ 1 & 1 & 0 \\ -2 & 0 & 1 \end{pmatrix}$ $E_2 = S_{31} = \begin{pmatrix} 1 & 0 & 0 \\ 0 & 1 & 0 \\ -2 & 0 & 1 \end{pmatrix}$

$\begin{pmatrix} 1 & 2 & 1 \\ 0 & 1 & -6 \\ 0 & -3 & 19 \end{pmatrix}$ $\begin{pmatrix} 1 & 0 & 0 \\ -1 & -1 & 0 \\ -2 & 0 & 1 \end{pmatrix}$ $E_3 = D_{22} = \begin{pmatrix} 1 & 0 & 0 \\ 0 & -1 & 0 \\ 0 & 0 & 1 \end{pmatrix}$

$$\begin{pmatrix} 1 & 2 & 1 \\ 0 & 1 & -6 \\ 0 & 0 & 1 \end{pmatrix} \qquad \begin{pmatrix} 1 & 0 & 0 \\ -1 & -1 & 0 \\ -5 & -3 & 1 \end{pmatrix} \qquad E_4 = S_{32} = \begin{pmatrix} 1 & 0 & 0 \\ 0 & 1 & 0 \\ 0 & 3 & 1 \end{pmatrix}$$

$$\begin{pmatrix} 1 & 2 & 1 \\ 0 & 1 & 0 \\ 0 & 0 & 1 \end{pmatrix} \qquad \begin{pmatrix} 1 & 0 & 0 \\ -31 & -19 & 6 \\ -5 & -3 & 1 \end{pmatrix} \qquad E_5 = S_{23} = \begin{pmatrix} 1 & 0 & 0 \\ 0 & 1 & 6 \\ 0 & 0 & 1 \end{pmatrix}$$

$$\begin{pmatrix} 1 & 2 & 0 \\ 0 & 1 & 0 \\ 0 & 0 & 1 \end{pmatrix} \qquad \begin{pmatrix} 6 & 3 & -1 \\ -31 & -19 & 6 \\ -5 & -3 & 1 \end{pmatrix} \qquad E_6 = S_{13} = \begin{pmatrix} 1 & 0 & -1 \\ 0 & 1 & 0 \\ 0 & 0 & 1 \end{pmatrix}$$

$$I = \begin{pmatrix} 1 & 0 & 0 \\ 0 & 1 & 0 \\ 0 & 0 & 1 \end{pmatrix} \qquad \text{and} \qquad A^{-1} = \begin{pmatrix} 68 & 41 & -13 \\ -31 & -19 & 6 \\ -5 & -3 & 1 \end{pmatrix}$$

$$E_7 = S_{12} = \begin{pmatrix} 1 & -2 & 0 \\ 0 & 1 & 0 \\ 0 & 0 & 1 \end{pmatrix}$$

Certain systems of n linear equations in n unknowns can now be solved using matrices. Suppose the system in matrix form is $AX = B$. If A is nonsingular, it follows that $X = A^{-1}B$. (Why?) Matrix equality then provides the values of the unknowns.

Illustration 8

Solve the system $\begin{cases} x - 6y = 10 \\ 5x + 2y = 18 \end{cases}$. In matrix form the system is $AX = B$,

where $A = \begin{pmatrix} 1 & -6 \\ 5 & 2 \end{pmatrix}$, $X = \begin{pmatrix} x \\ y \end{pmatrix}$, and $B = \begin{pmatrix} 10 \\ 18 \end{pmatrix}$. We compute A^{-1} as follows.

$$A = \begin{pmatrix} 1 & -6 \\ 5 & 2 \end{pmatrix} \qquad \text{and} \qquad I = \begin{pmatrix} 1 & 0 \\ 0 & 1 \end{pmatrix}$$

$$\begin{pmatrix} 1 & -6 \\ 0 & 32 \end{pmatrix} \qquad\qquad \begin{pmatrix} 1 & 0 \\ -5 & 1 \end{pmatrix}$$

$$\begin{pmatrix} 1 & -6 \\ 0 & 1 \end{pmatrix} \qquad\qquad \begin{pmatrix} 1 & 0 \\ -\frac{5}{32} & \frac{1}{32} \end{pmatrix}$$

$$I = \begin{pmatrix} 1 & 0 \\ 0 & 1 \end{pmatrix} \qquad \text{and} \qquad A^{-1} = \begin{pmatrix} \frac{2}{32} & \frac{6}{32} \\ -\frac{5}{32} & \frac{1}{32} \end{pmatrix} = \frac{1}{32}\begin{pmatrix} 2 & 6 \\ -5 & 1 \end{pmatrix}$$

Then, $X = \dfrac{1}{32}\begin{pmatrix} 2 & 6 \\ -5 & 1 \end{pmatrix}\begin{pmatrix} 10 \\ 18 \end{pmatrix} = \dfrac{1}{32}\begin{pmatrix} 128 \\ -32 \end{pmatrix} = \begin{pmatrix} 4 \\ -1 \end{pmatrix}$. Consequently, $x = 4$, $y = -1$, and the solution set $S = \{(4, -1)\}$.

Illustration 9

Solve the system $\begin{cases} x + 2y + z = -4 \\ -x - 3y + 5z = 0 \\ 2x + y + 21z = -21 \end{cases}$. In matrix form the system is $AX = B$, where $A = \begin{pmatrix} 1 & 2 & 1 \\ -1 & -3 & 5 \\ 2 & 1 & 21 \end{pmatrix}$, $X = \begin{pmatrix} x \\ y \\ z \end{pmatrix}$, and $B = \begin{pmatrix} -4 \\ 0 \\ -21 \end{pmatrix}$.

From Illustration 7, $A^{-1} = \begin{pmatrix} 68 & 41 & -13 \\ -31 & -19 & 6 \\ -5 & -3 & 1 \end{pmatrix}$. Therefore,

$$X = \begin{pmatrix} 68 & 41 & -13 \\ -31 & -19 & 6 \\ -5 & -3 & 1 \end{pmatrix} \begin{pmatrix} -4 \\ 0 \\ -21 \end{pmatrix} = \begin{pmatrix} 1 \\ -2 \\ -1 \end{pmatrix}$$

Matrix equality gives that $x = 1$, $y = -2$, $z = -1$, and the solution set $S = \{ (1, -2, -1) \}$.

Problem Set 3-3B

In Problems 1 through 10 obtain the inverses of the given matrices. Verify by multiplication.

1. $\begin{pmatrix} 6 & 3 \\ 5 & -4 \end{pmatrix}$
2. $\begin{pmatrix} 1 & 6 \\ -3 & 4 \end{pmatrix}$
3. $\begin{pmatrix} 0 & 3 \\ 3 & 0 \end{pmatrix}$

4. $\begin{pmatrix} 1 & 1 \\ 1 & -1 \end{pmatrix}$
5. $\begin{pmatrix} 3 & -2 \\ 6 & -4 \end{pmatrix}$
6. $\begin{pmatrix} 2 & -2 & 1 \\ -1 & 0 & 2 \\ 1 & 1 & 3 \end{pmatrix}$

7. $\begin{pmatrix} 2 & 1 & -1 \\ 0 & 3 & 1 \\ -1 & 0 & 2 \end{pmatrix}$
8. $\begin{pmatrix} 1 & 3 & 2 \\ 3 & 1 & 4 \\ -2 & -1 & 1 \end{pmatrix}$
9. $\begin{pmatrix} 1 & -1 & 1 \\ 1 & 1 & 1 \\ 1 & 1 & -1 \end{pmatrix}$

10. $\begin{pmatrix} -3 & 5 & -6 \\ 2 & -3 & 5 \\ 5 & 2 & -3 \end{pmatrix}$

Use the inverses obtained in Problems 1 through 10 to solve the systems of equations in Problems 11 through 20.

11. $\begin{cases} 6x + 3y = 5 \\ 5x - 4y = -3 \end{cases}$
12. $\begin{cases} x + 6y = -2 \\ -3x + 4y = 7 \end{cases}$

13. $\begin{cases} 0x + 3y = 9 \\ 3x + 0y = -12 \end{cases}$
14. $\begin{cases} x + y = 10 \\ x - y = 4 \end{cases}$

15. $\begin{cases} 3x - 2y = 5 \\ 6x - 4y = 11 \end{cases}$
16. $\begin{cases} 2x - 2y + z = 5 \\ -x + 2z = 3 \\ x + y + 3z = -6 \end{cases}$

17. $\begin{cases} 2x + y - z = 5 \\ 3y + z = -7 \\ -x + 2z = -1 \end{cases}$
18. $\begin{cases} x + 3y + 2z = 9 \\ 3x + y + 4z = 1 \\ -2x - y + z = 2 \end{cases}$

19. $\begin{cases} x - y + z = -6 \\ x + y + z = 4 \\ x + y - z = 2 \end{cases}$
20. $\begin{cases} -3x + 5y - 6z = -173 \\ 2x - 3y + 5z = 126 \\ 5x + 2y - 3z = -41 \end{cases}$

21. Solve the system $\begin{cases} x + 2y + z = a \\ -x - 3y + 5z = b \\ 2x + y + 21z = c \end{cases}$ for a, b, and c constants.

(See Illustration 9.)

22. Prove that the inverse of a nonsingular matrix is unique, that is, if B and C are inverses of A, then $B = C$.

23. If A and B are each nonsingular $n \times n$ matrices, prove that $(AB)^{-1} = B^{-1}A^{-1}$. (*Hint:* Argue that $B^{-1}A^{-1}$ is an inverse of AB.)

24. If A is nonsingular, prove that $(A^{-1})^{-1} = A$.

25. If A is nonsingular, prove that $(A^t)^{-1} = (A^{-1})^t$. (*Hint:* Use Theorem 2-3.3.)

26. If A is a square matrix and $AB = I$, prove that $BA = I$.

4

Determinants

4-1. THE DETERMINANT FUNCTION

As we have seen, square matrices play an important role in the theory of matrices. For example, recall that invertible matrices are necessarily square and identity matrices are square. If A is a square matrix, we will associate a real number with A, called the *determinant of A*. If $A = (a_{ij})$ is $n \times n$ the notations used to denote the determinant of A are *det A, det (a_{ij}),* or

$$\begin{vmatrix} a_{11} & a_{12} & \cdots & a_{1n} \\ a_{21} & a_{22} & \cdots & a_{2n} \\ \vdots & \vdots & \ddots & \vdots \\ a_{n1} & a_{n2} & \cdots & a_{nn} \end{vmatrix}$$

The last notation will only be used for $n \geq 2$. Before we describe a method of obtaining *det A* the concepts of the minor and cofactor of an entry of A are needed.

DEFINITION 4–1.1. *If $A = (a_{ij})$ is $n \times n$ with $n \geq 2$, the minor of an entry a_{ij} of A is $M[a_{ij}] = det\,B$, where B is that matrix obtained from A by deleting the ith row and jth column. The matrix B is called a submatrix of A.*

Illustration 1

If $A = \begin{pmatrix} 2 & -3 \\ -5 & 4 \end{pmatrix}$, then $M[2] = det\,(4)$, $M[-3] = det\,(-5)$,

$M[-5] = det\,(-3)$, and $M[4] = det\,(2)$. If $A = \begin{pmatrix} 3 & 0 & -1 \\ -2 & 5 & 2 \\ 1 & 4 & 6 \end{pmatrix}$, then

$M[3] = det \begin{pmatrix} 5 & 2 \\ 4 & 6 \end{pmatrix}$, $M[5] = det \begin{pmatrix} 3 & -1 \\ 1 & 6 \end{pmatrix}$, $M[2] = det \begin{pmatrix} 3 & 0 \\ 1 & 4 \end{pmatrix}$,

and $M[4] = det \begin{pmatrix} 3 & -1 \\ -2 & 2 \end{pmatrix}$.

DEFINITION 4-1.2. *If $A = (a_{ij})$ is $n \times n$ with $n \geq 2$, the cofactor of an entry a_{ij} of A is $C[a_{ij}] = (-1)^{i+j}M[a_{ij}]$.*

Illustration 2

For $A = \begin{pmatrix} 2 & -3 \\ -5 & 4 \end{pmatrix}$ of Illustration 1, $C[2] = (-1)^{1+1}M[2] =$
$M[2]$, $C[-3] = (-1)^{1+2}M[-3] = -M[-3]$, $C[-5] =$
$(-1)^{2+1}M[-5] = -M[-5]$, and $C[4] = (-1)^{2+2}M[4] = M[4]$.
For $A = \begin{pmatrix} 3 & 0 & -1 \\ -2 & 5 & 2 \\ 1 & 4 & 6 \end{pmatrix}$, $C[3] = (-1)^{1+1}M[3] = M[3]$, $C[5] =$
$(-1)^{2+2}M[5] = M[5]$, $C[2] = (-1)^{2+3}M[2] = -M[2]$, and
$C[4] = (-1)^{3+2}M[4] = -M[4]$.

Our next definition uses mathematical induction. Notice that the determinant of a 1×1 matrix is specified, then for $n \geq 2$ the determinant of an $n \times n$ matrix is defined if the determinant of an $(n - 1) \times (n - 1)$ matrix is defined. By the principle of mathematical induction, which we now state, the determinant of any square matrix is defined.

Principle of Mathematical Induction. If for each $n \in Z^+$, the statement $P(n)$ is true or false,

(a) $P(1)$ is true, and
(b) if $P(k)$ is true for $k \in Z^+$, then $P(k + 1)$ is true,

then $P(n)$ is true for all $n \in Z^+$.

Illustration 3

Prove that $\sum_{m=1}^{m=n} (2m - 1) = n^2$ for all $n \in Z^+$. For each $n \in Z^+$, this statement, $P(n)$ is clearly true or false.
For $n = 1$, $\sum_{m=1}^{m=1} (2m - 1) = 2(1) - 1 = 1$, which is equal to 1^2. Thus, $P(1)$ is true.

Next, if $P(k)$ is true we must prove that $P(k+1)$ is true, that is, if

$$\sum_{m=1}^{m=k} (2m-1) = k^2$$

then,

$$\sum_{m=1}^{m=k+1} (2m-1) = (k+1)^2$$

Thus, consider

$$\sum_{m=1}^{m=k+1} (2m-1) = \sum_{m=1}^{m=k} (2m-1) + 2(k+1) - 1$$
$$= k^2 + 2k + 2 - 1 \qquad \textit{Since } P(k) \textit{ is true.}$$
$$= k^2 + 2k + 1$$
$$= (k+1)^2$$

Therefore, $P(k+1)$ is true if $P(k)$ is true. By the principle of mathematical induction, the statement holds for all positive integers.

We are now prepared to define the *determinant function* as a function from the set of all square matrices into (actually onto) the set of all real numbers. The usual definition specifies the functional value of the determinant function.

DEFINITION 4-1.3. *If* $A = (a_{ij})$ *is* $n \times n$, *then*

a. *if* $n = 1$, *then* $\det A = a_{11}$,
b. *if* $n \geq 2$, *then* $\det A = \sum_{k=1}^{k=n} a_{1k} C[a_{1k}]$.

Thus, the determinant of a 1×1 matrix (a matrix with only one entry) is just the entry of the matrix. If $n \geq 2$, the determinant of A is the sum of the products of the entries in the first row of A and their corresponding cofactors. By *part (b)* of Definition 4-1.3,

$$\det A = a_{11}C[a_{11}] + a_{12}C[a_{12}] + \cdots + a_{1n}C[a_{1n}]$$

Each of these n cofactors involves the determinant of an $(n-1) \times (n-1)$ matrix. Thus, to evaluate the determinant of an $n \times n$ matrix we must know how to evaluate the determinant of an $(n-1) \times (n-1)$ matrix. Therefore, Definition 4-1.3 is an *inductive* definition.

Illustration 4

If $A = (3)$, then $\det A = 3$. For $B = (-5)$, we have $\det B = -5$. If $C = (0)$, then $\det C = 0$.

Illustration 5

Evaluate $\det A$ if $A = \begin{pmatrix} 2 & -3 \\ -5 & 4 \end{pmatrix}$. Now, $C[2] = M[2] = \det(4) = 4$ and $C[-3] = -M[-3] = -\det(-5) = -(-5) = 5$. Therefore, $\det A = 2 \cdot 4 + [-3]5 = 8 - 15 = -7$.

81

For $B = \begin{pmatrix} 5 & 2 \\ 4 & 6 \end{pmatrix}$, what is $det\ B$? We have $C[5] = M[5] = det\ (6) = 6$ and $C[2] = -M[2] = -det\ (4) = -4$. Consequently, $det\ B = 5 \cdot 6 + 2[-4] = 30 - 8 = 22$.

If $D = \begin{pmatrix} -2 & 5 \\ 1 & 4 \end{pmatrix}$, evaluate $det\ D$. Now, $C[-2] = M[-2] = det\ (4) = 4$ and $C[5] = -M[5] = -det\ (1) = -1$. Therefore, $det\ D = [-2]4 + 5[-1] = -8 - 5 = -13$.

Illustration 6

What is $det\ A$ if $A = \begin{pmatrix} 3 & 0 & -1 \\ -2 & 5 & 2 \\ 1 & 4 & 6 \end{pmatrix}$? First, $C[3] = M[3] = det \begin{pmatrix} 5 & 2 \\ 4 & 6 \end{pmatrix} = 22$ and $C[-1] = M[-1] = det \begin{pmatrix} -2 & 5 \\ 1 & 4 \end{pmatrix} = -13$, (see Illustration 5). Then,

$$det\ A = 3 \cdot 22 + 0 \cdot C[0] + [-1][-13] = 66 + 13 = 79$$

The summation in *part* (b) of Definition 4–1.3 can be easily obtained for a 2×2 or 3×3 matrix by using entries of the matrix. From Illustration 5, you can guess the result for a 2×2 matrix.

Illustration 7

Evaluate $det\ A$ if $A = \begin{pmatrix} a_{11} & a_{12} \\ a_{21} & a_{22} \end{pmatrix}$. Since $C[a_{11}] = a_{22}$ and $C[a_{12}] = -a_{21}$, we have

$$\begin{aligned} det\ A &= a_{11}C[a_{11}] + a_{12}C[a_{12}] \\ &= a_{11}a_{22} + a_{12}[-a_{21}] \\ &= a_{11}a_{22} - a_{12}a_{21} \end{aligned}$$

Therefore, $det\ A$ is the product of the entries on the main diagonal of A minus the product $a_{12}a_{21}$ of the entries a_{12} and a_{21} on the alternate diagonal.

Illustration 8

If $A = \begin{pmatrix} a_{11} & a_{12} & a_{13} \\ a_{21} & a_{22} & a_{23} \\ a_{31} & a_{32} & a_{33} \end{pmatrix}$, evaluate $det\ A$. First

$$C[a_{11}] = det \begin{pmatrix} a_{22} & a_{23} \\ a_{32} & a_{33} \end{pmatrix} = a_{22}a_{33} - a_{23}a_{32}$$

$$C[a_{12}] = -det \begin{pmatrix} a_{21} & a_{23} \\ a_{31} & a_{33} \end{pmatrix} = -[a_{21}a_{33} - a_{23}a_{31}] = a_{23}a_{31} - a_{21}a_{33}$$

and

$$C[a_{13}] = det \begin{pmatrix} a_{21} & a_{22} \\ a_{31} & a_{32} \end{pmatrix} = a_{21}a_{32} - a_{22}a_{31}$$

Therefore,

$$det A = a_{11}C[a_{11}] + a_{12}C[a_{21}] + a_{13}C[a_{13}]$$
$$= a_{11}[a_{22}a_{33} - a_{23}a_{32}] + a_{12}[a_{23}a_{31} - a_{21}a_{33}]$$
$$+ a_{13}[a_{21}a_{32} - a_{22}a_{31}]$$
$$= a_{11}a_{22}a_{33} + a_{12}a_{23}a_{31} + a_{13}a_{21}a_{32} - a_{13}a_{22}a_{31} - a_{11}a_{23}a_{32}$$
$$- a_{12}a_{21}a_{33}$$

This sum can be obtained from the following device, where the three elements on a line are multiplied, preceded by the sign indicated, then the six terms are added.

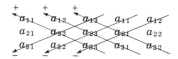

Illustration 9

Evaluate $det A$ if $A = \begin{pmatrix} 3 & 0 & -1 \\ -2 & 5 & 2 \\ 1 & 4 & 6 \end{pmatrix}$, (see Illustration 5). Now,

$$det A = (3)(5)(6) + (0)(2)(1) + (-1)(-2)(4) - (-1)(5)(1)$$
$$- (3)(2)(4) - (0)(-2)(6)$$
$$= 90 + 0 + 8 + 5 - 24 + 0$$
$$= 79$$

The following theorem states that the entries of any row (or column) and the cofactors of these entries can be used to evaluate the determinant of a square matrix with $n \geq 2$.

THEOREM 4-1.1. *If $A = (a_{ij})$ is $n \times n$ with $n \geq 2$, then $det A$ is the sum of the products of the entries in any row (or column) by their corresponding cofactors.*

Illustration 10

If $A = \begin{pmatrix} 2 & -3 \\ -5 & 4 \end{pmatrix}$, evaluate $det A$ using (a) the second row, and (b) the second column.

For (a), $C[-5] = 3$ and $C[4] = 2$. Thus, $det A = (-5)3 + (4)(2) = -15 + 8 = -7$.
For (b), $C[-3] = 5$ and $C[4] = 2$ give $det A = (-3)5 + 4(2) = -15 + 8 = -7$.

Theorem 4-1.1 is useful if zero is an entry of the matrix. The computation is shortened by using a row or column that has a maximum number of zero entries.

Illustration 11

For $A = \begin{pmatrix} 3 & 0 & -1 \\ -2 & 5 & 2 \\ 0 & 4 & 0 \end{pmatrix}$, we choose to use the third row to evaluate

$det\, A$. Now, $C[4] = -M[4] = -det\begin{pmatrix} 3 & -1 \\ -2 & 2 \end{pmatrix} = -4$. Therefore,

$$det\, A = 0C[a_{31}] + 4(-4) + 0C[a_{33}] = 0 - 16 + 0 = -16$$

Illustration 12

To evaluate $det\, A$ for $A = \begin{pmatrix} -2 & 1 & 0 & -1 \\ 0 & 2 & 1 & 5 \\ 1 & 0 & -2 & 1 \\ 3 & -1 & 0 & -4 \end{pmatrix}$, we will use the third

column since this column has two entries that are zero. Now,

$$C[a_{23}] = (-1)^{2+3}M[a_{23}] = -det\begin{pmatrix} -2 & 1 & -1 \\ 1 & 0 & 1 \\ 3 & -1 & -4 \end{pmatrix} = -6$$

and

$$C[a_{33}] = (-1)^{3+3}M[a_{33}] = det\begin{pmatrix} -2 & 1 & -1 \\ 0 & 2 & 5 \\ 3 & -1 & -4 \end{pmatrix} = 27$$

Then,

$$\begin{aligned} det\, A &= 0C[a_{13}] + 1C[a_{23}] + (-2)C[a_{33}] + 0C[a_{43}] \\ &= 0 + 1(-6) + (-2)(27) + 0 \\ &= -6 - 54 = -60 \end{aligned}$$

Problem Set 4-1

In Problems 1 through 13 evaluate the given determinants.

1. $\begin{vmatrix} 4 & -2 \\ 3 & 1 \end{vmatrix}$
2. $\begin{vmatrix} -2 & 4 \\ 1 & 3 \end{vmatrix}$
3. $\begin{vmatrix} 3 & 1 \\ 4 & -2 \end{vmatrix}$

4. $\begin{vmatrix} 4 & 3 \\ -2 & 1 \end{vmatrix}$
5. $\begin{vmatrix} 12 & -6 \\ 3 & 1 \end{vmatrix}$
6. $\begin{vmatrix} 4 & 10 \\ 3 & -5 \end{vmatrix}$

7. $\begin{vmatrix} 4 & -2 \\ 7 & -1 \end{vmatrix}$
8. $\begin{vmatrix} 10 & 0 \\ 3 & 1 \end{vmatrix}$
9. $\begin{vmatrix} 1 & 0 \\ 0 & 1 \end{vmatrix}$

10. $\begin{vmatrix} 5 & 0 \\ 0 & 6 \end{vmatrix}$
11. $\begin{vmatrix} 5 & 0 \\ -3 & 6 \end{vmatrix}$
12. $\begin{vmatrix} 5 & -7 \\ 0 & 6 \end{vmatrix}$

13. $\begin{vmatrix} 0 & 0 \\ 0 & 0 \end{vmatrix}$

In Problems 14 through 19 let $A = \begin{pmatrix} 3 & -5 & 4 \\ -2 & 1 & 7 \\ 0 & 2 & -3 \end{pmatrix}$. Obtain the minor

and the cofactor of each entry in the row or column indicated.

14. The first row   15. The second row   16. The third row

17. The first column   18. The second column   19. The third column

In Problems 20 through 35 evaluate the given determinants.

20. $\begin{vmatrix} 2 & 0 & -3 \\ 1 & 1 & 4 \\ 0 & 2 & 1 \end{vmatrix}$
21. $\begin{vmatrix} 1 & -4 & 2 \\ 0 & 1 & 0 \\ -2 & 3 & 5 \end{vmatrix}$
22. $\begin{vmatrix} 3 & -1 & 2 \\ 1 & 2 & -5 \\ 6 & 3 & -1 \end{vmatrix}$

23. $\begin{vmatrix} 1 & 0 & 0 \\ 0 & 1 & 0 \\ 0 & 0 & 1 \end{vmatrix}$
24. $\begin{vmatrix} 3 & 0 & 0 \\ 0 & -4 & 0 \\ 0 & 0 & 5 \end{vmatrix}$
25. $\begin{vmatrix} a & 0 & 0 \\ 0 & b & 0 \\ 0 & 0 & c \end{vmatrix}$

26. $\begin{vmatrix} 3 & 0 & 0 \\ 1 & -4 & 0 \\ 19 & 15 & 5 \end{vmatrix}$
27. $\begin{vmatrix} 3 & 2 & -6 \\ 0 & -4 & -8 \\ 0 & 0 & 5 \end{vmatrix}$
28. $\begin{vmatrix} 1 & 6 & -7 \\ 0 & 0 & 0 \\ 2 & -3 & 5 \end{vmatrix}$

29. $\begin{vmatrix} 1 & 1 & 4 \\ 2 & 0 & -3 \\ 0 & 2 & 1 \end{vmatrix}$
30. $\begin{vmatrix} 4 & 1 & 1 \\ -3 & 0 & 2 \\ 1 & 2 & 0 \end{vmatrix}$
31. $\begin{vmatrix} 8 & 2 & 2 \\ -3 & 0 & 2 \\ 1 & 2 & 0 \end{vmatrix}$

32. $\begin{vmatrix} 4 & 1 & 1 & -1 \\ -1 & -2 & -3 & 1 \\ 0 & 0 & 0 & 1 \\ -1 & 2 & -1 & 1 \end{vmatrix}$
33. $\begin{vmatrix} 1 & -4 & -4 & 3 \\ 2 & 0 & -2 & 3 \\ -4 & 2 & -5 & 2 \\ 3 & -4 & 1 & 0 \end{vmatrix}$

34. $\begin{vmatrix} 1 & -4 & -4 & 3 \\ 2 & 0 & -2 & 3 \\ 0 & -14 & -21 & 14 \\ 3 & -4 & 1 & 0 \end{vmatrix}$
35. $\begin{vmatrix} 1 & -3 & 2 & -4 & 4 \\ 2 & 1 & 0 & 4 & -1 \\ 3 & 0 & -2 & 2 & -4 \\ 1 & 2 & -1 & 4 & 0 \\ 1 & 1 & 1 & 2 & 1 \end{vmatrix}$

Use the principle of mathematical induction to prove the following statements for all positive integers n.

36. $\sum_{m=1}^{m=n} m = \dfrac{n(n+1)}{2}$

37. $\sum_{m=1}^{m=n} m^2 = \dfrac{n(n+1)(2n+1)}{6}$

38. $\sum_{m=1}^{m=n} m^3 = \dfrac{n^2(n+1)^2}{4}$

39. $\sum_{m=1}^{m=n} \dfrac{1}{(2m-1)(2m+1)} = \dfrac{n}{2n+1}$

40. $\sum_{m=1}^{m=n} ar^{m-1} = \dfrac{a(1-r^n)}{1-r}$, if $r \neq 1$

41. $x - y$ is a factor of $x^n - y^n$

4-2. SOME PROPERTIES OF DETERMINANTS

If $n \geq 4$, the problem of evaluating $\det A$ by Definition 4-1.3 may be tedious. However, if A is a triangular matrix (see *property 5*) or if one row (or column) is a scalar multiple of another row (or column) (see *property 4*), then $\det A$ is easily obtained. Furthermore, if B is a matrix obtained from A in certain ways (see *properties 1, 2, 3*), then $\det B$ and $\det A$ are related. The following properties are not only interesting, they provide new ways to evaluate determinants. Let A be a square matrix.

Property 1. If two rows (or columns) of A are interchanged to form a matrix B, then $det\ B = -det\ A$.

Property 2. If a row (or column) of A is multiplied by a scalar b to yield a matrix B, then $det\ B = b\ det\ A$.

Property 3. If a row (or column) of A is multiplied by a scalar and the result added to a different row (or column) of A to yield a matrix B, then $det\ B = det\ A$.

Property 4. If a row (or column) of A is a scalar multiple of another row (or column) of A, then $det\ A = 0$.

Property 5. If A is a triangular matrix, then $det\ A$ is the product of the entries on the main diagonal of A.

Property 6. $det\ A = det\ A^t$.

You will be asked to prove some of these properties or special cases of them in Problem Set 4-2. Here, we assume that the properties hold.

Illustration 1

If $A = \begin{pmatrix} 2 & 0 & 0 \\ -3 & 1 & 0 \\ 0 & 3 & 5 \end{pmatrix}$, what is $det\ A$? Notice that A is a triangular

matrix. By *property 5*, $det\ A = (2)(1)(5) = 10$.

Illustration 2

Evaluate $det\ A$ if $A = \begin{pmatrix} 1 & 0 & 3 & 2 \\ 3 & -5 & 0 & 7 \\ 6 & 2 & 5 & 1 \\ 9 & -15 & 0 & 21 \end{pmatrix}$. Since the fourth row is a

scalar multiple of the second row, then $det\ A = 0$. (See *property 4*.)

Illustration 3

If $B = \begin{pmatrix} 4 & 8 \\ 2 & 1 \end{pmatrix}$, then by *property 2* we have $det\ B = 4\ det \begin{pmatrix} 1 & 2 \\ 2 & 1 \end{pmatrix}$.

Also, $det\ B = 2\ det \begin{pmatrix} 2 & 8 \\ 1 & 1 \end{pmatrix}$. (What does this show?)

Illustration 4

If $A = \begin{pmatrix} 3 & 1 & -2 & 1 \\ 1 & 0 & -5 & -1 \\ 3 & -3 & 1 & 1 \\ 1 & 0 & 2 & -1 \end{pmatrix}$, evaluate $det\ A$ in three ways.

Solution 1. Use Theorem 4-1.1 and the second column of A to obtain

$$det\ A\ =\ -(1)\begin{vmatrix} 1 & -5 & -1 \\ 3 & 1 & 1 \\ 1 & 2 & -1 \end{vmatrix} - (-3)\begin{vmatrix} 3 & -2 & 1 \\ 1 & -5 & -1 \\ 1 & 2 & -1 \end{vmatrix} = 28 + 84 = 112$$

Solution 2. Apply *property 3* three times by multiplying the second column of A by -3, 2, and -1 and adding the results to the first, third, and fourth columns of A, respectively, to obtain

$$det\ A\ =\ \begin{vmatrix} 0 & 1 & 0 & 0 \\ 1 & 0 & -5 & -1 \\ 12 & -3 & -5 & 4 \\ 1 & 0 & 2 & -1 \end{vmatrix} = -\begin{vmatrix} 1 & -5 & -1 \\ 12 & -5 & 4 \\ 1 & 2 & -1 \end{vmatrix} = 112$$

Solution 3. Here, we change A to a triangular matrix. Now,

$$det\ A\ =\ -det\begin{pmatrix} 1 & 3 & -2 & 1 \\ 0 & 1 & -5 & -1 \\ -3 & 3 & 1 & 1 \\ 0 & 1 & 2 & -1 \end{pmatrix}$$

Interchange the first and second columns of A.

$$=\ -det\begin{pmatrix} 1 & 0 & 0 & 0 \\ 0 & 1 & -5 & -1 \\ -3 & 12 & -5 & 4 \\ 0 & 1 & 2 & -1 \end{pmatrix}$$

Add -3 times the first column to the second column. Others?

$$=\ -det\begin{pmatrix} 1 & 0 & 0 & 0 \\ 0 & 1 & 0 & 0 \\ -3 & 12 & 55 & 16 \\ 0 & 1 & 7 & 0 \end{pmatrix}$$

Why?

$$=\ -det\begin{pmatrix} 1 & 0 & 0 & 0 \\ 0 & 1 & 0 & 0 \\ -3 & 12 & 55 & 0 \\ 0 & 1 & 7 & -\frac{112}{55} \end{pmatrix}$$

Why?

$$=\ 112$$

This section is concluded with two theorems concerning determinants. The first involves the determinant of a product while the second involves the concept of the adjoint of a square matrix.

THEOREM 4-2.1. *If A and B are each $n \times n$ matrices, then det $AB = $ det A det B.*

COROLLARY 4-2.1. *If A is an invertible matrix, then*

$$det\ A\ det\ A^{-1} = 1$$

Proof: Let $B = A^{-1}$ in Theorem 4-2.1. Then, $det\ AA^{-1} = det\ A\ det\ A^{-1}$. Since $det\ AA^{-1} = det\ I = 1$, we have

$$det\ A\ det\ A^{-1} = 1$$

DEFINITION 4-2.1. *If $A = (a_{ij})$ is $n \times n$, the adjoint of A is adj $A = (C[a_{ij}])^t$.*

87

The adjoint of A is that matrix formed from A by replacing each entry in A by its cofactor, then taking the transpose of the resulting matrix. Thus, for the $n \times n$ matrix $A = (a_{ij})$, we have

$$adj\ A = \begin{pmatrix} C[a_{11}] & C[a_{12}] & \cdots & C[a_{1n}] \\ C[a_{21}] & C[a_{22}] & \cdots & C[a_{2n}] \\ \vdots & \vdots & \ddots & \vdots \\ C[a_{n1}] & C[a_{n2}] & \cdots & C[a_{nn}] \end{pmatrix}^t$$

THEOREM 4-2.2. *If $A = (a_{ij})$ is $n \times n$, then $A\ adj\ A = I\ det\ A$.*

You can easily verify that each entry on the main diagonal of $A\ adj\ A$ is $det\ A$. To verify that each entry off the main diagonal is zero is more difficult.

Illustration 5

Verify Theorem 4-2.1 for $A = \begin{pmatrix} 1 & -3 & 2 \\ 0 & 4 & -2 \\ 3 & 1 & -1 \end{pmatrix}$ and $B = \begin{pmatrix} -4 & 0 & 1 \\ 2 & 3 & 0 \\ 1 & -2 & 5 \end{pmatrix}$.

Now, $AB = \begin{pmatrix} -8 & -13 & 11 \\ 6 & 16 & -10 \\ -11 & 5 & -2 \end{pmatrix}$. Then, $det\ AB = 536$, $det\ A = -8$, $det\ B = -67$, and $536 = (-8)(-67)$.

Illustration 6

Obtain the adjoint of $A = \begin{pmatrix} 1 & -3 & 2 \\ 0 & 4 & -2 \\ 3 & 1 & -1 \end{pmatrix}$ and verify Theorem 4-2.2 for

the matrix A. Now,

$$adj\ A = \begin{pmatrix} -2 & -6 & -12 \\ -1 & -7 & -10 \\ -2 & 2 & 4 \end{pmatrix}^t = \begin{pmatrix} -2 & -1 & -2 \\ -6 & -7 & 2 \\ -12 & -10 & 4 \end{pmatrix} = -\begin{pmatrix} 2 & 1 & 2 \\ 6 & 7 & -2 \\ 12 & 10 & -4 \end{pmatrix}$$

Then,

$$A\ adj\ A = -\begin{pmatrix} 1 & -3 & 2 \\ 0 & 4 & -2 \\ 3 & 1 & -1 \end{pmatrix}\begin{pmatrix} 2 & 1 & 2 \\ 6 & 7 & -2 \\ 12 & 10 & -4 \end{pmatrix} = -\begin{pmatrix} 8 & 0 & 0 \\ 0 & 8 & 0 \\ 0 & 0 & 8 \end{pmatrix}$$

$$= -8I = I\ det\ A$$

since $det\ A = -8$.

Illustration 7

Prove *property 5*. Suppose A is a square matrix with all entries below the main diagonal zero, see Definition 2-3.4. For the proof we will use mathematical induction. If $A = (a_{11})$, a 1×1 matrix, then $det\ A = a_{11}$, which is the entry on the main diagonal of A. Thus, all 1×1 matrices have the property. If $k \in Z^+$ and all $k \times k$ matrices have the property, we must prove that all $(k + 1) \times (k + 1)$ matrices also have the property. Let

$$A = \begin{pmatrix} a_{11} & a_{12} & \cdots & a_{1k} & a_{1,k+1} \\ 0 & a_{22} & \cdots & a_{2k} & a_{2,k+1} \\ \vdots & \vdots & \ddots & \vdots & \vdots \\ 0 & 0 & \cdots & a_{kk} & a_{k,k+1} \\ 0 & 0 & \cdots & 0 & a_{k+1,k+1} \end{pmatrix}$$

Now,

$$\det A = a_{11}C[a_{11}] + a_{12}C[a_{22}] + \cdots + a_{1k}C[a_{1k}] + a_{1,k+1}C[a_{1,k+1}]$$
$$= a_{11}C[a_{11}]$$
$$= a_{11}a_{22}a_{33} \cdots a_{kk}a_{k+1,k+1}$$

since $C[a_{11}]$ is the determinant of a $k \times k$ matrix. Therefore, the property holds for 1 (all 1×1 matrices) and if the property holds for $k \in Z^+$ (all $k \times k$ matrices) then the property holds for $k + 1$ (all $(k + 1) \times (k + 1)$ matrices). By mathematical induction, the property holds for all positive integers. In Problem 34, Problem Set 4-2, you are asked to prove that this property holds for all square matrices with all entries above the main diagonal zero.

Problem Set 4-2

In Problems 1 through 8 use properties of determinants to evaluate each determinant in two ways.

1. $\begin{vmatrix} 2 & 0 & -3 \\ 1 & 1 & 4 \\ 0 & 2 & 1 \end{vmatrix}$
2. $\begin{vmatrix} 1 & -4 & 2 \\ 1 & 1 & 1 \\ -2 & 3 & 5 \end{vmatrix}$
3. $\begin{vmatrix} 3 & -1 & 2 \\ 1 & 2 & -5 \\ 6 & 3 & -1 \end{vmatrix}$

4. $\begin{vmatrix} 1 & 1 & 4 \\ 2 & 0 & -3 \\ 0 & 2 & 1 \end{vmatrix}$
5. $\begin{vmatrix} 8 & 2 & 2 \\ -3 & 0 & 2 \\ 1 & 2 & 0 \end{vmatrix}$
6. $\begin{vmatrix} 1 & -4 & -4 & 3 \\ 2 & 0 & -2 & 3 \\ -4 & 2 & -5 & 2 \\ 3 & -4 & 1 & 0 \end{vmatrix}$

7. $\begin{vmatrix} 2 & -1 & 1 & 1 \\ 1 & 1 & 0 & 1 \\ 2 & 2 & 0 & -1 \\ 1 & -3 & -2 & 1 \end{vmatrix}$
8. $\begin{vmatrix} 1 & -3 & 2 & -4 & 4 \\ 2 & 1 & 0 & 4 & -1 \\ 3 & 0 & -2 & 2 & -4 \\ 1 & 2 & -1 & 4 & 0 \\ 1 & 1 & 1 & 2 & 1 \end{vmatrix}$

In Problems 9 through 14 state properties of determinants that verify the given results.

9. $\begin{vmatrix} 5 & -2 \\ 3 & 4 \end{vmatrix} = \begin{vmatrix} 5 & 3 \\ -2 & 4 \end{vmatrix}$
10. $\begin{vmatrix} 4 & 3 & -4 \\ 5 & -6 & 0 \\ 1 & 2 & 3 \end{vmatrix} = \begin{vmatrix} 4 & 3 & 0 \\ 5 & -6 & 5 \\ 1 & 2 & 4 \end{vmatrix}$

11. $\begin{vmatrix} 3 & -2 & 5 \\ 2 & 1 & 0 \\ -15 & 10 & -25 \end{vmatrix} = 0$
12. $\begin{vmatrix} 2 & 3 & -5 & 4 \\ 0 & 1 & 2 & -8 \\ 0 & 0 & 3 & 1 \\ 0 & 0 & 0 & -5 \end{vmatrix} = -30$

13. $\begin{vmatrix} 3 & -2 & 5 \\ 8 & 4 & -2 \\ 0 & 3 & -1 \end{vmatrix} = 2 \begin{vmatrix} 3 & -2 & 5 \\ 4 & 2 & -1 \\ 0 & 3 & -1 \end{vmatrix}$

89

14. $\begin{vmatrix} 5 & -3 & -4 & 0 \\ 0 & 2 & 2 & -3 \\ 2 & 1 & 3 & -1 \\ -1 & 0 & 5 & 4 \end{vmatrix} = \begin{vmatrix} -4 & 0 & 5 & -3 \\ 2 & -3 & 0 & 2 \\ 3 & -1 & 2 & 1 \\ 5 & 4 & -1 & 0 \end{vmatrix}$

15. Solve $\begin{vmatrix} 16 & 1 \\ x & x \end{vmatrix} = 0$ for x.

16. Solve $\begin{vmatrix} x & x \\ x+3 & x-5 \end{vmatrix} = 0$ for x.

17. Solve $\begin{vmatrix} -x & 2-x & 0 \\ 2 & 2-x & 2 \\ 0 & 2 & -x \end{vmatrix} = 0$ for x.

In each of Problems 18 through 24 obtain the adjoint of the given matrix. Verify Theorem 4-2.2 for each matrix.

18. $\begin{pmatrix} 2 & 0 & -3 \\ 1 & 1 & 4 \\ 0 & 2 & 1 \end{pmatrix}$

19. $\begin{pmatrix} 1 & -4 & 2 \\ 1 & 1 & 1 \\ -2 & 3 & 5 \end{pmatrix}$

20. $\begin{pmatrix} 3 & -1 & 2 \\ 1 & 2 & -5 \\ 6 & 3 & -1 \end{pmatrix}$

21. $\begin{pmatrix} 1 & 1 & 4 \\ 2 & 0 & -3 \\ 0 & 2 & 1 \end{pmatrix}$

22. $\begin{pmatrix} 8 & 2 & 2 \\ -3 & 0 & 2 \\ 1 & 2 & 0 \end{pmatrix}$

23. $\begin{pmatrix} 1 & -4 & -4 & 3 \\ 2 & 0 & -2 & 3 \\ -4 & 2 & -5 & 2 \\ 3 & -4 & 1 & 0 \end{pmatrix}$ (See Problem 6.)

24. $\begin{pmatrix} 2 & -1 & 1 & 1 \\ 1 & 1 & 0 & 1 \\ 2 & 2 & 0 & -1 \\ 1 & -3 & -2 & 1 \end{pmatrix}$ (See Problem 7.)

In Problems 25 through 28 establish the identities.

25. $\begin{vmatrix} 1 & 1 & 1 \\ x & y & z \\ x^2 & y^2 & z^2 \end{vmatrix} = (x-y)(y-z)(z-x)$

26. $\begin{vmatrix} 1 & 1 & 1 \\ x & y & z \\ x^3 & y^3 & z^3 \end{vmatrix} = (x-y)(y-z)(z-x)(x+y+z)$

27. $\begin{vmatrix} x & 1 & 1 & 1 \\ 1 & x & 1 & 1 \\ 1 & 1 & x & 1 \\ 1 & 1 & 1 & x \end{vmatrix} = (x+3)(x-1)^3$

28. $\begin{vmatrix} x+y & y+z & z+x \\ y+z & z+x & x+y \\ z+x & x+y & y+z \end{vmatrix} = 2\begin{vmatrix} x & y & z \\ y & z & x \\ z & x & y \end{vmatrix}$

29. If (a, b) and (c, d) are distinct points in a plane, show that

$$\begin{vmatrix} 1 & x & y \\ 1 & a & b \\ 1 & c & d \end{vmatrix} = 0$$

is an equation of the line containing the two points.

30. Prove *property 2*.

31. Use *property 1* to prove that if two rows (or columns) of a square matrix A are identical, then $det\ A = 0$.

32. If a row (or column) vector of a square matrix is a zero vector, prove that $det\ A = 0$.

33. Prove *property 4*.

34. Prove *property 5* for all entries above the main diagonal zero.

35. If A is a square matrix, argue that each entry on the main diagonal of $A\ adj\ A$ is $det\ A$.

36. Argue that if A and B are row-equivalent square matrices, then $det\ A = \pm det\ B$.

4-3. CRAMER'S RULE

If $a_{11}a_{12}a_{21}a_{22} \neq 0$, and previous methods are applied to the system

$$\begin{cases} a_{11}x + a_{12}y = b_1 \\ a_{21}x + a_{22}y = b_2 \end{cases}$$

the equivalent system

(4-3.1)
$$\begin{cases} (a_{11}a_{22} - a_{12}a_{21})x = b_1a_{22} - a_{12}b_2 \\ (a_{11}a_{22} - a_{12}a_{21})y = a_{11}b_2 - b_1a_{21} \end{cases}$$

is obtained. Notice that $a_{11}a_{22} - a_{12}a_{21} = \begin{vmatrix} a_{11} & a_{12} \\ a_{21} & a_{22} \end{vmatrix}$, $b_1a_{22} -$

$a_{12}b_2 = \begin{vmatrix} b_1 & a_{12} \\ b_2 & a_{22} \end{vmatrix}$, and $a_{11}b_2 - b_1a_{21} = \begin{vmatrix} a_{11} & b_1 \\ a_{21} & b_2 \end{vmatrix}$.

If $\begin{vmatrix} a_{11} & a_{12} \\ a_{21} & a_{22} \end{vmatrix} \neq 0$, then *Cramer's rule* states that

(4-3.2)
$$x = \frac{\begin{vmatrix} b_1 & a_{12} \\ b_2 & a_{22} \end{vmatrix}}{\begin{vmatrix} a_{11} & a_{12} \\ a_{21} & a_{22} \end{vmatrix}}, \qquad y = \frac{\begin{vmatrix} a_{11} & b_1 \\ a_{12} & b_2 \end{vmatrix}}{\begin{vmatrix} a_{11} & a_{12} \\ a_{21} & a_{22} \end{vmatrix}}$$

Let

$$A = \begin{pmatrix} a_{11} & a_{12} \\ a_{21} & a_{22} \end{pmatrix}, \qquad D_1 = \begin{pmatrix} b_1 & a_{12} \\ b_2 & a_{22} \end{pmatrix}, \qquad \text{and} \qquad D_2 = \begin{pmatrix} a_{11} & b_1 \\ a_{21} & b_2 \end{pmatrix}$$

Then, Eqq. (4-3.2) can be expressed as

(4-3.2a)
$$x = \frac{det\ D_1}{det\ A}, \qquad y = \frac{det\ D_2}{det\ A}$$

From system (4-3.1), if $det\ A = 0$ and either $det\ D_1 \neq 0$ or $det\ D_2 \neq 0$, then either $0x \neq 0$ or $0y \neq 0$ and the system is inconsistent, that is, the solution set is empty. Geometrically, this means that the lines in R^2 defined by the equations do not intersect. If det $A = 0$, det $D_1 = 0$, and det $D_2 = 0$, then system (4–3.1) gives $0x = 0$ and $0y = 0$. In this case, the system is *dependent*, that is, there are many solutions. Geometrically, this means that the lines coincide. If $b_1 = 0$ and $b_2 = 0$, the equations of the system are homogeneous. Consequently, det $D_1 = 0$ and det $D_2 = 0$. For this case, if det $A \neq 0$, the only solution is the trivial one, $(0, 0)$, while if det $A = 0$ there exist many nontrivial solutions.

Illustration 1

Solve the system $\begin{cases} 3x - 5y = 2 \\ 2x + y = 10 \end{cases}$ by Cramer's rule. Since

$$A = \begin{pmatrix} 3 & -5 \\ 2 & 1 \end{pmatrix}, \qquad D_1 = \begin{pmatrix} 2 & -5 \\ 10 & 1 \end{pmatrix}, \qquad \text{and} \qquad D_2 = \begin{pmatrix} 3 & 2 \\ 2 & 10 \end{pmatrix}$$

we have det $A = 13$, det $D_1 = 52$, and det $D_2 = 26$. By Eqq. (4–3.2a), $x = \frac{52}{13} = 4$, $y = \frac{26}{13} = 2$, and the solution set $S = \{ (4, 2) \}$.

Illustration 2

Discuss the system $\begin{cases} 3x - 6y = 5 \\ 2x - 4y = 4 \end{cases}$. Now,

$$A = \begin{pmatrix} 3 & -6 \\ 2 & -4 \end{pmatrix}, \qquad D_1 = \begin{pmatrix} 5 & -6 \\ 4 & -4 \end{pmatrix}, \qquad \text{and} \qquad D_2 = \begin{pmatrix} 3 & 5 \\ 2 & 4 \end{pmatrix}$$

Then, det $A = 0$, det $D_1 = 4$, and det $D_2 = 2$. Since det $A = 0$ and at least one of det D_1 and det D_2 is not zero, the solution set $S = \emptyset$. The homogeneous system $\begin{cases} 3x - 6y = 0 \\ 2x - 4y = 0 \end{cases}$ has solution set

$$S = \{ (x, y) \mid x - 2y = 0 \}. \qquad \textit{Why?}$$

Either of Eqq. (4–3.2) or (4–3.2a) is the statement of Cramer's rule for a system of two linear equations in two unknowns. Cramer's rule can be applied to any system of linear equations with the same number of unknowns as equations, provided the determinant of the coefficient matrix is not zero. Thus, consider the system

(4–3.3)

$$\begin{cases} a_{11}x_1 + a_{12}x_2 + \cdots + a_{1n}x_n = b_1 \\ a_{21}x_1 + a_{22}x_2 + \cdots + a_{2n}x_n = b_2 \\ \vdots \qquad \vdots \qquad \ddots \qquad \vdots \qquad \vdots \\ a_{n1}x_1 + a_{n2}x_2 + \cdots + a_{nn}x_n = b_n \end{cases}$$

The matrix of coefficients is

$$A = \begin{pmatrix} a_{11} & a_{12} & \cdots & a_{1n} \\ a_{21} & a_{22} & \cdots & a_{2n} \\ \vdots & \vdots & \ddots & \vdots \\ a_{n1} & a_{n2} & \cdots & a_{nn} \end{pmatrix}$$

Let

$$jth$$
$$\text{column}$$

$$
D_j = \begin{pmatrix}
a_{11} & a_{12} & \cdots & b_1 & \cdots & a_{1n} \\
a_{21} & a_{22} & \cdots & b_2 & \cdots & a_{2n} \\
\vdots & \vdots & \ddots & \vdots & \ddots & \vdots \\
a_{n1} & a_{n2} & \cdots & b_n & \cdots & a_{nn}
\end{pmatrix}
$$

for $j \in \{1, 2, \ldots, n\}$ be obtained from A by replacing the jth column vector of A by the column vector $\begin{pmatrix} b_1 \\ b_2 \\ \vdots \\ b_n \end{pmatrix}$. Cramer's rule states that if $\det A \neq 0$, then for each $j \in \{1, 2, \ldots, n\}$, $x_j = \dfrac{\det D_j}{\det A}$. Thus,

(4-3.4) $\quad x_1 = \dfrac{\det D_1}{\det A}, \qquad x_2 = \dfrac{\det D_2}{\det A}, \qquad \ldots, \qquad x_n = \dfrac{\det D_n}{\det A}$

The system (4-3.3) is *inconsistent* if $\det A = 0$ and some $\det D_j \neq 0$ for $j \in \{1, 2, \ldots, n\}$, while the system is *dependent* if $\det A = 0$ and $\det D_j = 0$ for every $j \in \{1, 2, \ldots, n\}$.

Illustration 3

Use Cramer's rule to solve the system

$$
\begin{cases}
x + y - 2z = 1 \\
3x - 2y + z = -19 \\
x + 3y - 7z = 12
\end{cases}
$$

Now,

$$
A = \begin{pmatrix} 1 & 1 & -2 \\ 3 & -2 & 1 \\ 1 & 3 & -7 \end{pmatrix}, \qquad
D_1 = \begin{pmatrix} 1 & 1 & -2 \\ -19 & -2 & 1 \\ 12 & 3 & -7 \end{pmatrix}, \qquad
D_2 = \begin{pmatrix} 1 & 1 & -2 \\ 3 & -19 & 1 \\ 1 & 12 & -7 \end{pmatrix},
$$

and

$$
D_3 = \begin{pmatrix} 1 & 1 & 1 \\ 3 & -2 & -19 \\ 1 & 3 & 12 \end{pmatrix}
$$

Since $\det A = 11$, $\det D_1 = -44$, $\det D_2 = 33$, and $\det D_3 = -11$, Eq. (4-3.4) gives $x = -\frac{44}{11} = -4$, $y = \frac{33}{11} = 3$, and $z = -\frac{11}{11} = -1$. Therefore, $S = \{(-4, 3, -1)\}$. Geometrically, the three planes in R^3 defined by the equations intersect in the point $(-4, 3, -1)$.

Illustration 4

Solve the following system by Cramer's rule.

$$
\begin{cases}
x + y & = -1 \\
y - z & = 1 \\
z + w = 1 \\
x \quad\quad - w = -3
\end{cases}
$$

93

From

$$A = \begin{pmatrix} 1 & 1 & 0 & 0 \\ 0 & 1 & -1 & 0 \\ 0 & 0 & 1 & 1 \\ 1 & 0 & 0 & -1 \end{pmatrix}, \quad D_1 = \begin{pmatrix} -1 & 1 & 0 & 0 \\ 1 & 1 & -1 & 0 \\ 1 & 0 & 1 & 1 \\ -3 & 0 & 0 & -1 \end{pmatrix}$$

$$D_2 = \begin{pmatrix} 1 & -1 & 0 & 0 \\ 0 & 1 & -1 & 0 \\ 0 & 1 & 1 & 1 \\ 1 & -3 & 0 & -1 \end{pmatrix}, \quad D_3 = \begin{pmatrix} 1 & 1 & -1 & 0 \\ 0 & 1 & 1 & 0 \\ 0 & 0 & 1 & 1 \\ 1 & 0 & -3 & -1 \end{pmatrix}$$

and

$$D_4 = \begin{pmatrix} 1 & 1 & 0 & -1 \\ 0 & 1 & -1 & 1 \\ 0 & 0 & 1 & 1 \\ 1 & 0 & 0 & -3 \end{pmatrix}$$

we have $det\ A = det\ D_1 = det\ D_2 = det\ D_3 = det\ D_4 = 0$. (You should verify these.) Thus, the system has many solutions. If $x = k$, then $y = -1 - k$, $z = -2 - k$, and $w = 3 + k$. Therefore, the solution set $S = \{ (k,\ -1 - k,\ -2 - k,\ 3 + k) \mid k \in R \}$.

Problem Set 4-3

Solve the following problems from Section 3-3 using Cramer's rule, where applicable. Let Problems 11 through 21 of Problem Set 3-3B be Problems 1 through 11.

Obtain the solution set of each of the following systems of equations.

12. $\begin{cases} x + y + z = 4 \\ 2x - 3y + 4z = 17 \\ x - y - z = 2 \end{cases}$

13. $\begin{cases} x - 3y = 0 \\ -5x + 15y = 0 \end{cases}$

14. $\begin{cases} x - 3y = 4 \\ -5x + 15y = -19 \end{cases}$

15. $\begin{cases} x + y + z = 2 \\ x + y - z = 2 \\ -x - y + z = 2 \end{cases}$

16. $\begin{cases} x + y + z = 2 \\ x + y - z = 2 \\ x + y + 2z = 2 \end{cases}$

17. $\begin{cases} x + y + z = 0 \\ x + y - z = 0 \\ 3x - y + z = 0 \end{cases}$

18. $\begin{cases} x + y + z = 0 \\ x + y - z = 0 \\ x + y - 3z = 0 \end{cases}$

19. $\begin{cases} x + y = 8 \\ 2x - y = 7 \\ 5x + 2y = 10 \end{cases}$

20. $\begin{cases} x + y = 8 \\ 2x - y = 7 \\ 5x - y = 22 \end{cases}$

21. $\begin{cases} x + y + z = 6 \\ x - y = 6 \\ x + y - z = 2 \\ 3x - 2y + 5z = 15 \end{cases}$

22. $\begin{cases} x + y + z = 6 \\ x - y = 6 \\ x + y - z = 2 \\ -x + y + 4z = 2 \end{cases}$

23. $\begin{cases} x - y + z = 2 \\ 3x + 2y - z = 13 \end{cases}$

24. $\begin{cases} 3x + 2y + z = -7 \\ 6x + 4y - z = -20 \end{cases}$

4-4. MULTIPLICATIVE INVERSE OF A MATRIX

From Theorem 4-2.2, we know that $A \ adj \ A = I \ det \ A$, if A is a square matrix. If $det \ A \neq 0$, then $A \left[\dfrac{1}{det \ A} \right] adj \ A = I$ and $\left(\dfrac{1}{det \ A} \right) adj \ A$ is a right inverse of A. Since a right inverse of a square matrix is also a left inverse (see Problem 26 of Problem Set 3-3B), $\left(\dfrac{1}{det \ A} \right) adj \ A$ is an inverse of A. Thus, if $det \ A \neq 0$, there exists an inverse of A and this inverse is $\left(\dfrac{1}{det \ A} \right) adj \ A$. More actually holds, as given in the following two theorems.

THEOREM 4-4.1. *If $A = (a_{ij})$ is $n \times n$, then A is nonsingular if and only if $det \ A \neq 0$.*

THEOREM 4-4.2. *If A is a nonsingular matrix, then $A^{-1} = \left(\dfrac{1}{det \ A} \right) adj \ A$.*

The first theorem provides a test that allows us to decide whether a given matrix is singular or nonsingular, while the second theorem provides a method of obtaining the inverse of a nonsingular matrix.

Illustration 1

If $A = \begin{pmatrix} 2 & -1 \\ 3 & 4 \end{pmatrix}$, obtain A^{-1}. First, $det \ A = 11$. By Theorem 4-4.1, A^{-1} exists. Since $adj \ A = \begin{pmatrix} 4 & 1 \\ -3 & 2 \end{pmatrix}$, Theorem 4-4.2 gives that $A^{-1} = \dfrac{1}{11} \begin{pmatrix} 4 & 1 \\ -3 & 2 \end{pmatrix}$.

Illustration 2

Obtain A^{-1} if $A = \begin{pmatrix} 1 & -1 & 3 \\ -1 & 2 & 1 \\ 0 & 0 & -1 \end{pmatrix}$. First, $det \ A = -1$. Compute $adj \ A$ in the usual way to obtain $adj \ A = \begin{pmatrix} -2 & -1 & -7 \\ -1 & -1 & -4 \\ 0 & 0 & 1 \end{pmatrix}$. Then,

$$A^{-1} = \frac{1}{-1} \begin{pmatrix} -2 & -1 & -7 \\ -1 & -1 & -4 \\ 0 & 0 & 1 \end{pmatrix} = \begin{pmatrix} 2 & 1 & 7 \\ 1 & 1 & 4 \\ 0 & 0 & -1 \end{pmatrix}$$

The system of equations in (4–3.3) can be expressed as the

matrix equation $AX = B$ where $A = (a_{ij})$ is $n \times n$, $X = \begin{pmatrix} x_1 \\ x_2 \\ \vdots \\ x_n \end{pmatrix}$

and $B = \begin{pmatrix} b_1 \\ b_2 \\ \vdots \\ b_n \end{pmatrix}$. If A is nonsingular, we have

$$\begin{aligned} A^{-1}(AX) &= A^{-1}B \\ (A^{-1}A)X &= A^{-1}B \\ IX &= A^{-1}B \\ X &= A^{-1}B \end{aligned}$$

Provide all reasons.

From this last equation, matrix equality provides the solution of the system. The method of using a matrix equation to solve a system of linear equations is shown in the following illustrations.

Illustration 3

Solve the system $\begin{cases} 2x - y = 13 \\ 3x + 4y = 14 \end{cases}$. The matrix equation is $AX = B$,

where $A = \begin{pmatrix} 2 & -1 \\ 3 & 4 \end{pmatrix}$, $X = \begin{pmatrix} x \\ y \end{pmatrix}$, and $B = \begin{pmatrix} 13 \\ 14 \end{pmatrix}$. From Illustration 1,

$A^{-1} = \dfrac{1}{11}\begin{pmatrix} 4 & 1 \\ -3 & 2 \end{pmatrix}$. Therefore,

$$\begin{aligned} X &= \left[\frac{1}{11}\begin{pmatrix} 4 & 1 \\ -3 & 2 \end{pmatrix} \right]\begin{pmatrix} 13 \\ 14 \end{pmatrix} \\ &= \frac{1}{11}\left[\begin{pmatrix} 4 & 1 \\ -3 & 2 \end{pmatrix}\begin{pmatrix} 13 \\ 14 \end{pmatrix} \right] \\ &= \frac{1}{11}\begin{pmatrix} 66 \\ -11 \end{pmatrix} \\ &= \begin{pmatrix} 6 \\ -1 \end{pmatrix} \end{aligned}$$

Consequently, $x = 6$, $y = -1$ and the solution set $S = \{ (6, -1) \}$.

Illustration 4

Solve the system $\begin{cases} x - 3y + 2z = 2 \\ x - 2y - 3z = 6 \\ 4x + 7y - z = -2 \end{cases}$. In matrix form the system is

$AX = B$ where $A = \begin{pmatrix} 1 & -3 & 2 \\ 1 & -2 & -3 \\ 4 & 7 & -1 \end{pmatrix}$, $X = \begin{pmatrix} x \\ y \\ z \end{pmatrix}$, and $B = \begin{pmatrix} 2 \\ 6 \\ -2 \end{pmatrix}$. Since

$\det A = 86$ and $adj\ A = \begin{pmatrix} 23 & 11 & 13 \\ -11 & -9 & 5 \\ 15 & -19 & 1 \end{pmatrix}$, then

$$A^{-1} = \frac{1}{86} \begin{pmatrix} 23 & 11 & 13 \\ -11 & -9 & 5 \\ 15 & -19 & 1 \end{pmatrix}$$

Thus,

$$X = \frac{1}{86} \begin{pmatrix} 23 & 11 & 13 \\ -11 & -9 & 5 \\ 15 & -19 & 1 \end{pmatrix} \begin{pmatrix} 2 \\ 6 \\ -2 \end{pmatrix} = \begin{pmatrix} 1 \\ -1 \\ -1 \end{pmatrix}$$

Matrix equality gives $x = 1$, $y = -1$, and $z = -1$ from which the solution set $S = \{ (1, -1, -1) \}$.

If you are asked to solve a system of n linear equations in n unknowns or to obtain the inverse of a nonsingular $n \times n$ matrix, what methods will you use? Recall that for each of these problems we have two general methods, one involving reduction of a matrix and the other involving determinants. If $n \le 4$, either method is fairly easily applied. However, if n is large, the reduction method is much superior to that involving determinants since the number of multiplications required is about n^3 compared to $n!$. If we are seeking only an expression or formula for the answer, the methods involving determinants provide these while the reduction methods do not directly provide formulas. Using reduction we have to actually solve the problem to obtain an expression for the answer.

Problem Set 4–4

Let Problems 1 through 21 be Problems 1 through 21 of Problem Set 3–3B.

In Problems 22 through 28 use the results of Problems 1 through 7 and 18 through 24 of Problem Set 4–2 to solve the given systems of equations.

22. $\begin{cases} 2x \quad - 3z = 6 \\ x + y + 4z = -7 \\ 2y + z = 0 \end{cases}$

23. $\begin{cases} x - 4y + 2z = 11 \\ x + y + z = 3 \\ -2x + 3y + 5z = 10 \end{cases}$

24. $\begin{cases} 3x - y + 2z = 1 \\ x + 2y - 5z = -17 \\ 6x + 3y - z = -28 \end{cases}$

25. $\begin{cases} x + y + 4z = -1 \\ 2x \quad - 3z = 9 \\ 2y + z = -1 \end{cases}$

26. $\begin{cases} 8x + 2y + 2z = 10 \\ -3x \quad + 2z = -13 \\ x + 2y \quad = 3 \end{cases}$

27. $\begin{cases} x - 4y - 4z + 3w = -4 \\ 2x \quad - 2z + 3w = 3 \\ -4x + 2y - 5z + 2w = -5 \\ 3x - 4y + z \quad = 0 \end{cases}$

28. $\begin{cases} 2x - y + z + w = 6 \\ x + y \quad + w = -1 \\ 2x + 2y \quad - w = 4 \\ x - 3y - 2z + w = -3 \end{cases}$

5

Vector Spaces

5-1. EXAMPLES OF VECTOR SPACES

Since many mathematical systems are vector spaces, we can identify some properties common to these systems by studying vector spaces. By learning the properties of general vector spaces, we will know some properties of any system that is a vector space. Previously, we defined a vector space over R. (See Definition 1–1.1.) Although R will generally be used in the illustrations and problems, we will define (and prove results concerning) a vector space over any *field*. Notice that R satisfies the following definition of a field.

DEFINITION 5–1.1. *A field F consists of a set F with an equivalence relation $(=)$, an operation of addition $(+)$, and an operation of multiplication $(\cdot)$ such that for all a, b, $c \in F$ the following properties hold.*

a. *Closure*   *Each of $a + b$ and $a \cdot b$ is a unique element of F.*

b. *Commutative Laws*   *$a + b = b + a$ and $a \cdot b = b \cdot a$*

c. *Associative Laws*   *$a + (b + c) = (a + b) + c$ and $a \cdot (b \cdot c)$*
                                       $= (a \cdot b) \cdot c$

d. *Identities*   *There exists an element $0 \in F$ such that $a + 0 = 0 + a = a$ for all $a \in F$.*

There exists an element $1 \in F$, $1 \neq 0$, such that $a \cdot 1 = 1 \cdot a = a$ for all $a \in F$.

e. *Inverses*

For each $a \in F$ there exists an element $-a \in F$ such that $a + (-a) = (-a) + a = 0$. For each $a \in F$ with $a \neq 0$, there exists an element $a^{-1} \in F$ such that $a \cdot a^{-1} = a^{-1} \cdot a = 1$.

f. *Distributive Laws*

$a \cdot (b + c) = a \cdot b + a \cdot c$ and $(a + b) \cdot c = a \cdot c + b \cdot c$

The set Q of all rational numbers with the equality, addition, and multiplication of R is a field. Another example of a field is the set $C = \{a + bi \mid a, b \in R\}$ with $i^2 = -1$ and

(a) Equality $a + bi = c + di$ if and only if $a = c$ and $b = d$,

(b) Addition $(a + bi) + (c + di) = (a + c) + (b + d)i$, and

(c) Multiplication $(a + bi)(c + di) = (ac - bd) + (ad + bc)i$.

This field, C, is called the field of complex numbers. An example of a finite field is $Z_2 = \{0, 1\}$, with addition and multiplication defined by

+	0	1
0	0	1
1	1	0

·	0	1
0	0	0
1	0	1

A second finite field is $Z_3 = \{0, 1, 2\}$ with addition and multiplication defined by

+	0	1	2
0	0	1	2
1	1	2	0
2	2	0	1

·	0	1	2
0	0	0	0
1	0	1	2
2	0	2	1

If p is a prime number, then $Z_p = \{0, 1, 2, \ldots, p - 1\}$ is a field if modulo arithmetic is used for the addition and multiplication tables. For example, in Z_7, $3 + 2 = 5$, $3 + 4 = 0$, $5 + 6 = 4$, $3 \cdot 2 = 6$, $3 \cdot 4 = 5$, and $5 \cdot 6 = 2$. More generally, if $a, b \in Z_p$, then $a + b = cp + r_1$ and $a \cdot b = dp + r_2$ where r_1 and r_2 are nonnegative integers less than p. Thus, to perform either addition or multiplication in Z_p, perform the operation in the integers, divide by p, and take the remainder as the answer in Z_p.

In a field, or any other mathematical system, we assume that the *substitution principle* holds. Thus, if $a = b$, either one can replace the other one in any expression.

Problem Set 5-1A

In Problems 1 through 23 let a, b, and c be elements of a field F. Prove each statement or form the definition asked for. The notation ab is sometimes used instead of $a \cdot b$.

1. $(a + b) + (-a) = b$

2. $ab + b = b(a + 1)$

3. If $a + c = b + c$, then $a = b$.   4. $a \cdot 0 = 0$ for all $a \in F$

5. If $ac = bc$ and $c \neq 0$, then $a = b$.

6. The additive identity of F is unique, that is, if $0'$ is an additive identity of F, then $0' = 0$.

7. The multiplicative identity of F is unique. (See Problem 6.)

8. The additive inverse of an element in F is unique, that is, if b is an additive inverse of a, then $b = -a$.

9. If $a \neq 0$, the multiplicative inverse of a is unique. (See Problem 8.)

10. If $a + b = 0$, then $b = -a$ and $a = -b$.

11. $-(-a) = a$

12. If $ab = 1$, then $b = a^{-1}$ and $a = b^{-1}$.

13. If $ab \neq 0$, then $(ab)^{-1} = b^{-1}a^{-1}$.

14. $(-a)b = -(ab) = a(-b)$ 15. $(-a)(-b) = ab$

16. $(-1)a = -a$ 17. If $ab = 0$, then $a = 0$ or $b = 0$.

18. Define subtraction, $a - b$, for a field F.

19. $a(b - c) = ab - ac$ 20. $-(a - b) = b - a$

21. If $b \neq 0$, define division, a/b, for a field F.

22. If $b \neq 0$, then $\dfrac{a + c}{b} = \dfrac{a}{b} + \dfrac{c}{b}$.

23. $-\dfrac{a}{b} = \dfrac{-a}{b} = \dfrac{a}{-b}$

24. Show that equality for the set of all complex numbers is an equivalence relation.

25. Argue that C is a field.

26. Prove that parts (a), (b), (d), and (e) of Definition 5–1.1 hold for Z_2.

27. Repeat Problem 26 for Z_3.

28. Construct addition and multiplication tables for the field $Z_5 = \{0, 1, 2, 3, 4\}$. List the inverses of each element in Z_5.

Next, we consider some properties and examples of vector spaces over a field. First, Definition 1–1.1 is restated with the field R replaced with any field F.

DEFINITION 5–1.2. *A vector space V over a field F consists of a set V along with an equivalence relation $(=)$, an operation of addition $(+)$ in V, and scalar multiplication of elements of V by elements of F such that for all $c, d \in F$ and all $\mathbf{u}, \mathbf{v}, \mathbf{w} \in V$*

a. $\mathbf{u} + \mathbf{v}$ *is a unique element of V,*   *Closure*

b. $\mathbf{u} + \mathbf{v} = \mathbf{v} + \mathbf{u}$,   *Commutative Law*

c. $(\mathbf{u} + \mathbf{v}) + \mathbf{w} = \mathbf{u} + (\mathbf{v} + \mathbf{w})$,   *Associative Law*

d. *there exists an element $\mathbf{0} \in V$ such that*
$\mathbf{v} + \mathbf{0} = \mathbf{0} + \mathbf{v} = \mathbf{v}$, *for all $\mathbf{v} \in V$,*   *Additive Identity*

e. *for each* $\mathbf{v} \in V$, *there exists an element*
   $-\mathbf{v} \in V$ *such that*
   $\mathbf{v} + (-\mathbf{v}) = (-\mathbf{v}) + \mathbf{v} = \mathbf{0}$,　　　*Additive Inverse*

f. $c\mathbf{v}$ *is a unique element of* V,　　　*Closure for Scalar*
   Multiplication

g. $(cd)\mathbf{v} = c(d\mathbf{v})$,　　　*Associative Property*

h. $(c + d)\mathbf{v} = c\mathbf{v} + d\mathbf{v}$,　　　*Distributive Property*

i. $c(\mathbf{u} + \mathbf{v}) = c\mathbf{u} + c\mathbf{v}$, *and*　　　*Distributive Property*

j. $1\mathbf{v} = \mathbf{v}$, *where* 1 *is the multiplicative*
   identity of F.　　　*Identity Element*

The elements of V are called *vectors* while the elements of F are called *scalars*. As usual, vectors are denoted by boldface symbols. If $\mathbf{u}, \mathbf{v} \in V$, subtraction is defined in the usual way by $\mathbf{u} - \mathbf{v} = \mathbf{u} + (-\mathbf{v})$. Several additional algebraic properties, such as the following five, hold and are easily proved.

i. If $\mathbf{u} + \mathbf{w} = \mathbf{v} + \mathbf{w}$ or $\mathbf{w} + \mathbf{u} = \mathbf{w} + \mathbf{v}$, then $\mathbf{u} = \mathbf{v}$　　　*Cancellation Property*

ii. $c\mathbf{v} = \mathbf{0}$ if and only if $c = 0$ or $\mathbf{v} = \mathbf{0}$

iii. $-(c\mathbf{v}) = (-c)\mathbf{v} = c(-\mathbf{v})$

iv. $c(\mathbf{u} - \mathbf{v}) = c\mathbf{u} - c\mathbf{v}$

v. $-(\mathbf{u} - \mathbf{v}) = \mathbf{v} - \mathbf{u}$

Proof of Property i: If $\mathbf{u} + \mathbf{w} = \mathbf{v} + \mathbf{w}$, the substitution principle gives that $(\mathbf{u} + \mathbf{w}) + (-\mathbf{w}) = (\mathbf{v} + \mathbf{w}) + (-\mathbf{w})$. Then, $\mathbf{u} + [\mathbf{w} + (-\mathbf{w})] = \mathbf{v} + [\mathbf{w} + (-\mathbf{w})]$, which leads to $\mathbf{u} + \mathbf{0} = \mathbf{v} + \mathbf{0}$. Thus, $\mathbf{u} = \mathbf{v}$. (You can supply the reasons here.) A similar proof holds for the other part of the property.

Proof of Property iv: Now, $c(\mathbf{u} - \mathbf{v}) = c[\mathbf{u} + (-\mathbf{v})] = c\mathbf{u} + c(-\mathbf{v}) = c\mathbf{u} + [-(c\mathbf{v})] = c\mathbf{u} - c\mathbf{v}$. (Provide all reasons.)

Next, we consider some examples of vector spaces. We already know that for each positive integer n, R^n is a vector space over R. By Theorem 2-1.2, the set of all $m \times n$ dimension matrices (with real numbers for elements) is a vector space over R. If in Definition 5-1.2 we let $V = F$, then all parts of the definition hold. Therefore, any field is a vector space over itself. The set $\{0\}$ is a *trivial* vector space over R. In Euclidean three-space, any plane containing the origin is a vector space over R. At this point, you may need to review set theory (see Appendix), and read part of Section 6-1 for more information concerning functions.

Illustration 1

The solution set (space) S of all solutions of the homogeneous system of linear equations $\begin{cases} a_1x + b_1y = 0 \\ a_2x + b_2y = 0 \end{cases}$ is a vector space over R. Here, we think of the solutions as ordered pairs (x, y) in R^2. If $\mathbf{u} = (x_1, y_1) \in S$ and $\mathbf{v} = (x_2, y_2) \in S$, then $\mathbf{u} + \mathbf{v} = (x_1 + x_2, y_1 + y_2)$ and

$$\begin{cases} a_1(x_1 + x_2) + b_1(y_1 + y_2) = (a_1x_1 + b_1y_1) + (a_1x_2 + b_1y_2) \\ \qquad\qquad\qquad\qquad\qquad = 0 + 0 = 0 \\ a_2(x_1 + x_2) + b_2(y_1 + y_2) = (a_2x_1 + b_2y_1) + (a_2x_2 + b_2y_2) \\ \qquad\qquad\qquad\qquad\qquad = 0 + 0 = 0 \end{cases}$$

Thus, $\mathbf{u} + \mathbf{v} \in S$. *Parts (b), (c), (g), (h), (i), and (j)* of Definition 5-1.2 hold for all elements of S. Clearly, $\mathbf{0} = (0, 0) \in S$. If $\mathbf{v} = (x, y) \in S$, then $-\mathbf{v} = (-x, -y) \in S$ for

$$\begin{cases} a_1(-x) + b_1(-y) = -(a_1x + b_1y) = -0 = 0 \\ a_2(-x) + b_2(-y) = -(a_2x + b_2y) = -0 = 0 \end{cases}$$

If $\mathbf{v} = (x, y) \in S$ and $c \in R$, then $c\mathbf{v} = (cx, cy) \in S$ since

$$\begin{cases} a_1(cx) + b_1(cy) = c(a_1x + b_1y) = c(0) = 0 \\ a_2(cx) + b_2(cy) = c(a_2x + b_2y) = c(0) = 0 \end{cases}$$

Therefore, S is a vector space over R. In this example, the two lines intersect at the origin or they coincide. More generally, the solution space of the system of Eq. (3–1.1) is a vector space over R. For example, if $m = 2$ and $n = 3$, the two planes intersect in a line containing the origin or they coincide.

Illustration 2

If F is a field, the set of n-tuples $F_n = \{ (x_1, x_2, \ldots, x_n) \mid x_i \in F$ for $i = 1, 2, \ldots, n \}$ is a vector space over F. Here, we think of the elements of F_n as vectors and use the same definitions as for R^n, except that the equality, addition, and multiplication used are those of F instead of R. Specifically, if $\mathbf{u} = (a_1, a_2, \ldots, a_n) \in F_n$ and $\mathbf{v} = (x_1, x_2, \ldots, x_n) \in F_n$, then

$$\mathbf{u} = \mathbf{v} \text{ if and only if } a_1 = x_1, a_2 = x_2, \ldots, a_n = x_n$$
$$\mathbf{u} + \mathbf{v} = (a_1 + x_1, a_2 + x_2, \ldots, a_n + x_n)$$

and if $c \in F$,

$$c\mathbf{v} = (cx_1, cx_2, \ldots, cx_n)$$

With these definitions, the proof that F_n is a vector space over F is exactly like that of Theorem 2–1.1.

The next two illustrations involve functions. For functions over R, recall the usual definitions for equality, addition, and scalar multiplication. (See Section 6–1 for more information about functions.) If $c \in R$ and f and g are functions with the same domain, then for all x in this common domain

$$(5\text{–}1.1) \quad \begin{cases} f = g, \text{ if and only if } f(x) = g(x) \\ (f + g)(x) = f(x) + g(x) \\ (cf)(x) = cf(x) \end{cases}$$

Illustration 3

Let a_0, a_1, a_2, ..., a_n be particular real numbers and for each $x \in R$, define f by $f(x) = a_0 + a_1x + a_2x^2 + \cdots + a_nx^n$. Now, f is a real-valued polynomial function over R. Then $P[R] = \{f \mid f$ is a real-valued polynomial function over $R\}$ is a vector space over R. All properties of a vector space over R are easily verified. If x is restricted to the interval $[a, b]$, that is, $a \leq x \leq b$, then $P[a, b] = \{f \mid f$ is a real-valued polynomial function with domain $[a, b]\}$ is a vector space over R. You can also verify that with domain R (or $[a, b]$) the set consisting of the zero polynomial and all real-valued polynomial functions of degree $\leq n$ for a given n is a vector space over R.

The vector space in the next illustration is given only as an example of a vector space. We will not discuss vector spaces of this type in this book.

Illustration 4

The set $C[R] = \{f \mid f$ is a continuous real-valued function with domain $R\}$ is a vector space over R. This is easily verified if you recall from calculus that if $f, g \in C[R]$, then $f + g \in C[R]$ and if $c \in R$ then $cf \in C[R]$. If x is restricted to the interval $[a, b]$, then $C[a, b] = \{f \mid f$ is a continuous real-valued function with domain the interval $[a, b]\}$ is a vector space over R. Is the set of all differential functions on $[a, b]$ a vector space over R?

So far we have considered systems that are vector spaces. In the next illustration we mention some mathematical systems that are not vector spaces.

Illustration 5

The set of all real-valued polynomials over R of degree n for a particular n is not a vector space over R. You can easily show that the sum of two polynomials of degree n can have degree less than n. If the solution set S of a system of nonhomogeneous linear equations over R contains exactly one element, then S is not a vector space over R. Here, notice that S does not contain a zero element.

Problem Set 5–1B

In Problems 1, 2, and 3 let V be a vector space over a field F. If $\mathbf{u}$, $\mathbf{v} \in V$ and $c \in F$, prove the stated properties.

1. $c\mathbf{v} = \mathbf{0}$ if and only if $c = 0$ or $\mathbf{v} = \mathbf{0}$.
2. $-(c\mathbf{v}) = (-c)\mathbf{v} = c(-\mathbf{v})$
3. $-(\mathbf{u} - \mathbf{v}) = \mathbf{v} - \mathbf{u}$
4. Prove that F_n is a vector space over F.

5. Verify that $P[R]$ is a vector space over R.

6. Argue that the set consisting of the zero polynomial and all real-valued polynomials over R of degree 0, 1, or 2 is a vector space over R.

In Problems 7 through 17 argue that the given set is a vector space over R.

7. The line $\{ (x, 0) \mid x \in R \}$ 8. The line $\{ (x, y) \mid y = 2x \}$

9. The line $\{ (x, y, z) \mid x/2 = y/3 = z/6 \}$

10. The line $\{ (x, 0, 0) \mid x \in R \}$

11. The plane $\{ (x, y, 0) \mid x, y \in R \}$

12. The line $\{ (x, y, 0) \mid y = 2x \}$

13. The plane $\{ (x, y, z) \mid x - 2y + 3z = 0 \}$

14. $\{ \ln x \mid x > 0 \}$

15. $\left\{ \begin{pmatrix} x & 0 \\ 0 & 0 \end{pmatrix} \middle| x \in R \right\}$

16. $\{ f \mid f' - f = 0 \}$, where f' indicates the derivative of f.

17. $\{ f \mid f' + f = 0 \}$

In Problems 18 through 25 state at least one reason why the given set is not a vector space over R.

18. The line $\{ (x, 1) \mid x \in R \}$

19. The line $\left\{ (x, y, z) \middle| \dfrac{x}{2} = \dfrac{y}{3} = \dfrac{z - 1}{6} \right\}$

20. The line $\left\{ (x, y, z) \middle| \dfrac{x - x_0}{A} = \dfrac{y - y_0}{B} = \dfrac{z - z_0}{C} \right\}$, where $ABC \neq 0$ and not all of x_0, y_0, and z_0 are zero.

21. The plane $\{ (x, y, z) \mid x - 2y + 3z = 6 \}$

22. The plane $\{ (x, y, z) \mid ax + by + cz = d \}$, where $d \neq 0$ and not all of a, b, and c are zero.

23. $\left\{ \begin{pmatrix} x & 0 \\ 0 & 1 \end{pmatrix} \middle| x \in R \right\}$

24. $\{ (x, \ln x) \mid x > 0 \}$

25. $\{ e^x \mid x \in R \}$

26. Argue that the set of all functions from R into R is a vector space over R.

27. Prove that the set of all *even* functions from R into R is a vector space over R. [*Hint:* Recall that a function f from R into R is *even* means that $f(-x) = f(x)$, for all $x \in R$.]

28. Argue that the set of all *odd* functions from R into R is a vector space over R. [*Hint:* Recall that a function f from R into R is *odd* means that $f(-x) = -f(x)$, for all $x \in R$.]

29. Show that the solution set (space) of the system $\begin{cases} 3x - 2y + z = 0 \\ x + y - 2z = 0 \end{cases}$ is a vector space over R.

30. Argue that the solution set (space) of the system described in system (3–1.1) is a vector space over R.

5-2. LINEAR INDEPENDENCE AND DEPENDENCE

The concepts of linear combinations of vectors, linear independence, linear dependence, and spanning sets were mentioned in Chapter 1 in the study of R^2 and R^3. (See Problems 9, 10 of Problem Set 1–2 and Problem 32 of Problem Set 1–5.) For example, we know that $\mathbf{i}$ and $\mathbf{j}$ are linearly independent and span R^2. Also, $\mathbf{i}$, $\mathbf{j}$, and $\mathbf{k}$ are linearly independent and span R^3. In this section, these concepts are discussed as they apply to general vector spaces.

DEFINITION 5–2.1. *If V is a vector space over a field F, then an expression $c_1\mathbf{v}_1 + c_2\mathbf{v}_2 + \cdots + c_n\mathbf{v}_n$, where $c_i \in F$, is a linear combination of the n vectors $\mathbf{v}_1, \mathbf{v}_2, \ldots, \mathbf{v}_n$.*

Illustration 1

The set of all 2×2 dimension matrices over R is a vector space over R. For $a, b, c, d \in R$, the expression

$$a \begin{pmatrix} 1 & 0 \\ 0 & 0 \end{pmatrix} + b \begin{pmatrix} 0 & 1 \\ 0 & 0 \end{pmatrix} + c \begin{pmatrix} 0 & 0 \\ 1 & 0 \end{pmatrix} + d \begin{pmatrix} 0 & 0 \\ 0 & 1 \end{pmatrix}$$

is a linear combination of the matrices $\begin{pmatrix} 1 & 0 \\ 0 & 0 \end{pmatrix}$, $\begin{pmatrix} 0 & 1 \\ 0 & 0 \end{pmatrix}$, $\begin{pmatrix} 0 & 0 \\ 1 & 0 \end{pmatrix}$, and $\begin{pmatrix} 0 & 0 \\ 0 & 1 \end{pmatrix}$.

Illustration 2

Since $\mathbf{e}_1 = (1, 0, 0, \ldots, 0)$, $\mathbf{e}_2 = (0, 1, 0, \ldots, 0)$, $\ldots$, $\mathbf{e}_n = (0, 0, \ldots, 1) \in R^n$, then for $a_1, a_2, \ldots, a_n \in R$, $a_1\mathbf{e}_1 + a_2\mathbf{e}_2 + \cdots + a_n\mathbf{e}_n$ is a linear combination of the vectors $\mathbf{e}_1, \mathbf{e}_2, \ldots, \mathbf{e}_n$.

From Illustration 1, notice that any element $\begin{pmatrix} a & b \\ c & d \end{pmatrix}$ of the vector space can be expressed as a linear combination

$$\begin{pmatrix} a & b \\ c & d \end{pmatrix} = a \begin{pmatrix} 1 & 0 \\ 0 & 0 \end{pmatrix} + b \begin{pmatrix} 0 & 1 \\ 0 & 0 \end{pmatrix} + c \begin{pmatrix} 0 & 0 \\ 1 & 0 \end{pmatrix} + d \begin{pmatrix} 0 & 0 \\ 0 & 1 \end{pmatrix}$$

Thus, these four matrices *span* the vector space of all 2×2 matrices over R, (see Definition 5–2.2).

From Illustration 2, any vector $(a_1, a_2, \ldots, a_n) \in R^n$ can be expressed as a linear combination

$$(a_1, a_2, \ldots, a_n) = a_1\mathbf{e}_1 + a_2\mathbf{e}_2 + \cdots + a_n\mathbf{e}_n$$

Therefore, $\mathbf{e}_1, \mathbf{e}_2, \ldots, \mathbf{e}_n$ *span* R^n.

105

DEFINITION 5-2.2. *A subset S of a vector space V over a field F spans V if and only if every vector $\mathbf{v} \in V$ is a linear combination of some n vectors of S. If S spans V, then S is a spanning set for V. If $\{\mathbf{v}_1, \mathbf{v}_2, \ldots, \mathbf{v}_n\}$ is a spanning set for V, then the n vectors $\mathbf{v}_1, \mathbf{v}_2, \ldots, \mathbf{v}_n$ span V.* (See Appendix A for the definition and notation for a subset of a set.)

Referring to Illustration 1, we have that

$$a \begin{pmatrix} 1 & 0 \\ 0 & 0 \end{pmatrix} + b \begin{pmatrix} 0 & 1 \\ 0 & 0 \end{pmatrix} + c \begin{pmatrix} 0 & 0 \\ 1 & 0 \end{pmatrix} + d \begin{pmatrix} 0 & 0 \\ 0 & 1 \end{pmatrix} = \begin{pmatrix} 0 & 0 \\ 0 & 0 \end{pmatrix} = O$$

if and only if $\begin{pmatrix} a & b \\ c & d \end{pmatrix} = \begin{pmatrix} 0 & 0 \\ 0 & 0 \end{pmatrix}$. Therefore, $a = b = c = d = 0$ and we say that the four matrices are *linearly independent* (see Definition 5-2.3).

Using the vectors of Illustration 2, we see that

$$a_1 \mathbf{e}_1 + a_2 \mathbf{e}_2 + \cdots + a_n \mathbf{e}_n = (0, 0, \ldots, 0) = \mathbf{0}$$

if and only if $(a_1, a_2, \ldots, a_n) = (0, 0, \ldots, 0)$. Thus, $a_1 = a_2 = \cdots = a_n = 0$, and $\mathbf{e}_1, \mathbf{e}_2, \ldots, \mathbf{e}_n$ are *linearly independent.*

DEFINITION 5-2.3. *The vectors $\mathbf{v}_1, \mathbf{v}_2, \ldots, \mathbf{v}_n$ of a vector space V over a field F are linearly independent (over F) means that $c_1\mathbf{v}_1 + c_2\mathbf{v}_2 + \cdots + c_n\mathbf{v}_n = \mathbf{0}$ if and only if $c_1 = c_2 = \cdots = c_n = 0$. A subset S of V is a linearly independent set if and only if distinct vectors of every finite subset of S are linearly independent.*

If $\mathbf{v} \in V$ and $\mathbf{v} \neq \mathbf{0}$, then $\mathbf{v}$ is linearly independent for $a\mathbf{v} = \mathbf{0}$ if and only if $a = 0$. Thus, a single nonzero vector is linearly independent. The vectors $\mathbf{i}, \mathbf{j} \in R^2$ are linearly independent. However, the vectors $\mathbf{i}, \mathbf{j}$, and $\mathbf{i} + \mathbf{j}$ are not linearly independent since

$$c_1\mathbf{i} + c_2\mathbf{j} + c_3(\mathbf{i} + \mathbf{j}) = \mathbf{0} = (0, 0)$$

for $c_1 = c_2 = 1$ and $c_3 = -1$, as well as for $c_1 = c_2 = c_3 = 0$. Such vectors are said to be *linearly dependent.*

DEFINITION 5-2.4. *The vectors $\mathbf{v}_1, \mathbf{v}_2, \ldots, \mathbf{v}_n$ of a vector space V over a field F are linearly dependent (over F) if and only if they are not linearly independent. A subset S of V is a linearly dependent set if and only if S is not a linearly independent set.*

Illustration 3

If $\mathbf{0} \in \{\mathbf{v}_1, \mathbf{v}_2, \ldots, \mathbf{v}_n\} \subseteq V$, then this set of vectors is a linearly dependent set for $0\mathbf{v}_1 + 0\mathbf{v}_2 + \cdots + 1\mathbf{0} + \cdots + 0\mathbf{v}_n = \mathbf{0}$ and $1 \neq 0$. Here, V is a vector space over a field F, $1 \in F$, and $0 \in F$.

From Definition 5-2.4, the vectors $\mathbf{v}_1, \mathbf{v}_2, \ldots, \mathbf{v}_n$ are linearly dependent if and only if $c_1\mathbf{v}_1 + c_2\mathbf{v}_2 + \cdots + c_n\mathbf{v}_n = \mathbf{0}$ for some $c_i \neq 0$. Suppose $c_k \neq 0$. Then, we can write $\mathbf{v}_k = -(c_1\mathbf{v}_1 + c_2\mathbf{v}_2 + \cdots + c_{k-1}\mathbf{v}_{k-1} + c_{k+1}\mathbf{v}_{k+1} + \cdots + c_n\mathbf{v}_n)/c_k$. Thus, if $\mathbf{v}_1, \mathbf{v}_2, \ldots, \mathbf{v}_n$ are linearly dependent some vector is a linear combination of the remaining ones. The converse also holds (see Problem 36, Problem Set 5-2).

THEOREM 5-2.1. *The vectors $\mathbf{v}_1, \mathbf{v}_2, \ldots, \mathbf{v}_n$ of a vector space V over a field F are linearly dependent if and only if some one vector is a linear combination of the remaining $n - 1$ vectors.*

If $\mathbf{0} \notin \{\mathbf{v}_1, \mathbf{v}_2, \ldots, \mathbf{v}_n\}$ and the vectors of Theorem 5-2.1 are ordered by their subscripts, some vector is a linear combination of the preceding vectors. To see that $\mathbf{0}$ cannot be used, let $\mathbf{0}, \mathbf{i}, \mathbf{j} \in R^2$ be ordered as given. Here, no vector is a linear combination of the preceding vectors. (You should verify this.) The next two theorems involve two important and useful results concerning linear dependence of vectors.

THEOREM 5-2.2. *The nonzero vectors $\mathbf{v}_1, \mathbf{v}_2, \ldots, \mathbf{v}_n$ of a vector space V over a field F are linearly dependent if and only if some $\mathbf{v}_k \in \{\mathbf{v}_1, \mathbf{v}_2, \ldots, \mathbf{v}_n\}$ is a linear combination of the preceding vectors $\mathbf{v}_1, \mathbf{v}_2, \ldots, \mathbf{v}_{k-1}$.*

Proof: First, suppose $\mathbf{v}_k = c_1\mathbf{v}_1 + c_2\mathbf{v}_2 + \cdots + c_{k-1}\mathbf{v}_{k-1}$. If $n > k$, use 0 as the scalar to obtain $c_1\mathbf{v}_1 + c_2\mathbf{v}_2 + \cdots + c_{k-1}\mathbf{v}_{k-1} + (-1)\mathbf{v}_k + 0\mathbf{v}_{k+1} + \cdots + 0\mathbf{v}_n = \mathbf{0}$. Thus, $\mathbf{v}_1, \mathbf{v}_2, \ldots, \mathbf{v}_n$ are linearly dependent. This proves one part. Next, suppose that $c_1\mathbf{v}_1 + c_2\mathbf{v}_2 + \cdots + c_n\mathbf{v}_n = \mathbf{0}$ and some $c_i \neq 0$. Let k be the largest $i \in \{1, 2, \ldots, n\}$ such that $c_i \neq 0$. Now, $k \neq 1$, for if $k = 1$ we have $c_1\mathbf{v}_1 = \mathbf{0}$. Since $\mathbf{v}_1 \neq \mathbf{0}$, then $c_1 = 0$, a contradiction. Thus, $k > 1$ and for $i > k$, $c_i = 0$. Therefore,

$$\mathbf{v}_k = \left(-\frac{c_1}{c_k}\right)\mathbf{v}_1 + \left(-\frac{c_2}{c_k}\right)\mathbf{v}_2 + \cdots + \left(-\frac{c_{k-1}}{c_k}\right)\mathbf{v}_{k-1}$$

which gives $\mathbf{v}_k$ as a linear combination of $\mathbf{v}_1, \mathbf{v}_2, \ldots, \mathbf{v}_{k-1}$.

THEOREM 5-2.3. *If $n > m$, then n linear combinations of m vectors in a vector space V over R are linearly dependent.*

Proof: Let the m vectors be $\mathbf{v}_1, \mathbf{v}_2, \ldots, \mathbf{v}_m$, and suppose $c_1(d_{11}\mathbf{v}_1 + d_{12}\mathbf{v}_2 + \cdots + d_{1m}\mathbf{v}_m) + c_2(d_{21}\mathbf{v}_1 + d_{22}\mathbf{v}_2 + \cdots + d_{2m}\mathbf{v}_m) + \cdots + c_n(d_{n1}\mathbf{v}_1 + d_{n2}\mathbf{v}_2 + \cdots + d_{nm}\mathbf{v}_m) = \mathbf{0}$. This equation can be rewritten as $(c_1d_{11} + c_2d_{21} + \cdots + c_nd_{n1})\mathbf{v}_1 + (c_1d_{12} + c_2d_{22} + \cdots + c_nd_{n2})\mathbf{v}_2 + \cdots + (c_1d_{1m} + c_2d_{2m} + \cdots + c_nd_{nm})\mathbf{v}_m = \mathbf{0}$. That this last equation can hold with not all of $c_1, c_2, \ldots, c_n$

107

zero can be seen from the system of m equations

$$\begin{cases} c_1 d_{11} + c_2 d_{21} + \cdots + c_n d_{n1} = 0 \\ c_1 d_{12} + c_2 d_{22} + \cdots + c_n d_{n2} = 0 \\ \phantom{c_1 d_{11}} \vdots \phantom{+ c_2 d_{21}} \vdots \ddots \vdots \vdots \\ c_1 d_{1m} + c_2 d_{2m} + \cdots + c_n d_{nm} = 0 \end{cases}$$

in n unknowns, see Theorem 3–1.6. Thus, the theorem holds.

Problem Set 5–2

1. If $\mathbf{u} = \mathbf{v}_1 + \mathbf{v}_2$ and $\mathbf{v} = \mathbf{v}_1 - \mathbf{v}_2$, where $\mathbf{v}_1$ and $\mathbf{v}_2$ are vectors in a vector space V over R, express $5\mathbf{u} + 2\mathbf{v}$ as a linear combination of $\mathbf{v}_1$ and $\mathbf{v}_2$.

2. Repeat Problem 1 for $x\mathbf{u} + y\mathbf{v}$, where $x, y \in R$.

3. Which of $2\mathbf{v}_1$, $2\mathbf{v}_2$, $5\mathbf{v}_1 + 3\mathbf{v}_2$, $-2\mathbf{v}_1 + 3\mathbf{v}_2$ are linear combinations of $\mathbf{u}$ and $\mathbf{v}$ of Problem 1?

In Problems 4 through 13 obtain the set of all linear combinations of the given vectors in R^2 or R^3.

4. $(1, 0)$, $(1, 1)$ 5. $(-1, 0)$, $(0, -1)$
6. $(1, -2)$, $(5, -10)$ 7. $(3, 2)$, $(0, 0)$
8. $(-2, 1)$, $(5, 7)$ 9. $(1, 0, 0)$, $(1, 0, 1)$, $(1, 1, 1)$
10. $(1, -1, 0)$, $(-1, 0, 1)$, $(1, -2, 1)$
11. $(1, 2, 0)$, $(2, 0, 1)$, $(0, 1, 2)$
12. $(0, 1, 0)$, $(1, 0, 0)$, $(-1, 1, 0)$
13. $(1, 0, -2)$, $(0, 3, 5)$, $(1, 6, 8)$

For Problems 14 through 23 determine whether the vectors in each of Problems 4 through 13 span R^2 or R^3.

For Problems 24 through 33 classify the vectors in Problems 4 through 13 as linearly independent or linearly dependent over R.

34. Argue that (a_1, b_1), $(a_2, b_2) \in R^2$ are linearly independent over R if and only if $det \begin{pmatrix} a_1 & a_2 \\ b_1 & b_2 \end{pmatrix} \neq 0$.

35. Verify Theorem 5–2.3 for three linear combinations of the two vectors $(1, 0, 1)$ and $(1, 1, 1)$.

In Problems 36 through 44 let $\mathbf{v}_1, \mathbf{v}_2, \ldots, \mathbf{v}_n$ be elements of a vector space V over a field F. Prove each statement.

36. The vectors $\mathbf{v}_1, \mathbf{v}_2, \ldots, \mathbf{v}_n$ are linearly dependent if some one vector is a linear combination of the remaining $n - 1$ vectors.

37. If $\mathbf{v}_1, \mathbf{v}_2, \ldots, \mathbf{v}_n$ are linearly dependent and span V, then some $n - 1$ of these vectors span V.

38. If $\{\mathbf{v}_1, \mathbf{v}_2, \ldots, \mathbf{v}_n\}$ is an independent set, then every nonempty subset of $\{\mathbf{v}_1, \mathbf{v}_2, \ldots, \mathbf{v}_n\}$ is an independent set.

39. If some nonempty subset of $\{\mathbf{v}_1, \mathbf{v}_2, \ldots, \mathbf{v}_n\}$ is dependent, then $\{\mathbf{v}_1, \mathbf{v}_2, \ldots, \mathbf{v}_n\}$ is a dependent set.

In Problems 40 through 44 let A denote the set of all linear combinations of $\mathbf{v}_1, \mathbf{v}_2, \ldots, \mathbf{v}_n$.

40. If $\mathbf{u}, \mathbf{v} \in A$, then $\mathbf{u} + \mathbf{v} \in A$.

41. If $c \in F$ and $\mathbf{v} \in A$, then $c\mathbf{v} \in A$.

42. If $\mathbf{u}, \mathbf{v} \in A$, then $(\mathbf{u} - \mathbf{v}) \in A$.

43. If $\mathbf{u}, \mathbf{v} \in A$, then $(x\mathbf{u} + y\mathbf{v}) \in A$ for all $x, y \in F$.

44. If $\mathbf{u}_1, \mathbf{u}_2, \ldots, \mathbf{u}_m \in A$, then $(x_1\mathbf{u}_1 + x_2\mathbf{u}_2 + \cdots + x_m\mathbf{u}_m) \in A$ for all $x_1, x_2, \ldots, x_m \in F$.

5-3. BASIS OF A VECTOR SPACE

Since $\mathbf{i}$ and $\mathbf{j}$ are linearly independent over R and span R^2, we say that $\mathbf{i}$ and $\mathbf{j}$ *form a basis* for R^2, that is, $\{\mathbf{i}, \mathbf{j}\}$ is a basis for R^2. Also, we know that $\{\mathbf{i}, \mathbf{j}, \mathbf{k}\}$ is a basis for R^3. Here, bases are discussed as they apply to general vector spaces.

DEFINITION 5-3.1. *A basis of a vector space V over a field F is a set of linearly independent vectors of V that spans V. If a basis consists of a finite number of vectors, V is said to be finite-dimensional.*

Illustration 1

We have previously shown that $\begin{pmatrix} 1 & 0 \\ 0 & 0 \end{pmatrix}$, $\begin{pmatrix} 0 & 1 \\ 0 & 0 \end{pmatrix}$, $\begin{pmatrix} 0 & 0 \\ 1 & 0 \end{pmatrix}$, and $\begin{pmatrix} 0 & 0 \\ 0 & 1 \end{pmatrix}$ are linearly independent and span the vector space of all 2×2 real matrices over R. Thus, these four matrices form a basis for the vector space.

Illustration 2

The vectors $\mathbf{e}_1 = (1, 0, 0, \ldots, 0)$, $\mathbf{e}_2 = (0, 1, 0, \ldots, 0)$, $\ldots$, $\mathbf{e}_n = (0, 0, \ldots, 1)$ form a basis for R^n since they are linearly independent and span R^n. This basis is called the *standard basis* for R^n. These vectors also form a basis for the vector space F_n over a field F (see Illustration 2 of Section 5-1).

Illustration 3

The basis $\{\mathbf{i}, \mathbf{j}\}$ is the standard basis for R^2. Are there other bases for R^2? To see that the answer is yes, consider the vectors $\mathbf{i}$ and $\mathbf{i} + \mathbf{j}$. If $a\mathbf{i} + b(\mathbf{i} + \mathbf{j}) = \mathbf{0}$, then $(a + b)\mathbf{i} + b\mathbf{j} = \mathbf{0}$. Thus, $a + b = 0$ and $b = 0$. (Why?) Therefore, $a = 0$ and $b = 0$. This shows that $\mathbf{i}$ and $\mathbf{i} + \mathbf{j}$ are linearly independent. Next, let $(x\mathbf{i} + y\mathbf{j}) \in R^2$. Since $x\mathbf{i} + y\mathbf{j} =$

$(x - y)\mathbf{i} + y(\mathbf{i} + \mathbf{j})$, $\mathbf{i}$ and $\mathbf{i} + \mathbf{j}$ span R^2. Consequently, $\{\mathbf{i}, \mathbf{i} + \mathbf{j}\}$ is a basis for R^2. More generally, any two nonzero, nonparallel vectors in standard position form a basis for R^2. Can you make a similar statement for R^3?

The vector space with basis not finite in the next illustration is given only as an example. In general, we restrict ourselves to vector spaces with finite bases.

Illustration 4

The functions $1, x, x^2, \ldots, x^n$ form a basis for the vector space of all polynomials of degree $\leq n$ over R. The functions $1, x, x^2, \ldots, x^n, \ldots$ form a basis for the vector space $P[R]$. (This basis is not finite.) Does the vector space $C[R]$ (see Illustration 4 of Section 5-1) have a basis?

Next, we consider some fundamental results about bases of vector spaces.

THEOREM 5-3.1. *If $V \neq \{\mathbf{0}\}$ is a vector space over a field F and V is spanned by a finite subset not containing $\mathbf{0}$, then V has a finite basis.*

Proof: Suppose V is spanned by the vectors $\mathbf{v}_1, \mathbf{v}_2, \ldots, \mathbf{v}_m$. If these m vectors are linearly independent, they form a basis for V. If the m vectors are linearly dependent, then some vector, say $\mathbf{v}_{k_1}$, is a linear combination of the preceding vectors $\mathbf{v}_1, \mathbf{v}_2, \ldots, \mathbf{v}_{k_1-1}$, by Theorem 5-2.2. Eliminate $\mathbf{v}_{k_1}$, and renumber the remaining $m - 1$ vectors, if necessary, in order to obtain the $m - 1$ vectors $\mathbf{v}'_1, \mathbf{v}'_2, \ldots, \mathbf{v}'_{m-1}$. These $m - 1$ vectors span V. If they are linearly independent, they form a basis for V. If not, Theorem 5-2.2 can be applied again to obtain the $m - 2$ vectors $\mathbf{v}''_1, \mathbf{v}''_2, \ldots, \mathbf{v}''_{m-2}$ that span V. Theorem 5-2.2 can be applied at most $m - 1$ times, since a single nonzero vector is linearly independent. Therefore, by the elimination process we obtain a basis of n elements, where $1 \leq n \leq m$.

THEOREM 5-3.2. *If a vector space V over a field F has a finite basis of n elements, then every basis of V has exactly n elements.*

Proof: Suppose $\{\mathbf{v}_1, \mathbf{v}_2, \ldots, \mathbf{v}_n\}$ and $\{\mathbf{x}_1, \mathbf{x}_2, \ldots, \mathbf{x}_m\}$ are bases of V. Then, $\{\mathbf{x}_1, \mathbf{v}_1, \mathbf{v}_2, \ldots, \mathbf{v}_n\}$ clearly spans V and is linearly dependent, since $\mathbf{x}_1$ is a linear combination of $\mathbf{v}_1, \mathbf{v}_2, \ldots, \mathbf{v}_n$. Since $\mathbf{x}_1 \neq \mathbf{0}$, Theorem 5-2.2 gives some $\mathbf{v}_i$ as being a linear combination of the preceding vectors $\mathbf{x}_1, \mathbf{v}_1, \mathbf{v}_2, \ldots, \mathbf{v}_{i-1}$. By renumbering, if necessary, we can assume that $\mathbf{v}_n$ is a linear combination of $\mathbf{x}_1, \mathbf{v}_1, \mathbf{v}_2, \ldots, \mathbf{v}_{n-1}$. Then, $\{\mathbf{x}_1, \mathbf{v}_1, \mathbf{v}_2, \ldots, \mathbf{v}_{n-1}\}$ spans V. Next, $\{\mathbf{x}_1, \mathbf{x}_2, \mathbf{v}_1, \mathbf{v}_2, \ldots, \mathbf{v}_{n-1}\}$ spans V and is a linearly dependent set since $\mathbf{x}_2$ is a linear combination of $\mathbf{x}_1$,

$\mathbf{v}_1, \mathbf{v}_2, \ldots, \mathbf{v}_{n-1}$. Since $\mathbf{x}_1$ and $\mathbf{x}_2$ are in a basis of V, Theorem 5-2.2 gives some $\mathbf{v}_i$ as being a linear combination of the preceding vectors $\mathbf{x}_1, \mathbf{x}_2, \mathbf{v}_1, \mathbf{v}_2, \ldots, \mathbf{v}_{i-1}$. Renumbering, if necessary, we can assume that $\mathbf{v}_{n-1}$ is a linear combination of $\mathbf{x}_1, \mathbf{x}_2, \mathbf{v}_1, \mathbf{v}_2, \ldots, \mathbf{v}_{n-2}$. Then, $\{\mathbf{x}_1, \mathbf{x}_2, \mathbf{v}_1, \mathbf{v}_2, \ldots, \mathbf{v}_{n-2}\}$ spans V. Suppose $n < m$. By the elimination process we obtain a set $\{\mathbf{x}_1, \mathbf{x}_2, \ldots, \mathbf{x}_n\}$ that spans V. This gives a contradiction since none of the vectors $\mathbf{x}_{n+1}, \mathbf{x}_{n+2}, \ldots, \mathbf{x}_m$ are a linear combination of $\mathbf{x}_1, \mathbf{x}_2, \ldots, \mathbf{x}_n$. Hence $n \not< m$, that is, $n \geq m$. An entirely similar argument with the roles of the $\mathbf{v}$s and $\mathbf{x}$s interchanged will show that $m \geq n$. Therefore, $m = n$.

DEFINITION 5-3.2. *The dimension n of a finite-dimensional vector space V over a field F is the number of vectors in a basis of V. In notation, dim $V = n$.*

THEOREM 5-3.3. *If $\{\mathbf{v}_1, \mathbf{v}_2, \ldots, \mathbf{v}_n\}$ is a basis of a vector space V over a field F, then each vector $\mathbf{v} \in V$ can be expressed in exactly one way as a linear combination of these basis vectors.*

Proof: Since $\{\mathbf{v}_1, \mathbf{v}_2, \ldots, \mathbf{v}_n\}$ is a basis of V, this set spans V. Thus, a vector $\mathbf{v} \in V$ can be expressed in at least one way as a linear combination of these basis vectors. If $\mathbf{v} = c_1\mathbf{v}_1 + c_2\mathbf{v}_2 + \cdots + c_n\mathbf{v}_n$ and $\mathbf{v} = d_1\mathbf{v}_1 + d_2\mathbf{v}_2 + \cdots + d_n\mathbf{v}_n$, then since

$$\mathbf{0} = \mathbf{v} - \mathbf{v} = c_1\mathbf{v}_1 + c_2\mathbf{v}_2 + \cdots + c_n\mathbf{v}_n$$
$$- (d_1\mathbf{v}_1 + d_2\mathbf{v}_2 + \cdots + d_n\mathbf{v}_n)$$

we have

$$(c_1 - d_1)\mathbf{v}_1 + (c_2 - d_2)\mathbf{v}_2 + \cdots + (c_n - d_n)\mathbf{v}_n = \mathbf{0}$$

Since the vectors $\mathbf{v}_1, \mathbf{v}_2, \ldots, \mathbf{v}_n$ are linearly independent, we have

$$c_1 - d_1 = 0, c_2 - d_2 = 0, \ldots, c_n - d_n = 0$$

This implies that $c_1 = d_1, c_2 = d_2, \ldots, c_n = d_n$. Therefore, each vector $\mathbf{v} \in V$ can be expressed in exactly one way as a linear combination of the vectors in the given basis.

THEOREM 5-3.4. *If $\mathbf{v}_1, \mathbf{v}_2, \ldots, \mathbf{v}_p$ are linearly independent vectors in an n-dimensional vector space V over a field F, then there exists a basis containing $\mathbf{v}_1, \mathbf{v}_2, \ldots, \mathbf{v}_p$.*

Proof: Let $\{\mathbf{x}_1, \mathbf{x}_2, \ldots, \mathbf{x}_n\}$ be a basis for V. Since these n vectors span V, the $p + n$ vectors $\mathbf{v}_1, \mathbf{v}_2, \ldots, \mathbf{v}_p, \mathbf{x}_1, \mathbf{x}_2, \ldots, \mathbf{x}_n$ also span V. Furthermore, these $p + n$ vectors are linearly dependent. By the process of elimination used in the proof of Theorem 5-3.1, where a vector is eliminated if it is a linear combination of the preceding vectors, a basis of V can be obtained. Here, if $\mathbf{x}_i = \mathbf{v}_k$, then $\mathbf{x}_i$ is eliminated but $\mathbf{v}_k$ is not eliminated. This basis necessarily contains $\mathbf{v}_1, \mathbf{v}_2, \ldots, \mathbf{v}_p$, since none of these vectors are eliminated because they are linearly independent.

111

COROLLARY 5-3.1. *Any* $n + 1$ *vectors of an n-dimensional vector space V over a field F are linearly dependent.*

This section is closed with a result concerning the existence of a basis for a vector space. The proof of this theorem is beyond the scope of this book.

THEOREM 5-3.5. *If V is a vector space over a field F and V $\neq$ {0},* *then V has a basis.*

Problem Set 5-3

In Problems 1 through 7 use the elimination method illustrated in the proof of Theorem 5-3.1 to obtain a basis of R^2 or R^3 from the given linearly dependent sets.

1. { $(2, -3)$, $(-6, 9)$, $(1, 3)$ }
2. { $(5, 4)$, $(0, 4)$, $(-8, -7)$ }
3. { $(-3, 5)$, $(6, -10)$, $(5, 0)$, $(2, 3)$ }
4. { $(1, 0, 0)$, $(0, 1, 0)$, $(0, 0, 5)$, $(0, 0, 1)$ }
5. { $(1, 0, 0)$, $(0, 1, 0)$, $(5, -3, 0)$, $(0, 0, -1)$ }
6. { $(1, 3, 0)$, $(2, -5, 3)$, $(4, 1, 3)$, $(0, 4, 1)$ }
7. { $(1, 1, 1)$, $(0, 1, 1)$, $(1, 0, 0)$, $(4, 4, 4)$, $(0, -2, -4)$ }

In Problems 8 through 15 extend the linearly independent sets to bases of R^2 or R^3. Use the standard bases for R^2 and R^3 and refer to the proof of Theorem 5-3.4.

8. { $(2, -5)$ }
9. { $(5, 0)$ }
10. { $(-3, 0)$ }
11. { $(1, 0, 0)$, $(0, 0, 5)$ }
12. { $(2, 0, 0)$, $(0, -3, 0)$ }
13. { $(1, 1, 1)$, $(0, 1, 1)$ }
14. { $(1, 3, 0)$, $(2, -5, 3)$ }
15. { $(-3, 2, -4)$, $(5, -2, 10)$ }

16. Extend $\left\{ \begin{pmatrix} 3 & 0 \\ 0 & 0 \end{pmatrix}, \begin{pmatrix} 1 & 2 \\ 0 & 1 \end{pmatrix} \right\}$ to a basis for the vector space of all 2×2 real matrices over R.

17. Prove Corollary 5-3.1.

18. How many elements are in a basis for the vector space of all $m \times n$ real matrices over R? Answer the same question for the vector space F over the field F.

19. If θ is the measure of a given angle, argue that { $(\cos \theta, \sin \theta)$, $(-\sin \theta, \cos \theta)$ } is a basis for R^2.

20. Argue that Corollary 5-3.1 is also a corollary of Theorem 5-2.3, that is, that Corollary 5-3.1 can be proved easily by applying Theorem 5-2.3.

21. If A is a finite basis for a vector space V over a field F and B is a basis for V, prove that B is a finite set.

22. Argue that the $p + n$ vectors in the proof of Theorem 5-3.4 are linearly dependent.

5-4. SUBSPACES

Those subsets of a vector space V over a field F that are also vector spaces over F are of particular importance in the study of vector spaces. If the same equality and operations are used for the subset and V, the subset is called a *subspace* of V.

DEFINITION 5-4.1.   *If V is a vector space over a field F, then M is a subspace of V if and only if*

a.   *$M \subseteq V$, and*
b.   *M with the same equality and operations as V is a vector space over F.*

We already know some subspaces of certain vector spaces. For example:

i. V and $\{\mathbf{0}\}$ are trivial subspaces of any vector space V over a field F,
ii.   a line that contains the origin is a subspace of R^2,
iii.   a line that contains the origin is a subspace of R^3,
iv.   a plane that contains the origin is a subspace of R^3,
v. $P[R]$ is a subspace of $C[R]$,
vi.   the vector space of all polynomial functions over R of degree $\leq n$ for a particular n is a subspace of $P[R]$.
vii.   the vector space of all differentiable functions over R is a subspace of $C[R]$.

If we wish to prove that a given subset of a vector space V over a field F is a subspace of V, we could verify that all properties of a vector space hold for the subset. Since there are several properties, this verification would be tedious. The following theorem states that we only need to verify two properties of a vector space, rather than all properties.

THEOREM 5-4.1.   *If V is a vector space over a field F, then M is a subspace of V if and only if*

a.   *$M \subseteq V$ and $M \neq \emptyset$,*
b.   *$\mathbf{u} + \mathbf{v} \in M$, for all $\mathbf{u}, \mathbf{v} \in M$, and*
c.   *$c\mathbf{v} \in M$, for all $\mathbf{v} \in M$ and all $c \in F$.*

Proof: If M is a subspace of V, then *parts (a), (b),* and *(c)* clearly hold. Next, we suppose that *parts (a), (b),* and *(c)* of the theorem hold and prove that M is a subspace of V. The only parts of Definition 5-1.2 that need to be verified are *parts (d)* and *(e)*. All other parts hold for all vectors in V, and thus hold for all vectors in M. Recall that $-1 \in F$. If $\mathbf{v} \in M$, then $(-1)\mathbf{v} \in M$. Since $(-1)\mathbf{v} = -\mathbf{v}$, we have $-\mathbf{v} \in M$. Thus, the inverse of each element of M is in M. If $\mathbf{v} \in M$, then $\mathbf{v} + (-\mathbf{v}) \in M$. Since $\mathbf{v} + (-\mathbf{v}) = \mathbf{0}$, then $\mathbf{0} \in M$. Therefore, M is a subspace of V.

113

Illustration 1

Show that $M = \left\{ \begin{pmatrix} x & 0 \\ 0 & 0 \end{pmatrix} \middle| x \in R \right\}$ is a subspace of the vector space of all 2×2 real matrices over R. Part (a) of Theorem 5-4.1 clearly holds. If $\mathbf{u} = \begin{pmatrix} a & 0 \\ 0 & 0 \end{pmatrix} \in M$ and $\mathbf{v} = \begin{pmatrix} x & 0 \\ 0 & 0 \end{pmatrix} \in M$, then $\mathbf{u} + \mathbf{v} = \begin{pmatrix} a+x & 0 \\ 0 & 0 \end{pmatrix} \in M$. Furthermore, if $c \in R$, then

$$cv = \begin{pmatrix} cx & 0 \\ 0 & 0 \end{pmatrix} \in M$$

Illustration 2

Prove that $M = \{ (x_1, x_2, \ldots, x_n) \mid x_i \in R$ and $x_1 = 0 \}$ is a subspace of R^n. We note that *part* (a) of Theorem 5-4.1 holds. If $\mathbf{u} = (0, a_2, a_3, \ldots, a_n) \in M$ and $\mathbf{v} = (0, x_2, x_3, \ldots, x_n) \in M$, then $\mathbf{u} + \mathbf{v} = (0, a_2 + x_2, a_3 + x_3, \ldots, a_n + x_n) \in M$. If $c \in R$, then $cv = (0, cx_2, cx_3, \ldots, cx_n) \in M$. Consequently, M is a subspace of R^n.

Illustration 3

The set $S = \{ (x_1, x_2, \ldots, x_n) \mid x_i \in R$ and $x_1 = 1 \}$ is *not* a subspace of R^n. One reason is that S is not closed under addition. Another reason is that $\mathbf{0} \notin S$.

The next two examples of subspaces are so important that the results are stated as theorems. Recall that $M_1 \cap M_2 = \{ \mathbf{v} \mid \mathbf{v} \in M_1$ and $\mathbf{v} \in M_2 \}$ is the intersection of the sets M_1 and M_2. (See Appendix.)

THEOREM 5-4.2.   If M_1 and M_2 are subspaces of a vector space V over a field F, then $M_1 \cap M_2$ is a subspace of V.

Proof: Since $\mathbf{0} \in M_1$ and $\mathbf{0} \in M_2$, then $\mathbf{0} \in (M_1 \cap M_2)$. Thus, $M_1 \cap M_2 \neq \emptyset$. We know that $(M_1 \cap M_2) \subseteq V$. Next, if $\mathbf{u} \in (M_1 \cap M_2)$ and $\mathbf{v} \in (M_1 \cap M_2)$, then $\mathbf{u}, \mathbf{v} \in M_1$ and $\mathbf{u}, \mathbf{v} \in M_2$. Since M_1 and M_2 are subspaces of V, $\mathbf{u} + \mathbf{v} \in M_1$ and $\mathbf{u} + \mathbf{v} \in M_2$. Hence, $\mathbf{u} + \mathbf{v} \in (M_1 \cap M_2)$. Furthermore, if $c \in F$, then $cv \in M_1$ and $cv \in M_2$, which implies that $cv \in (M_1 \cap M_2)$. By Theorem 5-4.1, $M_1 \cap M_2$ is a subspace of V.

In the Problem Set you will be asked to prove that the intersection of *any* number of subspaces of a vector space V over a field F is a subspace of V.

To see that Theorem 5-4.2 does not necessarily hold if intersection, $\cap$, is replaced with union, $\cup$, consider

$$M_1 = \left\{ \begin{pmatrix} x & 0 \\ 0 & 0 \end{pmatrix} \middle| x \in R \right\}$$

and

$$M_2 = \left\{ \begin{pmatrix} 0 & y \\ 0 & 0 \end{pmatrix} \middle| y \in R \right\}$$

Now, M_1 and M_2 are subspaces of the vector space of all 2×2 matrices over R but $M_1 \cup M_2$ is not a subspace. Since $\begin{pmatrix} 1 & 0 \\ 0 & 0 \end{pmatrix} \in M_1$ and $\begin{pmatrix} 0 & 1 \\ 0 & 0 \end{pmatrix} \in M_2$, then $\begin{pmatrix} 1 & 0 \\ 0 & 0 \end{pmatrix} \in M_1 \cup M_2$ and $\begin{pmatrix} 0 & 1 \\ 0 & 0 \end{pmatrix} \in M_1 \cup M_2$. However, the sum

$$\begin{pmatrix} 1 & 0 \\ 0 & 0 \end{pmatrix} + \begin{pmatrix} 0 & 1 \\ 0 & 0 \end{pmatrix} = \begin{pmatrix} 1 & 1 \\ 0 & 0 \end{pmatrix} \notin M_1 \cup M_2$$

The next theorem does provide another way of combining two subspaces to obtain a subspace. Before the theorem is stated, the definition of a certain sum of subspaces is needed.

DEFINITION 5-4.2. *If M_2 and M_2 are subspaces of a vector space V over a field F, the sum $M_1 + M_2 = \{ \mathbf{u} + \mathbf{v} \mid \mathbf{u} \in M_1 \text{ and } \mathbf{v} \in M_2 \}$. If $M_1 \cap M_2 = \{ \mathbf{0} \}$, the sum is called the direct sum and is denoted by $M_1 \oplus M_2$.*

Notice that $M_1 + M_2$ may not be equal to $M_1 \cup M_2$, that is, the sum of M_1 and M_2 is not necessarily the same as the union of the sets M_1 and M_2. To see this, let $M_1 = \{ (x, 0) \mid x \in R \}$ and $M_2 = \{ (0, y) \mid y \in R \}$. Now, M_1 and M_2 are subspaces of R^2. Notice that $(1, 1) \in (M_1 + M_2)$, but $(1, 1) \notin (M_1 \cup M_2)$.

THEOREM 5-4.3. *If M_1 and M_2 are subspaces of a vector space V over a field F, then $M_1 + M_2$ is a subspace of V.*

Proof: Since $M_1 \subseteq (M_1 + M_2)$ and $M_1 \neq \emptyset$, then $M_1 + M_2 \neq \emptyset$. Clearly, $(M_1 + M_2) \subseteq V$, since each element in $M_1 + M_2$ is a sum of vectors in V. If $\mathbf{u}, \mathbf{v} \in (M_1 + M_2)$, there exist vectors $\mathbf{u}_1$, $\mathbf{v}_1 \in M_1$ and $\mathbf{u}_2, \mathbf{v}_2 \in M_2$ such that $\mathbf{u} = \mathbf{u}_1 + \mathbf{u}_2$ and $\mathbf{v} = \mathbf{v}_1 + \mathbf{v}_2$. Then, $\mathbf{u} + \mathbf{v} = (\mathbf{u}_1 + \mathbf{u}_2) + (\mathbf{v}_1 + \mathbf{v}_2) = (\mathbf{u}_1 + \mathbf{v}_1) + (\mathbf{u}_2 + \mathbf{v}_2)$. Thus, $\mathbf{u} + \mathbf{v} \in (M_1 + M_2)$. (Why?) If $c \in F$, then $c\mathbf{v} = c(\mathbf{v}_1 + \mathbf{v}_2) = c\mathbf{v}_1 + c\mathbf{v}_2$ where $c\mathbf{v}_1 \in M_1$ and $c\mathbf{v}_2 \in M_2$. Thus, $c\mathbf{v} \in (M_1 + M_2)$. By Theorem 5-4.1, $M_1 + M_2$ is a subspace of V.

In the Problem Set you will be asked to prove that the sum of any finite number of subspaces of a vector space V over a field F is a subspace of V.

The following statements can now be made and little would be required to prove them. If M_1 and M_2 are subspaces of a vector

115

space V over a field F, then $\{\mathbf{0}\}$ is a subspace of $M_1 \cap M_2$, $M_1 \cap M_2$ is a subspace of both M_1 and M_2, M_1 and M_2 are subspaces of $M_1 + M_2$, and $M_1 + M_2$ is a subspace of V.

The next theorem provides an interesting result concerning $M_1 + M_2$, namely that $M_1 + M_2$ is the *smallest* subspace of V that contains both M_1 and M_2.

THEOREM 5-4.4.   *If M, M_1 and M_2 are subspaces of a vector space V over a field F, $M_1 \subseteq M$, and $M_2 \subseteq M$, then $(M_1 + M_2) \subseteq M$.*

Since the subspaces $M_1 \cap M_2$ and $M_1 + M_2$ can be compared as sets and each can be compared with M_1 and M_2, you may wonder if there is a connection between the dimensions of these subspaces. If V is finite-dimensional, the connection is given in our next theorem. Also, notice that the theorem provides a reason for defining the dimension of the *trivial subspace*, $\{\mathbf{0}\}$, to be zero.

THEOREM 5-4.5.   *If M_1 and M_2 are subspaces of a finite-dimensional vector space V over a field F, then*

$$dim\ (M_1 + M_2) = dim\ M_1 + dim\ M_2 - dim\ (M_1 \cap M_2)$$

Proof: Let V be a finite-dimensional vector space over a field F, and let M_1 and M_2 be subspaces of V. Suppose $M_1 \cap M_2 \neq \{\mathbf{0}\}$. Let $\{\mathbf{x}_1, \mathbf{x}_2, \ldots, \mathbf{x}_r\}$ be a basis for $M_1 \cap M_2$. Since $(M_1 \cap M_2) \subseteq M_1$ and $(M_1 \cap M_2) \subseteq M_2$, these r vectors are part of some basis for M_1 and part of some basis for M_2. Let $\{\mathbf{x}_1, \mathbf{x}_2, \ldots, \mathbf{x}_r, \mathbf{y}_1, \mathbf{y}_2, \ldots, \mathbf{y}_s\}$ be a basis for M_1 and let $\{\mathbf{x}_1, \mathbf{x}_2, \ldots, \mathbf{x}_r, \mathbf{z}_1, \mathbf{z}_2, \ldots, \mathbf{z}_t\}$ be a basis for M_2. Then, $dim\ (M_1 \cap M_2) = r$, $dim\ M_1 = r + s$, and $dim\ M_2 = r + t$. Now, the vectors $\mathbf{x}_1, \mathbf{x}_2, \ldots, \mathbf{x}_r$, $\mathbf{y}_1, \mathbf{y}_2, \ldots, \mathbf{y}_s$, $\mathbf{z}_1, \mathbf{z}_2, \ldots, \mathbf{z}_t$ span $M_1 + M_2$. Therefore, $dim\ (M_1 + M_2) \leq r + s + t$. Since $dim\ M_1 + dim\ M_2 - dim\ (M_1 \cap M_2) = (r + s) + (r + t) - r = r + s + t$, we need to verify that $dim\ (M_1 + M_2) = r + s + t$. This will be proved if we prove that the $r + s + t$ vectors that span $M_1 + M_2$ are linearly independent. Thus, suppose a_i, b_i, $c_i \in F$ and

(1) $a_1 \mathbf{x}_1 + a_2 \mathbf{x}_2 + \cdots + a_r \mathbf{x}_r + b_1 \mathbf{y}_1 + b_2 \mathbf{y}_2 + \cdots + b_s \mathbf{y}_s$
$$+ c_1 \mathbf{z}_1 + c_2 \mathbf{z}_2 + \cdots + c_t \mathbf{z}_t = \mathbf{0}$$

This equation can be rewritten as

$$\overbrace{a_1 \mathbf{x}_1 + a_2 \mathbf{x}_2 + \cdots + a_r \mathbf{x}_r + b_1 \mathbf{y}_1 + b_2 \mathbf{y}_2 + \cdots + b_s \mathbf{y}_s}^{\mathbf{u}} =$$
$$\underbrace{- (c_1 \mathbf{z}_1 + c_2 \mathbf{z}_2 + \cdots + c_t \mathbf{z}_t)}_{\mathbf{v}}$$

In this equation, the vector $\mathbf{u}$ on the left is in M_1 and the vector $\mathbf{v}$ on the right is in M_2. This observation holds since the $\mathbf{x}$s and $\mathbf{y}$s form a basis for M_1 and the $\mathbf{z}$s are part of a basis for M_2. Since $\mathbf{u} = \mathbf{v}$, we conclude that $\mathbf{u}, \mathbf{v} \in (M_1 \cap M_2)$. Now, $\mathbf{u} \in (M_1 \cap M_2)$

implies that $\mathbf{u}$ can be expressed as $\mathbf{u} = d_1\mathbf{x}_1 + d_2\mathbf{x}_2 + \cdots + d_r\mathbf{x}_r$. Then, $\mathbf{u} = \mathbf{v}$ gives

$$d_1\mathbf{x}_1 + d_2\mathbf{x}_2 + \cdots + d_r\mathbf{x}_r = -(c_1\mathbf{z}_1 + c_2\mathbf{z}_2 + \cdots + c_t\mathbf{z}_t)$$

or

$$d_1\mathbf{x}_1 + d_2\mathbf{x}_2 + \cdots + d_r\mathbf{x}_r + c_1\mathbf{z}_1 + c_2\mathbf{z}_2 + \cdots + c_t\mathbf{z}_t = \mathbf{0}$$

Recall that $\{\mathbf{x}_1, \mathbf{x}_2, \ldots, \mathbf{x}_r, \mathbf{z}_1, \mathbf{z}_2, \ldots, \mathbf{z}_t\}$ is a basis for M_2. Consequently, these $r + t$ vectors are linearly independent. Thus,

$$d_1 = d_2 = \cdots = d_r = c_1 = c_2 = \cdots = c_t = 0$$

and Eq. (1) reduces to

$$a_1\mathbf{x}_1 + a_2\mathbf{x}_2 + \cdots + a_r\mathbf{x}_r + b_1\mathbf{y}_1 + b_2\mathbf{y}_2 + \cdots + b_s\mathbf{y}_s = \mathbf{0}$$

Since $\{\mathbf{x}_1, \mathbf{x}_2, \ldots, \mathbf{x}_r, \mathbf{y}_1, \mathbf{y}_2, \ldots, \mathbf{y}_s\}$ is a basis for M_1, it is a linearly independent set. Thus,

$$a_1 = a_2 = \cdots = a_r = b_1 = b_2 = \cdots = b_s = 0$$

Therefore, if Eq. (1) holds, all of the scalars must be zero. By Definition 5-2.3, the vectors $\mathbf{x}_1, \mathbf{x}_2, \ldots, \mathbf{x}_r, \mathbf{y}_1, \mathbf{y}_2, \ldots, \mathbf{y}_s, \mathbf{z}_1, \mathbf{z}_2, \ldots, \mathbf{z}_t$ are linearly independent. Since these $r + s + t$ vectors span $M_1 + M_2$ and are linearly independent, they form a basis for $M_1 + M_2$. Therefore, $dim\,(M_1 + M_2) = r + s + t$, and the theorem holds.

The case for $M_1 \cap M_2 = \{\mathbf{0}\}$ is given as a problem. In this case, $M_1 + M_2 = M_1 \oplus M_2$ and $dim\,(M_1 + M_2) = s + t = dim\,M_1 + dim\,M_2$. Thus, in order for the theorem to hold we need to agree that $dim\,(M_1 \cap M_2) = dim\,\{\mathbf{0}\} = 0$.

Problem Set 5-4

In each of Problems 1 through 11 decide if the given set is a subspace of R^2 or R^3, whichever is applicable.

1. $\{(x, y) \mid y = 2x\}$
2. $\{(x, y) \mid y \geq 0\}$
3. $\{(x, y) \mid y = x^2\}$
4. $\{(x, y) \mid x$ and y are rational numbers$\}$
5. $\{(x, y) \mid x$ is a rational number$\}$
6. $\{(x, y) \mid xy = 0\}$
7. $\{(x, y, z) \mid x + y + z = 0\}$
8. $\{(x, y, z) \mid z = x + 2y\}$
9. $\{(x, y, z) \mid z = x^2 + y^2\}$
10. $\{(x, y, z) \mid xyz = 0\}$
11. $\{(x, y, z) \mid y$ is a rational number$\}$

In Problems 12 through 17 decide which of the sets are subspaces of the vector space V over R of all functions from R into R. Let each function be from R into R.

12. $\{f \mid f(1) = 0\}$
13. $\{f \mid f(-1) = f(1)\}$
14. $\{f \mid f(1) = 2 + f(-1)\}$
15. $\{f \mid f(x^2) = [f(x)]^2\}$
16. $\{f \mid f$ is an even function$\}$ (See Problem 27 of Problem Set 5-1B.)

17. $\{f \mid f$ is an odd function$\}$ (See Problem 28 of Problem Set 5–1B.)

18. Argue that the sum of the subspaces of Problems 16 and 17 is V.

19. Argue that the intersection of the subspaces of Problems 16 and 17 is $\{\mathbf{0}\}$.

20. If V is a vector space over a field F and $\mathbf{v}_1, \mathbf{v}_2, \ldots, \mathbf{v}_n \in V$, prove that the set of all linear combinations of $\mathbf{v}_1, \mathbf{v}_2, \ldots, \mathbf{v}_n$ is a subspace of V. (See Problems 40 through 44 of Problem Set 5–2.)

21. Prove that the intersection of any number of subspaces of a vector space V over a field F is a subspace of V.

22. Prove that the intersection of all subspaces of a vector space V over a field F that contain $\mathbf{v}_1, \mathbf{v}_2, \ldots, \mathbf{v}_n$ is a subspace of V.

23. Argue that the subspace of Problem 20 is the same as the subspace of Problem 22. This subspace is the subspace *spanned* or *generated* by the vectors $\mathbf{v}_1, \mathbf{v}_2, \ldots, \mathbf{v}_n$.

24. Let A be an $m \times n$ dimension matrix over R. Prove that the set spanned by the row vectors of A is a subspace of R^n. This subspace is the *row space* of A.

25. Obtain the row space of each matrix over R.

(a) $\begin{pmatrix} 1 & 0 \\ 0 & 0 \end{pmatrix}$ (b) $\begin{pmatrix} 1 & 0 \\ 0 & 1 \end{pmatrix}$ (c) $\begin{pmatrix} 1 & 1 & 0 \\ 0 & 1 & 0 \end{pmatrix}$

(d) $\begin{pmatrix} 0 & 0 & 0 \\ 0 & 0 & 0 \end{pmatrix}$ (e) $\begin{pmatrix} 1 & 0 \\ 1 & 1 \\ 0 & 1 \end{pmatrix}$ (f) $\begin{pmatrix} 0 & 0 \\ 0 & 0 \\ 0 & 0 \end{pmatrix}$

In Problems 26 through 29 let n be a positive integer not 1 and let V be the vector space of all $n \times n$ matrices over R. Let all matrices be $n \times n$ over R.

26. Is $M = \{A \mid A$ is nonsingular$\}$ a subspace of V?

27. Is $M = \{A \mid A$ is singular$\}$ a subspace of V?

28. Is $M = \{A \mid a_{ij} = a_{ji}\}$ a subspace of V? The matrices in M are called *symmetric* matrices.

29. If B is a particular element of V, is $M = \{A \mid AB = BA\}$ a subspace of V?

30. If A and B are finite sets and $N(A)$ denotes the number of elements in A, state a theorem similar to Theorem 5–4.4 involving $N(A)$, $N(B)$, $N(A \cup B)$, and $N(A \cap B)$.

31. Argue that the sum of any finite number of subspaces of a vector space V over a field F is a subspace of V.

32. If M_1 and M_2 are subspaces of a vector space V over a field F, show that $M_1 \cap M_2$ is a subspace of both M_1 and M_2.

33. If M_1 and M_2 are subspaces of a vector space V over a field F, argue that M_1 and M_2 are subspaces of $M_1 + M_2$.

34. Prove Theorem 5–4.4.

35. Argue that Theorem 5–4.5 holds in case $M_1 \cap M_2 = \{\mathbf{0}\}$.

36. Show that $M_1 = \left\{ \begin{pmatrix} x & 0 \\ 0 & y \end{pmatrix} \middle| x, y \in R \right\}$ and $M_2 = \left\{ \begin{pmatrix} x & 0 \\ y & 0 \end{pmatrix} \middle| x, \right.$ $\left. y \in R \right\}$ are subspaces of the vector space V of all 2×2 real matrices over R. Obtain bases for M_1, M_2, $M_1 \cap M_2$, and $M_1 + M_2$. Verify Theorem 5–4.5 for this special case.

5-5. COORDINATES IN VECTOR SPACES

In Section 1–2, a rectangular coordinate system was imposed on a Euclidean plane, then the vector space R^2 was described. The same technique was used in Section 1–5 to describe R^3. Here, we begin with a finite-dimensional vector space V over a field F and introduce coordinates in V. This will be done in such a way that the usual rectangular coordinate systems can be obtained from R^2 and R^3.

Suppose V is a finite-dimensional vector space over a field F. Let $[\mathbf{v}_1, \mathbf{v}_2, \ldots, \mathbf{v}_n]$ denote an *ordered basis* for V, where the basis vectors are ordered according to their subscripts. Here, the ordered basis $[\mathbf{v}_2, \mathbf{v}_1, \mathbf{v}_3, \mathbf{v}_4, \ldots, \mathbf{v}_n]$ is considered different from $[\mathbf{v}_1, \mathbf{v}_2, \ldots, \mathbf{v}_n]$, since these bases are ordered differently. For the ordered basis $[\mathbf{v}_1, \mathbf{v}_2, \ldots, \mathbf{v}_n]$, each vector $\mathbf{v} \in V$ can be expressed uniquely as

$$\mathbf{v} = a_1\mathbf{v}_1 + a_2\mathbf{v}_2 + \cdots + a_n\mathbf{v}_n$$

for $a_i \in F$ (see Theorem 5–3.3). The ordered n-tuple $(a_1, a_2, \ldots, a_n)$ is called the *coordinates of* $\mathbf{v}$ *relative to* (or *with respect to*) *the ordered basis* $[\mathbf{v}_1, \mathbf{v}_2, \ldots, \mathbf{v}_n]$. Notice that each vector is associated with exactly one n-tuple and each n-tuple is associated with exactly one vector. This statement holds because there exists a natural one-to-one pairing between V and

$$\{(a_1, a_2, \ldots, a_n) \mid a_i \in F\}$$

If $\mathbf{w} = b_1\mathbf{v}_1 + b_2\mathbf{v}_2 + \cdots + b_n\mathbf{v}_n$, then

$$\mathbf{v} + \mathbf{w} = (a_1 + b_1)\mathbf{v}_1 + (a_2 + b_2)\mathbf{v}_2 + \cdots + (a_n + b_n)\mathbf{v}_n$$

and

$$c\mathbf{v} = (ca_1)\mathbf{v}_1 + (ca_2)\mathbf{v}_2 + \cdots + (ca_n)\mathbf{v}_n, \text{ for } c \in F$$

Thus, if $\mathbf{v}$ and $\mathbf{w}$ have coordinates $(a_1, a_2, \ldots, a_n)$ and $(b_1, b_2, \ldots, b_n)$, respectively, then $\mathbf{v} + \mathbf{w}$ has coordinates $(a_1 + b_1, a_2 + b_2, \ldots, a_n + b_n)$ and $c\mathbf{v}$ has coordinates $(ca_1, ca_2, \ldots, ca_n)$. With the algebra of n-tuples, we have

i. the coordinates of $\mathbf{v} + \mathbf{w}$ is the sum of the coordinates of $\mathbf{v}$ and $\mathbf{w}$, and

ii. the coordinates of $c\mathbf{v}$ is c times the coordinates of $\mathbf{v}$.

Illustration 1

Let $[\mathbf{i}, \mathbf{j}]$, where $\mathbf{i} = (1, 0)$ and $\mathbf{j} = (0, 1)$, be an ordered basis for R^2. Now, $\mathbf{v} = (x, y) \in R^2$ can be uniquely expressed as $\mathbf{v} = x\mathbf{i} + y\mathbf{j}$. Thus, the ordered pair (x, y) is the coordinates of $\mathbf{v}$ relative to the ordered basis $[\mathbf{i}, \mathbf{j}]$.

119

Illustration 2

Let $[\mathbf{j}, \mathbf{i}]$ be an ordered basis for R^2. Then, $\mathbf{v} = (x, y) \in R^2$ can be uniquely expressed as $\mathbf{v} = y\mathbf{j} + x\mathbf{i}$. Consequently, the ordered pair (y, x) is the coordinates of $\mathbf{v}$ relative to the ordered basis $[\mathbf{j}, \mathbf{i}]$.

In the two preceding illustrations, the basis vectors are orthogonal. However, in defining coordinates of a vector no mention was made concerning orthogonality of the basis vectors. In the next illustration, the basis vectors are not orthogonal.

Illustration 3

We know that $\{\mathbf{i}, \mathbf{i} + \mathbf{j}\}$ is a basis for R^2, see Illustration 3 of Section 5-3. Consider the ordered basis $[\mathbf{i}, \mathbf{i} + \mathbf{j}]$ with $\mathbf{i}$ the first vector and $\mathbf{i} + \mathbf{j}$ the second vector. Here, a vector $\mathbf{v} = (x, y) \in R^2$ can be uniquely expressed as $\mathbf{v} = (x - y)\mathbf{i} + y(\mathbf{i} + \mathbf{j})$. Therefore, the ordered pair $(x - y, y)$ is the coordinates of $\mathbf{v}$ relative to the ordered basis $[\mathbf{i}, \mathbf{i} + \mathbf{j}]$.

Illustration 4

If θ is the measure of a given angle, then $[\,(\cos \theta, \sin \theta), (-\sin \theta, \cos \theta)\,]$ is an ordered basis for R^2. (See Problem 19, Section 5-3.) Then, $\mathbf{v} = (x, y) \in R^2$ can be expressed uniquely as $\mathbf{v} = x'(\cos \theta, \sin \theta) + y'(-\sin \theta, \cos \theta)$. From this equation,

$$\begin{cases} x = x' \cos \theta - y' \sin \theta \\ y = x' \sin \theta + y' \cos \theta \end{cases}$$

the usual rotation formulas for two-space. Solving for x' and y', we have

$$\begin{cases} x' = x \cos \theta + y \sin \theta \\ y' = -x \sin \theta + y \cos \theta \end{cases}$$

Therefore, the ordered pair $(x \cos \theta + y \sin \theta, -x \sin \theta + y \cos \theta)$ is the coordinates of $\mathbf{v}$ relative to the ordered basis $[\,(\cos \theta, \sin \theta), (-\sin \theta, \cos \theta)\,]$. Geometrically, the standard basis vectors $\mathbf{i}$ and $\mathbf{j}$ have been rotated through the angle θ to obtain the basis $[\,(\cos \theta, \sin \theta), (-\sin \theta, \cos \theta)\,]$.

Illustration 5

If $\mathbf{i} = (1, 0, 0)$, $\mathbf{j} = (0, 1, 0)$, and $\mathbf{k} = (0, 0, 1)$, then $\{\mathbf{i}, \mathbf{i} + \mathbf{j}, \mathbf{i} + \mathbf{k}\}$ is easily shown to be a basis for R^3. For the ordered basis $[\mathbf{i}, \mathbf{i} + \mathbf{j}, \mathbf{i} + \mathbf{k}]$, $\mathbf{v} = (x, y, z) \in R^3$ can be uniquely expressed as $\mathbf{v} = a\mathbf{i} + b(\mathbf{i} + \mathbf{j}) + c(\mathbf{i} + \mathbf{k})$. Vector equality gives

$$\begin{cases} x = a + b + c \\ y = b \\ z = c \end{cases}$$

from which $a = x - y - z$, $b = y$, and $c = z$. Consequently, the ordered triple $(x - y - z, y, z)$ is the coordinates of $\mathbf{v}$ relative to the ordered basis $[\mathbf{i}, \mathbf{i} + \mathbf{j}, \mathbf{i} + \mathbf{k}]$.

Illustration 6

Let $\left[\begin{pmatrix} 1 & 0 \\ 0 & 0 \end{pmatrix}, \begin{pmatrix} 0 & 1 \\ 0 & 0 \end{pmatrix}, \begin{pmatrix} 0 & 0 \\ 1 & 0 \end{pmatrix}, \begin{pmatrix} 0 & 0 \\ 0 & 1 \end{pmatrix} \right]$ be an ordered basis for the vector space of all 2×2 real matrices over R. Then, $\mathbf{v} = \begin{pmatrix} x & y \\ z & w \end{pmatrix}$ can be uniquely expressed as

$$\mathbf{v} = a \begin{pmatrix} 1 & 0 \\ 0 & 0 \end{pmatrix} + b \begin{pmatrix} 0 & 1 \\ 0 & 0 \end{pmatrix} + c \begin{pmatrix} 0 & 0 \\ 1 & 0 \end{pmatrix} + d \begin{pmatrix} 0 & 0 \\ 0 & 1 \end{pmatrix}$$

Then, matrix equality gives that $x = a$, $y = b$, $z = c$, and $w = d$. Therefore, the ordered 4-tuple (x, y, z, w) is the coordinates of $\mathbf{v}$ relative to the given ordered basis.

Problem Set 5-5

1. In the vector space R over R, the standard basis is $\{1\}$. What are the coordinates of 5, 10, 12, 0, -5, -10, and x for $x \in R$ with respect to $\{1\}$? Answer the same question for the basis $\{5\}$.

In Problems 2 through 8, what are the coordinates of $(x, y) \in R^2$ relative to the given ordered bases? Here, $\mathbf{i} = (1, 0)$ and $\mathbf{j} = (0, 1)$.

2. $[2\mathbf{i}, 3\mathbf{j}]$

3. $[2\mathbf{i}, -3\mathbf{j}]$

4. $[-2\mathbf{i}, 3\mathbf{j}]$

5. $[-2\mathbf{i}, -3\mathbf{j}]$

6. $[\mathbf{i}, \mathbf{i} - 2\mathbf{j}]$

7. $[\mathbf{i} + \mathbf{j}, \mathbf{i} - \mathbf{j}]$

8. $[2\mathbf{i} - 5\mathbf{j}, -3\mathbf{i} - 7\mathbf{j}]$

In Problems 9 through 15, what are the coordinates of $(x, y, z) \in R^3$ with respect to the given ordered bases? Here, $\mathbf{i} = (1, 0, 0)$, $\mathbf{j} = (0, 1, 0)$, and $\mathbf{k} = (0, 0, 1)$.

9. $[3\mathbf{i}, 2\mathbf{j}, 5\mathbf{k}]$

10. $[\mathbf{j}, \mathbf{i}, \mathbf{k}]$

11. $[\mathbf{i}, \mathbf{k}, \mathbf{j}]$

12. $[\mathbf{j}, \mathbf{k}, \mathbf{i}]$

13. $[\mathbf{k}, \mathbf{i}, \mathbf{j}]$

14. $[-\mathbf{i}, -\mathbf{j}, -\mathbf{k}]$

15. $[\mathbf{i} + \mathbf{j}, \mathbf{i} + \mathbf{k}, \mathbf{j} + \mathbf{k}]$

6

Linear Mappings

6-1. INTRODUCTION

Recall that if A is an $m \times n$ matrix over R, B and C are each $n \times t$, and $c \in R$, the properties

(6-1.1)
$$A(B + C) = AB + AC$$
$$A(cB) = c(AB)$$

hold. In this chapter, we will study functions from a vector space over a field F to a vector space over F for which these two properties hold. In terms of functions, the properties are

(6-1.1a)
$$f(x + y) = f(x) + f(y)$$
$$f(cx) = cf(x)$$

Such functions are called *linear mappings, linear functions,* or *linear transformations.* The familiar operations of rotation, reflection, projection, differentiation, and integration are examples of linear mappings. Since we will study functions (for which certain properties hold), we first recall the definition of a function.

DEFINITION 6-1.1. *If A is a set and B is a set, a function, or mapping, f from A into B is a correspondence that associates to each element $x \in A$ a unique element $y \in B$.*

The *domain* of f is A and the *range* of f (or the *image* of A under f) is a subset of B. If the range of f is B, then f is called an *onto* mapping. If each element of the range is associated with exactly one element of the domain, then f is a *one-to-one* mapping. If $x \in A$, then $f(x)$ denotes the unique element of the range associated with x. With this notation, f is one-to-one means that if $f(x_1) = f(x_2)$, then $x_1 = x_2$. At times the range of f is denoted by $f(A)$.

Problem Set 6–1A

In each of Problems 1 through 14 let the domain of f consist of all $x \in R$ such that $f(x) \in R$. Obtain the domain and range of the indicated functions.

1. $f(x) = 4$ 2. $f(x) = 5x$ 3. $f(x) = x^2$

4. $f(x) = (x + 1)/x$ 5. $f(x) = x/(x + 5)$ 6. $f(x) = \sqrt{x^2 - 4}$

7. $f(x) = -\sqrt{x^2 - 4}$ 8. $f(x) = \sqrt{4 - x^2}$ 9. $f(x) = \ln x$

10. $f(x) = e^x$ 11. $f(x) = |x|$ 12. $f(x) = \cos x$

13. $f(x) = \tan x$ 14. $f(x) = [x]$, the greatest integer function

15. Describe a mapping from the set Z^+ onto the set of all negative integers which is
    (a) one-to-one
    (b) not one-to-one

16. Describe a mapping from Z^+ onto the set of all positive even integers that is
    (a) one-to-one
    (b) not one-to-one

17. Repeat Problem 16 if *even* is replaced with *odd*.

18. Suppose f is a mapping from A into B. If f is an onto mapping, must there exist a function from B onto A? If f is one-to-one and onto, does there exist a one-to-one function from B onto A?

With the previous review of functions, we are now ready to define a linear mapping from a vector space to a vector space. As in Chapter 5, most illustrations and problems will involve vector spaces over R. However, most definitions and theorems will be stated for vector spaces over any field F.

DEFINITION 6–1.2. *If V and W are vector spaces over a field F, then f is a linear mapping or linear transformation from V into W if and only if*

a. *f is a mapping from V into W,*
b. *$f(\mathbf{v}_1 + \mathbf{v}_2) = f(\mathbf{v}_1) + f(\mathbf{v}_2)$, for all $\mathbf{v}_1, \mathbf{v}_2 \in V$, and*
c. *$f(c\mathbf{v}) = cf(\mathbf{v})$, for all $\mathbf{v} \in V$ and all $c \in F$.*

We will employ the usual function notation for a linear mapping since a linear mapping is a function. (Not all functions are linear.)

However, two particular mappings are important enough to be denoted by special symbols. The *identity mapping I* is defined by $I(\mathbf{v}) = \mathbf{v}$, for all $\mathbf{v} \in V$, and the *zero mapping 0* is defined by $0(\mathbf{v}) = \mathbf{0}$, for all $\mathbf{v} \in V$. Also, we will denote the set of all linear mappings from V into W by $T(V, W)$.

Illustration 1

If V is a vector space over a field F, then the identity mapping, I, is a linear mapping from V into (actually onto) V. This holds, for

(a) I is a function from V into V since $I(\mathbf{v}) = \mathbf{v}$, for all $\mathbf{v} \in V$,

(b) $I(\mathbf{v}_1 + \mathbf{v}_2) = \mathbf{v}_1 + \mathbf{v}_2 = I(\mathbf{v}_1) + I(\mathbf{v}_2)$, for all $\mathbf{v}_1, \mathbf{v}_2 \in V$, and

(c) $I(c\mathbf{v}) = c\mathbf{v} = cI(\mathbf{v})$, for all $\mathbf{v} \in V$ and all $c \in F$.

Illustration 2

If V is a vector space over a field F, then the zero mapping, 0, is a linear mapping from V into V. This holds, because

(a) 0 is a function from V into V since $0(\mathbf{v}) = \mathbf{0}$, for all $\mathbf{v} \in V$,

(b) $0(\mathbf{v}_1 + \mathbf{v}_2) = \mathbf{0} = \mathbf{0} + \mathbf{0} = 0(\mathbf{v}_1) + 0(\mathbf{v}_2)$, for all $\mathbf{v}_1, \mathbf{v}_2 \in V$, and

(c) $0(c\mathbf{v}) = \mathbf{0} = c\mathbf{0} = c0(\mathbf{v})$, for all $\mathbf{v} \in V$ and all $c \in F$.

At times brackets will be used in the function notation. Let us agree that $f(\mathbf{v})$ and $f[\mathbf{v}]$ both mean the value of f at $\mathbf{v}$, that is, $f(\mathbf{v}) = f[\mathbf{v}]$.

Illustration 3

The function f defined by $f[(x, y)] = x$ projects each point $(x, y) \in R^2$ onto the x-axis. Show that f is a linear mapping from R^2 into R^1. Now f is clearly a function from R^2 into R^1. If $(x_1, y_1) \in R^2$ and $(x_2, y_2) \in R^2$, then

$$f[(x_1, y_1) + (x_2, y_2)] = f[(x_1 + x_2, y_1 + y_2)] \quad \text{Addition in } R^2.$$
$$= x_1 + x_2 \quad \text{Definition of } f.$$
$$= f[(x_1, y_1)] + f[(x_2, y_2)] \quad \text{Why?}$$

Also, if $c \in R$ and $(x, y) \in R^2$, then

$$f[c(x, y)] = f[(cx, cy)] = cx = cf[(x, y)] \quad \text{Provide the reasons.}$$

Illustration 4

Show that the function f that projects each point (x, y, z) in space onto the point (x, y) in R^2 is a linear mapping from R^3 into R^2. Here, f is defined by $f[(x, y, z)] = (x, y)$ and is a function. If (x_1, y_1, z_1),

$(x_2, y_2, z_2) \in R^3$, then

$$f[(x_1, y_1, z_1) + (x_2, y_2, z_2)]$$

$= f[(x_1 + x_2, y_1 + y_2, z_1 + z_2)]$	*Why?*
$= (x_1 + x_2, y_1 + y_2)$	*Definition of f.*
$= (x_1, y_1) + (x_2, y_2)$	*Addition in R^2.*
$= f[(x_1, y_1, z_1)] + f[(x_2, y_2, z_2)]$	*Why?*

Also, if $c \in R$ and $(x, y, z) \in R^3$, then

$$f[c(x, y, z)] = f[(cx, cy, cz)]$$

$= (cx, cy) = c(x, y) = cf[(x, y, z)]$	*Provide all reasons.*

Illustration 5

Show that f defined by $f[(x, y)] = (x + y, y)$ for all $(x, y) \in R^2$ is a linear mapping from R^2 into R^2. Clearly, f is a function from R^2 into R^2. If $(x_1, y_1), (x_2, y_2) \in R^2$, then

$$f[(x_1, y_1) + (x_2, y_2)]$$

$= f[(x_1 + x_2, y_1 + y_2)]$	*Why?*
$= ([x_1 + x_2] + [y_1 + y_2], y_1 + y_2)$	*Why?*
$= ([x_1 + y_1] + [x_2 + y_2], y_1 + y_2)$	*Properties of R.*
$= (x_1 + y_1, y_1) + (x_2 + y_2, y_2)$	*Addition in R^2.*
$= f[(x_1, y_1)] + f[(x_2, y_2)]$	*Why?*

Also, if $c \in R$ and $(x, y) \in R^2$, then

$$f[c(x, y)] = f[(cx, cy)] = (cx + cy, cy)$$

$= c(x + y, y) = cf[(x, y)]$	*Provide all reasons.*

Illustration 6

From calculus, we know that if $c \in R$ and g and h are differentiable functions over R, then $D(g + h) = Dg + Dh$ and $D(cg) = c(Dg)$. Therefore, D is a linear mapping from the vector space V of all differentiable functions over R into the vector space of all real-valued functions over R.

Illustration 7

We know, again from calculus, that if g and h are each continuous over R, then for $c \in R$,

$$\int_0^x (g + h)(t)\, dt = \int_0^x g(t)\, dt + \int_0^x h(t)\, dt$$

and

$$\int_0^x cg(t)\, dt = c \int_0^x g(t)\, dt$$

Therefore, the mapping L defined by $L[f(x)] = \int_0^x f(t)\, dt$ is a linear mapping from the space of all continuous functions over R into R.

125

Illustration 8

The sine function is *not* a linear mapping from R^1 into R^1 since generally $\sin (x + y) \neq \sin x + \sin y$. Furthermore, $\sin cx \neq c \sin x$ for all $x \in R$. The function f defined by $f[\,(x, y)\,] = (x, y^2)$ is *not* a linear mapping from R^2 into R^2, for

$$f[\,(x_1, y_1) + (x_2, y_2)\,] = f[\,(x_1 + x_2, y_1 + y_2)\,] = (x_1 + x_2, [\,y_1 + y_2\,]^2)$$

$$f[\,(x_1, y_1)\,] + f[\,(x_2, y_2)\,] = (x_1, y_1^2) + (x_2, y_2^2) = (x_1 + x_2, y_1^2 + y_2^2)$$

and $(y_1 + y_2)^2 \neq y_1^2 + y_2^2$ for all $y_1, y_2 \in R$. Also,

$$f[\,c(x, y)\,] = f[\,(cx, cy)\,] = (cx, c^2 y^2) = c(x, cy^2)$$

while

$$cf[\,(x, y)\,] = c(x, y^2)$$

Notice that $cy^2 \neq y^2$ for all $c, y \in R$.

Problem Set 6–1B

In Problems 1 through 9 decide which of the indicated functions are linear mappings from R^1 into R^1.

1. $f(x) = -x$ 2. $f(x) = 2$ 3. $f(x) = 5x$

4. $f(x) = -2x$ 5. $f(x) = mx$, m constant

6. $f(x) = mx + b$, m, b constants   7. $f(x) = \cos x$

8. $f(x) = e^x$ 9. $f(x) = x^2$

In Problems 10 through 18 decide which of the indicated functions are linear mappings from R^2 into R^2.

10. $f[\,(x, y)\,] = (y, x)$ 11. $f[\,(x, y)\,] = (x, -y)$

12. $f[\,(x, y)\,] = (-x, y)$ 13. $f[\,(x, y)\,] = (-x, -y)$

14. $f[\,(x, y)\,] = c(x, y)$, c constant   15. $f[\,(x, y)\,] = (x + 1, y)$

16. $f[\,(x, y)\,] = (x, y + 1)$ 17. $f[\,(x, y)\,] = \sqrt{x^2 + y^2}$

18. $f[\,(x, y)\,] = (x \cos \theta + y \sin \theta, -x \sin \theta + y \cos \theta)$, θ constant

19. Interpret Problems 10, 11, 12, 13, and 18 geometrically.

20. Which of the following are linear mappings from R^2 into R^1
    (a) $f[\,(x, y)\,] = xy$ (b) $f[\,(x, y)\,] = 3x - y$
    (c) $f[\,(x, y)\,] = x + y$ (d) $f(\mathbf{v}) = \mathbf{i} \cdot \mathbf{v}$

21. Is f defined by $f[\,(x, y, z)\,] = x - 3y + 2z$ a linear mapping from R^3 into R^1 ?

22. Show that $f[\,(x, y, z)\,] = (x, y, 0)$ defines a linear mapping f from R^3 into R^3. Compare with Illustration 4.

In Problems 23, 24, and 25 argue that the functions are linear mappings from R^3 into R^2.

23. $f[\,(x, y, z)\,] = (x, z)$ 24. $f[\,(x, y, z)\,] = (3x - 2y, 5x - 2z)$

25. $f[\,(x, y, z)\,] = (c_1 x + c_2 y + c_3 z, d_1 x + d_2 y + d_3 z)$, c_i, d_i constant for $i = 1, 2, 3$

26. If f is a linear mapping from R^2 into R^2, $f(\mathbf{i}) = \mathbf{i} + \mathbf{j}$, and $f(\mathbf{j}) = \mathbf{i} - \mathbf{j}$, obtain
    (a) $f(5\mathbf{i} - 3\mathbf{j})$ (b) $f[\,(0, 0)\,]$ (c) $f[\,(5, -3)\,]$
    (d) $f(x\mathbf{i} + y\mathbf{j})$ (e) all $\mathbf{v}$ such that $f(\mathbf{v}) = \mathbf{0}$

27. If f is a linear mapping from R^2 into R^3, $f(\mathbf{i}) = \mathbf{i} + \mathbf{j}$, and $f(\mathbf{j}) = \mathbf{i} - \mathbf{k}$, determine
    (a) $f(2\mathbf{i} + 3\mathbf{j})$ (b) $f[\,(2, 3)\,]$
    (c) $f[\,(x, y)\,]$ (d) $f[\,(0, 0)\,]$
    (e) all $\mathbf{v}$ such that $f(\mathbf{v}) = \mathbf{0}$

28. If f is a linear mapping from R^2 into R^1, $f(\mathbf{i} + \mathbf{j}) = 0$, and $f(\mathbf{i} - \mathbf{j}) = 6$, obtain
    (a) $f(\mathbf{i})$ (b) $f(\mathbf{j})$ (c) $f[\,(x, y)\,]$
    (d) all $\mathbf{v}$ such that $f(\mathbf{v}) = \mathbf{0}$

29. If f is a linear mapping from R^3 into R^1, $f(\mathbf{i} + \mathbf{j}) = 0$, $f(\mathbf{i} - \mathbf{j}) = 2$, and $f(2\mathbf{i} - \mathbf{j} + \mathbf{k}) = -4$, determine
    (a) $f(\mathbf{i})$ (b) $f(\mathbf{j})$ (c) $f(\mathbf{k})$
    (d) $f[\,(x, y, z)\,]$ (e) all $\mathbf{v}$ such that $f(\mathbf{v}) = \mathbf{0}$

30. Let V be the vector space of all real $n \times 1$ matrices over R and let A be a given $m \times n$ real matrix. Prove that f defined by $f(X) = AX$, for all $X \in V$, is a linear mapping from V into the vector space W of all real $m \times 1$ matrices over R.

31. Argue that the function f of Problem 30 is the zero mapping if and only if A is the zero $m \times n$ matrix.

32. Let V be the vector space of all real $m \times n$ matrices over R. Let P be a given $m \times m$ real matrix and let Q be a given $n \times n$ real matrix. Prove that the function f defined by $f(A) = PAQ$, for all $A \in V$, is a linear mapping from V into V.

33. Let V be the vector space of all $n \times n$ real matrices over R and let B be a given $n \times n$ matrix. Argue that the function f defined by $f(A) = AB - BA$ for all $A \in V$, is a linear mapping from V into V.

34. Prove that $f(c\mathbf{v}_1 + \mathbf{v}_2) = cf(\mathbf{v}_1) + f(\mathbf{v}_2)$, for all $c \in F$ and all $\mathbf{v}_1$, $\mathbf{v}_2 \in V$, is equivalent to parts (b) and (c) of Definition 6-1.2.

35. Argue that $f(a\mathbf{v}_1 + b\mathbf{v}_2) = af(\mathbf{v}_1) + bf(\mathbf{v}_2)$, for all $a, b \in F$ and all $\mathbf{v}_1$, $\mathbf{v}_2 \in V$, is equivalent to parts (b) and (c) of Definition 6-1.2.

In each of Illustrations 1 through 7, notice that the linear mapping pairs the zero vector in the domain with the zero vector in the range. This is always the case with linear mappings, as the following theorem shows.

THEOREM 6-1.1.   If f is a linear mapping from a vector space V over a field F into a vector space W over F, then $f(\mathbf{0}) = \mathbf{0}$.

Proof: Now, $f(\mathbf{0}) = f(\mathbf{0} + \mathbf{0}) = f(\mathbf{0}) + f(\mathbf{0})$. Therefore, $f(\mathbf{0}) = \mathbf{0}$. (Supply all reasons.)

If f and g are functions from R into R, recall that the functions af and $f + g$ are defined as follows (see Eqq. (5–1.1)).

(6–1.2)
$$\begin{cases} \text{If } a \in R, \ (af)(x) = a\,[f(x)]\text{, for all } x \in R \\ \qquad\qquad\qquad \text{and} \\ (f + g)(x) = f(x) + g(x) \text{ for all } x \in R \end{cases}$$

If f and g are linear mappings, entirely similar definitions hold. We next indicate that af and $f + g$ are linear mappings.

THEOREM 6–1.2. *If f and g are linear mappings from a vector space V over a field F into a vector space W over F, then*

a. *if $a \in F$, af is a linear mapping from V into W, and*
b. *$f + g$ is a linear mapping from V into W.*

Proof of Part (b): Now, $f + g$ is a function from V into W. If $\mathbf{v}_1, \mathbf{v}_2 \in V$, then

$(f + g)(\mathbf{v}_1 + \mathbf{v}_2)$

$\qquad = f(\mathbf{v}_1 + \mathbf{v}_2) + g(\mathbf{v}_1 + \mathbf{v}_2)$ *Definition of $f + g$.*

$\qquad = [f(\mathbf{v}_1) + f(\mathbf{v}_2)] + [g(\mathbf{v}_1) + g(\mathbf{v}_2)]$
$\qquad\qquad\qquad\qquad\qquad\qquad\qquad$ *Why?*

$\qquad = [f(\mathbf{v}_1) + g(\mathbf{v}_1)] + [f(\mathbf{v}_2) + g(\mathbf{v}_2)]$
$\qquad\qquad\qquad\qquad\qquad$ *Properties of addition in W.*

$\qquad\quad = (f + g)(\mathbf{v}_1) + (f + g)(\mathbf{v}_2)$ *Why?*

If $\mathbf{v} \in V$ and $c \in F$, then

$\qquad (f + g)(c\mathbf{v}) = f(c\mathbf{v}) + g(c\mathbf{v})$ *Why?*

$\qquad\qquad\qquad = cf(\mathbf{v}) + cg(\mathbf{v})$ *Why?*

$\qquad\qquad\qquad = c[f(\mathbf{v}) + g(\mathbf{v})]$ *Distributive property for W.*

$\qquad\qquad\qquad = c[(f + g)(\mathbf{v})]$ *Why?*

DEFINITION 6–1.3. *If f is a linear mapping from a vector space V over a field F into a vector space W over F, the kernel of f (or the null space of f) is the set of all elements of V that are paired with the zero vector of W. In set notation, the kernel of f, $\ker f = \{\,\mathbf{v} \mid f(\mathbf{v}) = \mathbf{0}\,\}$.*

THEOREM 6–1.3. *If f is a linear mapping from a vector space V over a field F into a vector space W over F, then*

a. *the range of f is a subspace of W, and*
b. *the kernel of f is a subspace of V.*

Proof of Part (a): First, the range of f is a subset of W. (Why?) If $\mathbf{w}_1$ and $\mathbf{w}_2$ are in the range of f, then there exist $\mathbf{v}_1, \mathbf{v}_2 \in V$ such that $f(\mathbf{v}_1) = \mathbf{w}_1$ and $f(\mathbf{v}_2) = \mathbf{w}_2$. Now, $\mathbf{w}_1 + \mathbf{w}_2 = f(\mathbf{v}_1) + f(\mathbf{v}_2) = f(\mathbf{v}_1 + \mathbf{v}_2)$. Since $(\mathbf{v}_1 + \mathbf{v}_2) \in V$ and $f(\mathbf{v}_1 + \mathbf{v}_2) =$

$\mathbf{w}_1 + \mathbf{w}_2$, then $\mathbf{w}_1 + \mathbf{w}_2$ is in the range of f. Next, if $\mathbf{w}$ is in the range of f there exists a $\mathbf{v} \in V$ such that $f(\mathbf{v}) = \mathbf{w}$. For $c \in F$, we have $f(c\mathbf{v}) = cf(\mathbf{v}) = c\mathbf{w}$. Since $c\mathbf{v} \in V$ and $f(c\mathbf{v}) = c\mathbf{w}$, then $c\mathbf{w}$ is in the range of f. By Theorem 5–4.1, the range of f is a subspace of W.

Proof of Part (b): Now, the kernel of f is a subset of V. If $\mathbf{v}_1$ and $\mathbf{v}_2$ are in the kernel of f, then

$$f(\mathbf{v}_1 + \mathbf{v}_2) = f(\mathbf{v}_1) + f(\mathbf{v}_2) = \mathbf{0} + \mathbf{0} = \mathbf{0}$$

Since $(\mathbf{v}_1 + \mathbf{v}_2) \in V$ and $f(\mathbf{v}_1 + \mathbf{v}_2) = \mathbf{0}$, then $\mathbf{v}_1 + \mathbf{v}_2$ is in the kernel of f. Next, if $c \in F$ and $\mathbf{v}$ is in the kernel of f, then

$$f(c\mathbf{v}) = cf(\mathbf{v}) = c\mathbf{0} = \mathbf{0}$$

Now, $c\mathbf{v} \in V$ and $f(c\mathbf{v}) = \mathbf{0}$ imply that $c\mathbf{v}$ is in the kernel of f. Therefore, the kernel of f is a subspace of V, by Theorem 5–4.1.

Problem Set 6–1C

In Problems 1 through 9 describe the kernel of f (the null space of f) and the range of f for the linear mappings of the following problems from Problem Set 6–1B.

1. Problem 1
2. Problem 5
3. Problem 10
4. Problem 13
5. Problem 14
6. Problem 18
7. Problem 20
8. Problem 21
9. Problem 24

In Problems 10 through 16 let f be a linear mapping from a vector space V over a field F into a vector space W over F. The kernel of f and the range of f are denoted by $ker f$ and $f(V)$, respectively.

10. Argue that $ker f = \{\mathbf{0}\}$ if and only if f is a one-to-one mapping.
11. Prove that if $ker f = \{\mathbf{0}\}$ and $\mathbf{v}_1, \mathbf{v}_2, \ldots, \mathbf{v}_n$ are linearly independent in V, then $f(\mathbf{v}_1), f(\mathbf{v}_2), \ldots, f(\mathbf{v}_n)$ are linearly independent in W.
12. Show that if $\mathbf{v}_1, \mathbf{v}_2, \ldots, \mathbf{v}_n$ span V, then $f(\mathbf{v}_1), f(\mathbf{v}_2), \ldots, f(\mathbf{v}_n)$ span $f(V)$.
13. If f is one-to-one and $\{\mathbf{v}_1, \mathbf{v}_2, \ldots, \mathbf{v}_n\}$ is a basis of V, argue that $\{f(\mathbf{v}_1), f(\mathbf{v}_2), \ldots, f(\mathbf{v}_n)\}$ is a basis of $f(V)$. (Apply Problems 10, 11, and 12.)
14. Prove that if f is one-to-one and V is finite-dimensional, then $dim V = dim f(V)$. (See Problem 13.)
15. What is $ker 0$? $ker I$?
16. If f is one-to-one, V is finite-dimensional, and $dim V = dim W$, prove that $W = f(V)$, that is, prove that f is from V onto W. (Notice that $dim f(V) = dim W$.)
17. Prove part (a) of Theorem 6–1.2.

6-2. LINEAR MAPPINGS AND MATRICES

Suppose V and W are finite-dimensional vector spaces over R and f is a linear mapping from V into W. Let $[\mathbf{v}_1, \mathbf{v}_2, \ldots, \mathbf{v}_n]$ be an ordered basis of V and let $[\mathbf{w}_1, \mathbf{w}_2, \ldots, \mathbf{w}_m]$ be an ordered basis of W. Now, we know that for $i \in \{1, 2, \ldots, n\}$, $f(\mathbf{v}_i) \in W$ and every element of W can be expressed uniquely as a linear combination of the basis vectors $\mathbf{w}_1, \mathbf{w}_2, \ldots, \mathbf{w}_m$. The image of each basis vector of V is thus a unique linear combination of the basis vectors of W. Therefore, we are led to the system of equations

(6-2.1)
$$\begin{cases} f(\mathbf{v}_1) = a_{11}\mathbf{w}_1 + a_{21}\mathbf{w}_2 + \cdots + a_{m1}\mathbf{w}_m \\ f(\mathbf{v}_2) = a_{12}\mathbf{w}_1 + a_{22}\mathbf{w}_2 + \cdots + a_{m2}\mathbf{w}_m \\ \quad\vdots \qquad\quad \vdots \qquad\quad \vdots \qquad \ddots \qquad \vdots \\ f(\mathbf{v}_n) = a_{1n}\mathbf{w}_1 + a_{2n}\mathbf{w}_2 + \cdots + a_{mn}\mathbf{w}_m \end{cases}$$

with $a_{ji} \in R$ for $1 \leq j \leq m$ and $1 \leq i \leq n$. This system of equations can be expressed as

(6-2.1a)
$$f(\mathbf{v}_i) = \sum_{j=1}^{j=m} a_{ji}\mathbf{w}_j \qquad (i = 1, 2, \ldots, n)$$

The set of elements a_{ji} determines an $m \times n$ matrix

(6-2.2)
$$A = \begin{pmatrix} a_{11} & a_{21} & \cdots & a_{m1} \\ a_{12} & a_{22} & \cdots & a_{m2} \\ \vdots & \vdots & \ddots & \vdots \\ a_{1n} & a_{2n} & \cdots & a_{mn} \end{pmatrix}^t = \begin{pmatrix} a_{11} & a_{12} & \cdots & a_{1n} \\ a_{21} & a_{22} & \cdots & a_{2n} \\ \vdots & \vdots & \ddots & \vdots \\ a_{m1} & a_{m2} & \cdots & a_{mn} \end{pmatrix}$$

which is called the *matrix of the mapping f with respect to (or relative to) the two given ordered bases.* (Notice that the matrix (a_{ji}) is the transpose of the matrix (a_{ij}).) The elements of A depend on the ordered bases chosen for V and W, and for a given mapping f the elements of A are uniquely determined by the bases used. Also, given any $m \times n$ matrix A over R and a pair of ordered bases of V and W, then A determines a unique linear mapping from V into W.

Illustration 1

Obtain the matrix of the linear mapping of Illustration 4 of Section 6-1 with respect to the standard ordered bases of R^3 and R^2. From

$$f[\,(1, 0, 0)\,] = (1, 0) = 1(1, 0) + 0(0, 1)$$
$$f[\,(0, 1, 0)\,] = (0, 1) = 0(1, 0) + 1(0, 1)$$

and

$$f[\,(0, 0, 1)\,] = (0, 0) = 0(1, 0) + 0(0, 1)$$

we have

$$A = \begin{pmatrix} 1 & 0 \\ 0 & 1 \\ 0 & 0 \end{pmatrix}^t = \begin{pmatrix} 1 & 0 & 0 \\ 0 & 1 & 0 \end{pmatrix}$$

Illustration 2

Repeat Illustration 1 except use $[\,(1, 0),\ (1, 1)\,]$ for an ordered basis of R^2, see Illustration 3 of Section 5–3. Now,

$$f[\,(1, 0, 0)\,] = (1, 0) = 1(1, 0) + 0(1, 1)$$
$$f[\,(0, 1, 0)\,] = (0, 1) = -1(1, 0) + 1(1, 1)$$

and

$$f[\,(0, 0, 1)\,] = (0, 0) = 0(1, 0) + 0(1, 1)$$

Therefore,

$$A = \begin{pmatrix} 1 & 0 \\ -1 & 1 \\ 0 & 0 \end{pmatrix}^t = \begin{pmatrix} 1 & -1 & 0 \\ 0 & 1 & 0 \end{pmatrix}$$

Illustration 3

The function f with

$$f(\mathbf{i}) = (2, 1)$$

and

$$f(\mathbf{j}) = (1, -4)$$

defines a linear mapping from R^2 into R^2. Here, $\mathbf{i} = (1, 0)$ and $\mathbf{j} = (0, 1)$ form the standard ordered basis of R^2. What is the matrix of f with respect to the standard basis? From

$$f(\mathbf{i}) = (2, 1) = 2(1, 0) + 1(0, 1) = 2\mathbf{i} + 1\mathbf{j}$$

and

$$f(\mathbf{j}) = (1, -4) = 1(1, 0) - 4(0, 1) = 1\mathbf{i} - 4\mathbf{j}$$

we have

$$A = \begin{pmatrix} 2 & 1 \\ 1 & -4 \end{pmatrix}^t = \begin{pmatrix} 2 & 1 \\ 1 & -4 \end{pmatrix}$$

Illustration 4

Show that $A = \begin{pmatrix} 1 & 3 & -2 \\ 0 & -1 & 5 \end{pmatrix}$ is the matrix of a unique linear mapping f from R^3 into R^2 with respect to the standard ordered bases. Now,

$$f[\,(1, 0, 0)\,] = 1(1, 0) + 0(0, 1) = (1, 0)$$
$$f[\,(0, 1, 0)\,] = 3(1, 0) - 1(0, 1) = (3, -1)$$

and

$$f[\,(0, 0, 1)\,] = -2(1, 0) + 5(0, 1) = (-2, 5)$$

Furthermore,

$$f[\,(x, y, z)\,] = x(1, 0) + y(3, -1) + z(-2, 5) = (x + 3y - 2z, \ -y + 5z)$$

Next, if $\mathbf{v}$ is *any* one element in V, we will obtain an expression for $f(\mathbf{v})$ that involves the matrix A. If $\mathbf{v} \in V$, then $\mathbf{v}$ can be expressed

131

uniquely as

$$\mathbf{v} = c_1\mathbf{v}_1 + c_2\mathbf{v}_2 + \cdots + c_n\mathbf{v}_n$$

where $c_i \in R$ for $1 \le i \le n$. Then,

$$
\begin{aligned}
f(\mathbf{v}) &= f(c_1\mathbf{v}_1 + c_2\mathbf{v}_2 + \cdots + c_n\mathbf{v}_n) \\
&= f(c_1\mathbf{v}_1) + f(c_2\mathbf{v}_2) + \cdots + f(c_n\mathbf{v}_n) \\
&= c_1 f(\mathbf{v}_1) + c_2 f(\mathbf{v}_2) + \cdots + c_n f(\mathbf{v}_n) \\
&= c_1 \sum_{j=1}^{j=m} a_{j1}\mathbf{w}_j + c_2 \sum_{j=1}^{j=m} a_{j2}\mathbf{w}_j + \cdots + c_n \sum_{j=1}^{j=m} a_{jn}\mathbf{w}_j \\
&= \sum_{k=1}^{k=n} \left[c_k \sum_{j=1}^{j=m} a_{jk}\mathbf{w}_j \right] \\
&= \sum_{j=1}^{j=m} \left[\left(\sum_{k=1}^{k=n} a_{jk}c_k \right) \mathbf{w}_j \right]
\end{aligned}
$$

Now, $f(\mathbf{v}) \in W$ and $f(\mathbf{v})$ can be expressed uniquely as a linear combination of the basis vectors $\mathbf{w}_1, \mathbf{w}_2, \ldots, \mathbf{w}_m$. Thus, if

$$f(\mathbf{v}) = d_1\mathbf{w}_1 + d_2\mathbf{w}_2 + \cdots + d_m\mathbf{w}_m = \sum_{j=1}^{j=m} d_j\mathbf{w}_j$$

then $d_j = \sum_{k=1}^{k=n} a_{jk}c_k$. With the coordinates of $\mathbf{v}$ relative to the ordered basis $[\mathbf{v}_1, \mathbf{v}_2, \ldots, \mathbf{v}_n]$ expressed as the $n \times 1$ matrix

$$
B = \begin{pmatrix} c_1 \\ c_2 \\ \vdots \\ c_n \end{pmatrix}
$$

we have

(6-2.3) $$f(\mathbf{v}) = AB$$

which gives the coordinates of $f(\mathbf{v})$ relative to the ordered basis $[\mathbf{w}_1, \mathbf{w}_2, \ldots, \mathbf{w}_m]$ as an $m \times 1$ matrix. The transpose of the coefficient matrix from Eq. (6-2.1) was used for A so that Eq. (6-2.3) could be obtained.

Illustration 5

Use Eq. (6-2.3) to obtain $f[(x, y, z)]$ for (a) Illustration 1, and (b) Illustration 2.
For (a)

$$
\begin{pmatrix} 1 & 0 & 0 \\ 0 & 1 & 0 \end{pmatrix} \begin{pmatrix} x \\ y \\ z \end{pmatrix} = \begin{pmatrix} x \\ y \end{pmatrix}
$$

Hence, $f[(x, y, z)] = (x, y)$.
For (b)

$$
\begin{pmatrix} 1 & -1 & 0 \\ 0 & 1 & 0 \end{pmatrix} \begin{pmatrix} x \\ y \\ z \end{pmatrix} = \begin{pmatrix} x - y \\ y \end{pmatrix}
$$

Therefore, $f[(x, y, z)] = (x - y, y)$.

Illustration 6

Use Eq. (6–2.3) to obtain (a) $f[(x, y)]$ in Illustration 3, and (b) $f[(x, y, z)]$ in Illustration 4.

For (a)

$$\begin{pmatrix} 2 & 1 \\ 1 & -4 \end{pmatrix} \begin{pmatrix} x \\ y \end{pmatrix} = \begin{pmatrix} 2x + y \\ x - 4y \end{pmatrix}$$

from which $f[(x, y)] = (2x + y, x - 4y)$.

For (b)

$$\begin{pmatrix} 1 & 3 & -2 \\ 0 & -1 & 5 \end{pmatrix} \begin{pmatrix} x \\ y \\ z \end{pmatrix} = \begin{pmatrix} x + 3y - 2z \\ - y + 5z \end{pmatrix}$$

which gives $f[(x, y, z)] = (x + 3y - 2z, -y + 5z)$.

Problem Set 6–2

In Problems 1 through 5 obtain the matrices of the given linear mappings with respect to the standard ordered bases of the indicated vector spaces. Verify Eq. (6–2.3) for each matrix.

1. From R^2 into R^2:
    (a) $f[(x, y)] = (y, x)$ (b) $f[(x, y)] = (x, -y)$
    (c) $f[(x, y)] = (-x, y)$ (d) $f[(x, y)] = (-x, -y)$
    (e) $f[(x, y)] = (x \cos \theta + y \sin \theta, -x \sin \theta + y \cos \theta)$, θ constant

2. From R^2 into R^1:
    (a) $f[(x, y)] = x + y$ (b) $f[(x, y)] = 3x - y$
    (c) $f[(x, y)] = 0$ (d) $f[(x, y)] = ax + by$

3. From R^3 into R^2:
    (a) $f[(x, y, z)] = (3x - 2y, 5x - 2z)$
    (b) $f[(x, y, z)] = (x, z)$

4. From R^2 into R^4:
    (a) $f[(x, y)] = (0, x, x + y, y)$
    (b) $f[(x, y)] = (x - y, y, 0, x + y)$

5. From R^4 into R^4:
    (a) $f[(x, y, z, w)] = (x - y, y - z, z - w, w - x)$
    (b) $f[(x, y, z, w)] = (3x, 2x + y, y - 2z, w)$

In each of Problems 6 through 14 obtain the matrix of f if f is a linear mapping from R^2 or R^3 with the standard ordered bases into R^2 with the ordered basis $[\mathbf{u}, \mathbf{v}]$, where $\mathbf{u} = (1, 1)$ and $\mathbf{v} = (0, 1)$.

6. $f[(x, y)] = (y, x)$ 7. $f[(x, y)] = (x, -y)$
8. $f[(x, y)] = (-x, y)$ 9. $f[(x, y)] = (-x, -y)$
10. $f[(x, y)] = (2x + y, x - y)$
11. $f[(x, y)] = (5x - 3y, -3x + 5y)$
12. $f[(x, y, z)] = (3x - 2y, 5x - 2z)$
13. $f[(x, y, z)] = (x, z)$
14. $f[(x, y, z)] = (x + y + z, 2x + 2y + 2z)$

In each of Problems 15 through 21 describe the linear mapping having the given matrix with respect to the standard ordered bases.

15. $\begin{pmatrix} 1 & -3 \\ 0 & 1 \end{pmatrix}$, R^2 into R^2

16. $\begin{pmatrix} 3 & 1 & -2 \\ -1 & 0 & 5 \end{pmatrix}$, R^3 into R^2

17. $\begin{pmatrix} 3 & -1 \\ 1 & 0 \\ -2 & 5 \end{pmatrix}$, R^2 into R^3

18. $\begin{pmatrix} 1 & 0 & 0 \\ 0 & 1 & 0 \\ 0 & 0 & 1 \end{pmatrix}$, R^3 into R^3

19. $\begin{pmatrix} 0 & 0 & 0 \\ 0 & 0 & 0 \\ 0 & 0 & 0 \end{pmatrix}$, R^3 into R^3

20. $\begin{pmatrix} 1 & -2 & 3 \\ 0 & 1 & -1 \\ 2 & 0 & 1 \end{pmatrix}$, R^3 into R^3

21. $\begin{pmatrix} 0 & 2 & -3 & 1 \\ 1 & 0 & 0 & 2 \\ 0 & 0 & 0 & 1 \end{pmatrix}$, R^4 into R^3

6-3. SUMS AND PRODUCTS

Since a linear mapping is a function, we already have a definition of addition of two linear mappings. Thus, addition of linear mappings is addition of functions. If V and W are vector spaces over a field F and f and g are linear mappings from V into W, then

(6-3.1) $(f + g)(\mathbf{v}) = f(\mathbf{v}) + g(\mathbf{v})$ for all $\mathbf{v} \in V$

From Theorem 6–1.2, $f + g$ is a linear mapping from V into W. You can easily show (see Problem 12) that the matrix of the sum $f + g$ relative to a pair of ordered bases of V and W is the sum of the matrices of f and g relative to the same bases. Since addition of linear mappings from V into W is defined in terms of the addition of W, we expect many of the algebraic properties of W to hold for $T(V, W)$. (Recall that $T(V, W)$ is the set of all linear mappings from V into W.) In fact, all properties of a vector space over F hold for $T(V, W)$. We first state the properties, with proofs of some properties, then state the theorem. To apply Definition 5–1.2, we use the set $T(V, W)$ with the usual equivalence relation for functions, the addition defined above, and scalar multiplication defined by

(6-3.2) $(cf)(\mathbf{v}) = cf(\mathbf{v})$ for all $\mathbf{v} \in V$

Now, if $f, g, h \in T(V, W)$, then

i. $f + g$ is a unique element of $T(V, W)$,

ii. $f + g = g + f$, and

iii. $(f + g) + h = f + (g + h)$.

Proof of ii: Now, $(f + g)(\mathbf{v}) = f(\mathbf{v}) + g(\mathbf{v}) = g(\mathbf{v}) + f(\mathbf{v}) = (g + f)(\mathbf{v})$. (Supply all reasons.) The zero mapping, 0, has the properties

iv. $f + 0 = 0 + f = f$, for all $f \in T(V, W)$.

Next, if $f \in T(V, W)$, then $-f$ is defined by

(6-3.3) $$(-f)(\mathbf{v}) = -f(\mathbf{v}) \qquad \text{for all } \mathbf{v} \in V$$

Now, $-f \in T(V, W)$ since, if $\mathbf{v}_1, \mathbf{v}_2 \in V$ and $c \in F$, we have

$$(-f)(\mathbf{v}_1 + \mathbf{v}_2) = -[f(\mathbf{v}_1 + \mathbf{v}_2)] = -[f(\mathbf{v}_1) + f(\mathbf{v}_2)]$$
$$= -f(\mathbf{v}_1) + [-f(\mathbf{v}_2)] = (-f)(\mathbf{v}_1) + (-f)(\mathbf{v}_2)$$

and

$$(-f)(c\mathbf{v}) = -[f(c\mathbf{v})] = -[cf(\mathbf{v})] = c[-f(\mathbf{v})] = c[(-f)(\mathbf{v})]$$

Furthermore, $-f$ has the properties

v. $f + (-f) = -f + f = 0$.

The following properties concerning scalar multiplication are easily proved for $c, d \in F$.

vi. cf is a unique element of $T(V, W)$,

vii. $(cd)f = c(df)$,

viii. $(c + d)f = cf + df$,

ix. $c(f + g) = cf + cg$, and

x. $1f = f$, where 1 is the identity of F.

Proof of viii: Now, $[(c + d)f](\mathbf{v}) = (c + d)[f(\mathbf{v})] = c[f(\mathbf{v})] + d[f(\mathbf{v})] = (cf)(\mathbf{v}) + (df)(\mathbf{v})$. (Provide the needed reasons here and in the following proof.)

Proof of ix: Here, $[c(f + g)](\mathbf{v}) = c[(f + g)(\mathbf{v})] = c[f(\mathbf{v}) + g(\mathbf{v})] = cf(\mathbf{v}) + cg(\mathbf{v}) = (cf)(\mathbf{v}) + (cg)(\mathbf{v})$.

THEOREM 6-3.1. *If V and W are vector spaces over a field F, then $T(V, W)$ is a vector space over F.*

For a product of linear mappings we use *composition* of functions. Thus, if V, W, and U are vector spaces over a field F, $g \in T(V, W)$, and $f \in T(W, U)$, then fg is defined by

(6-3.4) $$(fg)(\mathbf{v}) = f[g(\mathbf{v})] \qquad \text{for all } \mathbf{v} \in V$$

Notice that the domain of fg is V, the range of g is a subset of W, and the range of fg is a subset of U. If $W = U = V$, then fg is a mapping from V into V. In this important case, $T(V, V)$ is closed under composition.

135

Illustration 1

Let g and f be functions from Z (the set of all integers) into Q and from Q into R, respectively, where $g(x) = (x/5) - 1$, for all $x \in Z$, and $f(y) = \sqrt{2}y$, for all $y \in Q$. Then, the composite function fg is specified by

$$(fg)(x) = f[g(x)] = f[(x/5) - 1] = \sqrt{2}[(x/5) - 1]$$

for all $x \in Z$.

Illustration 2

Let g be the mapping from R^3 into R^2 of Illustration 4 of Section 6-1 and let f be the mapping from R^2 into R^1 of Illustration 3 in the same section. The composite mapping fg from R^3 into R^1 is then

$$(fg)[(x, y, z)] = f(g[(x, y, z)]) = f[(x, y)] = x$$

for all $(x, y, z) \in R^3$.

We next show that with certain restrictions fg is a linear mapping and the matrix of fg is the product of the matrices of f and g.

THEOREM 6–3.2. *If V, W, and U are vector spaces over a field F, $g \in T(V, W)$, and $f \in T(W, U)$, then $fg \in T(V, U)$.*

Proof: If $g \in T(V, W)$, $f \in T(W, U)$, and $\mathbf{v}_1, \mathbf{v}_2 \in V$, then

$$
\begin{aligned}
(fg)(\mathbf{v}_1 + \mathbf{v}_2) &= f[g(\mathbf{v}_1 + \mathbf{v}_2)] \\
&= f[g(\mathbf{v}_1) + g(\mathbf{v}_2)] \\
&= f[g(\mathbf{v}_1)] + f[g(\mathbf{v}_2)] \\
&= (fg)(\mathbf{v}_1) + (fg)(\mathbf{v}_2)
\end{aligned}
$$

Provide all reasons.

If $c \in F$ and $\mathbf{v} \in V$, then

$$
\begin{aligned}
(fg)(c\mathbf{v}) &= f[g(c\mathbf{v})] \\
&= f[cg(\mathbf{v})] \\
&= cf[g(\mathbf{v})] \\
&= c(fg)(\mathbf{v})
\end{aligned}
$$

If V, W, and U are finite-dimensional vector spaces over R, $g \in T(V, W)$, and $f \in T(W, U)$, then the matrix of fg with respect to a triple of bases of V, W, and U is the product of the matrices of f and g with respect to these bases. To see this, let $[\mathbf{v}_1, \mathbf{v}_2, \ldots, \mathbf{v}_n]$, $[\mathbf{w}_1, \mathbf{w}_2, \ldots, \mathbf{w}_m]$, and $[\mathbf{u}_1, \mathbf{u}_2, \ldots, \mathbf{u}_p]$ be ordered bases of V, W, and U, respectively. Let $B(m \times n)$, and $A(p \times m)$, be the matrices of g and f relative to the given bases. Then,

$$g(\mathbf{v}_i) = \sum_{j=1}^{j=m} b_{ji}\mathbf{w}_j \qquad (i = 1, 2, \ldots, n)$$

and

$$f(\mathbf{w}_j) = \sum_{k=1}^{k=p} a_{kj}\mathbf{u}_k \qquad (j = 1, 2, \ldots, m)$$

Therefore, the matrix of fg is $p \times n$ and is determined from

$$(fg)(\mathbf{v}_i) = f[g(\mathbf{v}_i)] \qquad (i = 1, 2, \ldots, n)$$

$$= f\left[\sum_{j=1}^{j=m} b_{ji}\mathbf{w}_j\right]$$

$$= \sum_{j=1}^{j=m} b_{ji}f(\mathbf{w}_j)$$

$$= \sum_{j=1}^{j=m}\left[b_{ji}\sum_{k=1}^{k=p} a_{kj}\mathbf{u}_k\right]$$

$$= \sum_{k=1}^{k=p}\left[\sum_{j=1}^{j=m} a_{kj}b_{ji}\right]\mathbf{u}_k$$

Therefore, $\sum_{j=1}^{j=m} a_{kj}b_{ji}$ is the kth entry of the matrix of fg as well as the kth entry of the product AB. (You may need to verify this.) Hence, the matrix of fg is the product of the matrices of f and g.

Problem Set 6–3

1. If A, B, and C are sets, g is a one-to-one mapping from A into B, and f is a one-to-one mapping from B into C, argue that fg is a one-to-one mapping from A into C.

2. If A, B, and C are sets, g is a mapping from A onto B, and f is a mapping from B onto C, prove that fg is a mapping from A onto C.

In Problems 3 through 7, let V and W be vector spaces over a field F. If $f, g, h \in T(V, W)$, and $1, c, d \in F$, prove the assertions.

3. $(f + g) + h = f + (g + h)$ 4. $f + 0 = f$

5. $f + (-f) = 0$ 6. $(cd)f = c(df)$

7. $1f = f$

In Problems 8 through 11, let V, W, U, and Y be vector spaces over a field F.

8. If $h \in T(V, W)$, $g \in T(W, U)$, and $f \in T(U, Y)$, prove that $(fg)h = f(gh)$.

9. If $g, h \in T(V, W)$ and $f \in T(W, U)$, argue that $f(g + h) = fg + fh$.

10. If $h \in T(V, W)$ and $f, g \in T(W, U)$, show that $(f + g)h = fh + gh$.

11. If $c \in F$, $g \in T(V, W)$, and $f \in T(W, U)$, prove that $c(fg) = (cf)g = f(cg)$.

12. Let V and W be finite-dimensional vector spaces over R and let $f, g \in T(V, W)$. If A and B are the matrices of f and g with respect to a pair of ordered bases of V and W, argue that the matrix of $f + g$ is $A + B$.

13. Let f be the mapping of Illustration 1 of Section 6–2. Define a linear mapping g from R^2 into R^2 by

$$g[\,(1, 0, 0)\,] = (1, 1)$$
$$g[\,(0, 1, 0)\,] = (1, 0)$$

and
$$g[\,(0, 0, 1)\,] = (0, 2)$$

Obtain the matrix B of g with respect to the standard ordered bases of R^3 and R^2. Determine the matrix of $f + g$ and verify that it is $A + B$.

14. Let g be the mapping of Illustration 4 in Section 6–2 and let f be the mapping of Illustration 3 in the same section. Obtain the matrix of fg with respect to the standard ordered bases of R^3 and R^2 and verify that it is equal to the product, $\begin{pmatrix} 2 & 1 \\ 1 & -4 \end{pmatrix} \begin{pmatrix} 1 & 3 & -2 \\ 0 & -1 & 5 \end{pmatrix}$, of the matrices of f and g.

6–4. SOME THEORY

If $f \in T(V, W)$ we know that the range of f, denoted by $f(V)$, is a subspace of W and the kernel of f, denoted by $ker\, f$, is a subspace of V (see Theorem 6–1.3). If V is finite-dimensional, the following theorem provides information concerning the dimensions of the spaces V, $f(V)$, and $ker\, f$.

THEOREM 6–4.1.   *If V and W are vector spaces over a field F, V is finite-dimensional, and $f \in T(V, W)$, then*
$$dim\ V = dim\ (ker\ f) + dim\ f\ (V)$$

Proof: Let $dim\ V = n$ and $dim\ (ker\ f) = m$. Clearly, $m \leq n$. Let $\{\,\mathbf{v}_1, \mathbf{v}_2, \ldots, \mathbf{v}_m\,\}$ be a basis for $ker\, f$ and extend this basis to a basis $\{\,\mathbf{v}_1, \mathbf{v}_2, \ldots, \mathbf{v}_m, \mathbf{v}_{m+1}, \ldots, \mathbf{v}_n\,\}$ of V. We will show that $\{\,f(\mathbf{v}_{m+1}), f(\mathbf{v}_{m+2}), \ldots, f(\mathbf{v}_n)\,\}$ is a basis of $f(V)$. Now a vector in $f(V)$ is of the form $f(\mathbf{v})$ where $\mathbf{v} \in V$. Since any vector $\mathbf{v} \in V$ can be expressed as
$$\mathbf{v} = c_1\mathbf{v}_1 + c_2\mathbf{v}_2 + \cdots + c_m\mathbf{v}_m + c_{m+1}\mathbf{v}_{m+1} + \cdots + c_n\mathbf{v}_n$$

for $c_i \in F$ we have

$$
\begin{aligned}
f(\mathbf{v}) &= f(c_1\mathbf{v}_1 + c_2\mathbf{v}_2 + \cdots + c_m\mathbf{v}_m + c_{m+1}\mathbf{v}_{m+1} + \cdots + c_n\mathbf{v}_n) \\
&= f(c_1\mathbf{v}_1) + f(c_2\mathbf{v}_2) + \cdots + f(c_m\mathbf{v}_m) + f(c_{m+1}\mathbf{v}_{m+1}) \\
&\qquad\qquad\qquad\qquad\qquad\qquad\qquad\qquad + \cdots + f(c_n\mathbf{v}_n) \\
&= c_1 f(\mathbf{v}_1) + c_2 f(\mathbf{v}_2) + \cdots + c_m f(\mathbf{v}_m) + c_{m+1}f(\mathbf{v}_{m+1}) \\
&\qquad\qquad\qquad\qquad\qquad\qquad\qquad\qquad + \cdots + c_n f(\mathbf{v}_n) \\
&= c_1(\mathbf{0}) + c_2(\mathbf{0}) + \cdots + c_m(\mathbf{0}) + c_{m+1}f(\mathbf{v}_{m+1}) + \cdots + c_n f(\mathbf{v}_n) \\
&= c_{m+1}f(\mathbf{v}_{m+1}) + \cdots + c_n f(\mathbf{v}_n)
\end{aligned}
$$

Therefore, $\{\,f(\mathbf{v}_{m+1}), f(\mathbf{v}_{m+2}), \ldots, f(\mathbf{v}_n)\,\}$ spans $f(V)$. This set is also linearly independent, for suppose $k_1 f(\mathbf{v}_{m+1}) + k_2 f(\mathbf{v}_{m+2}) + \cdots + k_{n-m}f(\mathbf{v}_n) = \mathbf{0}$. Then,
$$f(k_1\mathbf{v}_{m+1} + k_2\mathbf{v}_{m+2} + \cdots + k_{n-m}\mathbf{v}_n) = \mathbf{0}$$

which shows that $(k_1\mathbf{v}_{m+1} + k_2\mathbf{v}_{m+2} + \cdots + k_{n-m}\mathbf{v}_n) \in ker f$. Thus, this vector can be expressed as a linear combination of the basis vectors of $ker f$

$$k_1\mathbf{v}_{m+1} + k_2\mathbf{v}_{m+2} + \cdots + k_{n-m}\mathbf{v}_n = K_1\mathbf{v}_1 + K_2\mathbf{v}_2 + \cdots + K_m\mathbf{v}_m$$

Then, $K_1\mathbf{v}_1 + K_2\mathbf{v}_2 + \cdots + K_m\mathbf{v}_m - k_1\mathbf{v}_{m+1} - k_2\mathbf{v}_{m+2} - \cdots - k_{n-m}\mathbf{v}_n = \mathbf{0}$, from which $K_1 = K_2 = \cdots = K_m = k_1 = k_2 = \cdots = k_{n-m} = 0$. (Why?) Hence, $\{ f(\mathbf{v}_{m+1}), f(\mathbf{v}_{m+2}), \ldots, f(\mathbf{v}_n) \}$ is a linearly independent set. Since this set of $n - m$ elements also spans $f(V)$, it is a basis for $f(V)$. Therefore, $dim \, f(V) = n - m$. Since $dim \, V = n$ and $dim \, (ker f) = m$, we have $n = m + (n - m)$ or $dim \, V = dim \, (ker f) + dim \, f(V)$.

There are other terms commonly used to denote $dim \, (ker f)$ and $dim \, f(V)$. These terms are particularly useful in connecting linear mappings and matrices. First, a definition is made, then Theorem 6–4.1 is restated using the alternate notations.

DEFINITION 6–4.1.   *If V and W are vector spaces over a field F, V is finite-dimensional, and $f \in T(V, W)$, then*

a.   *the nullity of f is $dim \, (ker f)$, and*

b.   *the rank of f is $dim \, f(V)$.*

THEOREM 6–4.1'.   *If V and W are vector spaces over a field F, V is finite-dimensional, and $f \in T(V, W)$, then*

$$dim \, V = nullity \; of \; f + rank \; of \; f$$

In Problems 24 and 25 of Problem Set 5–4 the row space of a matrix was defined and obtained for certain matrices. Here, we need the row rank and column rank of a matrix.

DEFINITION 6–4.2.   *If A is an $m \times n$ matrix over R, then*

a.   *the row rank of A is the maximum number of linearly independent rows of A, and*

b.   *the column rank of A is the maximum number of linearly independent columns of A.*

Illustration 1

For the matrices in Problem 25 of Problem Set 5–4, the row ranks are 1, 2, 2, 0, 2, and 0, respectively. Notice that for each matrix the column rank is the same as the row rank. That this result always holds is indicated by the following theorem.

THEOREM 6–4.2.   *If A is an $m \times n$ real matrix, then the row rank and column rank of A are equal.*

Since the row rank and column rank of a matrix A are equal, we will define this common value to be the *rank* of A. Thus, the term rank is associated with matrices and with certain linear mappings. Our next theorem connects these two concepts.

DEFINITION 6–4.3.   *If A is an $m \times n$ real matrix, then the rank of A is the row (column) rank of A.*

THEOREM 6–4.3.   *If V and W are finite-dimensional vector spaces over R, $f \in T(V, W)$, and A is the matrix of f relative to a pair of ordered bases, then the rank of f and the rank of A are equal.*

Proof: Let $[\mathbf{v}_1, \mathbf{v}_2, \dots, \mathbf{v}_n]$ and $[\mathbf{w}_1, \mathbf{w}_2, \dots, \mathbf{w}_m]$ be ordered bases of V and W, respectively. Then, $\mathbf{v} \in V$ and $f(\mathbf{v}) = \mathbf{w} \in W$ can be expressed as

$$\mathbf{v} = a_1\mathbf{v}_1 + a_2\mathbf{v}_2 + \cdots + a_n\mathbf{v}_n$$

and

$$\mathbf{w} = b_1\mathbf{w}_1 + b_2\mathbf{w}_2 + \cdots + b_m\mathbf{w}_m$$

Since A is the matrix of f relative to the given bases, we know that $\mathbf{w} = A\mathbf{v}$. If $\mathbf{t}_1, \mathbf{t}_2, \dots, \mathbf{t}_n$ denote the column vectors of A, then $A\mathbf{v} = a_1\mathbf{t}_1 + a_2\mathbf{t}_2 + \cdots + a_n\mathbf{t}_n$. Hence, $f(V)$ is spanned by the n column vectors. Therefore, the maximum number of linearly independent vectors in $\{\mathbf{t}_1, \mathbf{t}_2, \dots, \mathbf{t}_n\}$ is the column rank of A and also the dimension of $f(V)$. From Definition 6–4.1 and Definition 6–4.3, the rank of f and the rank of A are equal.

This section is concluded with two important theorems concerning systems of linear equations. One part of one theorem will be proved to indicate the method of proof.

THEOREM 6–4.4.   *Let $AX = O$ be a system of m homogeneous linear equations in n unknowns. If A has rank r and S is the solution space of the system, then*

a.   *$dim\ S = n - r$*
b.   *if $m < n$, then S contains a nonzero element,*
c.   *if $m = n$, then $S = \{(0, 0, \dots, 0)\}$ if and only if A is nonsingular, and*
d.   *$S = \{(0, 0, \dots, 0)\}$ if and only if the rank of A is n.*

Proof of Part (a):   Let f be that linear mapping in $T(R^n, R^m)$ having matrix A with respect to the standard ordered bases. Now, $(x_1, x_2, \dots, x_n) \in S$ if and only if $(x_1, x_2, \dots, x_n) \in ker\ f$. Therefore,

$$
\begin{aligned}
dim\ S &= dim\ (ker\ f) \\
&= dim\ R^n - dim\ f(R^n) \qquad & \text{Theorem 6–4.1} \\
&= n - \text{rank of } f \qquad & \text{Definition 6–4.1} \\
&= n - \text{rank of } A \qquad & \text{Why?} \\
&= n - r
\end{aligned}
$$

THEOREM 6–4.5. *Let $AX = B$ be a nonhomogeneous system of m linear equations in n unknowns. If A has rank r and S is the solution set of the system, then*

a. $S \neq \emptyset$ *if and only if B^t is in the column space of A,*
b. *all elements of S can be obtained by adding any one element of S to each solution of $AX = O$, and*
c. $S \neq \emptyset$ *if and only if the rank of A is equal to the rank of aug A*

These last two theorems provide an important way of solving the system $AX = B$. First, we obtain *dim S* where S is the solution space of $AX = O$. Next, we obtain a basis of S and a particular solution of $AX = B$. Finally, from this basis and particular solution all solutions of $AX = B$ can be exhibited. The following illustrations emphasize this method of solving linear systems of equations.

Illustration 2

Solve the system $\begin{cases} x + 5y = 8 \\ -2x - 10y = -16 \end{cases}$. In matrix notation, the system is $AX = B$ where

$$A = \begin{pmatrix} 1 & 5 \\ -2 & -10 \end{pmatrix}, \qquad X = \begin{pmatrix} x \\ y \end{pmatrix}, \qquad \text{and} \qquad B = \begin{pmatrix} 8 \\ -16 \end{pmatrix}$$

Since A can be reduced to $\begin{pmatrix} 1 & 5 \\ 0 & 0 \end{pmatrix}$, the rank of A is 1. If S is the solution space of $AX = O$, then $dim\ S = 2 - 1 = 1$, by *part (a)* of Theorem 6-4.4. This means that S is a line. From $\begin{pmatrix} 1 & 5 \\ 0 & 0 \end{pmatrix} \begin{pmatrix} x \\ y \end{pmatrix} = \begin{pmatrix} 0 \\ 0 \end{pmatrix}$, we have $x = -5y$. Thus, $x = 5$ when $y = -1$, and $\{ (5, -1) \}$ is a basis for S. (Any basis for S can be used here.) Now, $(-2, 2)$ clearly satisfies $AX = B$. Therefore, by *part (b)* of Theorem 6-4.5, the solution set of $AX = B$ is

$$\{ a(5, -1) + (-2, 2) \mid a \in R \} = \{ (5a - 2, -a + 2) \mid a \in R \}$$

Using another method, the solution set $\{ (8 - 5y, y) \mid y \in R \}$ is obtained. You can easily show that these last two sets are equal.

Illustration 3

Solve the system $\begin{cases} x + 2y - z = 3 \\ -3x + y + 5z = -22 \end{cases}$, see Illustration 3 of Section 3-2. In matrix notation, the system is $AX = B$ where

$$A = \begin{pmatrix} 1 & 2 & -1 \\ -3 & 1 & 5 \end{pmatrix}, \qquad B = \begin{pmatrix} 3 \\ -22 \end{pmatrix}, \qquad \text{and} \qquad X = \begin{pmatrix} x \\ y \\ z \end{pmatrix}$$

Since A can be reduced to $\begin{pmatrix} 1 & 0 & -\frac{11}{7} \\ 0 & 1 & \frac{2}{7} \end{pmatrix}$, the rank of A is 2. If S denotes the solution space of $AX = O$, then $dim\ S = 3 - 2 = 1$ by *part (a)*

141

of Theorem 6-4.4. As in Illustration 2, S is a line. From

$$\begin{pmatrix} 1 & 0 & -\frac{11}{7} \\ 0 & 1 & \frac{2}{7} \end{pmatrix} \begin{pmatrix} x \\ y \\ z \end{pmatrix} = \begin{pmatrix} 0 \\ 0 \\ 0 \end{pmatrix}$$

we obtain $x = (\frac{11}{7})z$ and $y = (-\frac{2}{7})z$. Letting $z = 7$, we have $x = 11$ and $y = -2$. Hence, $\{ (11, -2, 7) \}$ is one basis for S. (As before, any basis can be used.) Setting $z = 0$ in $AX = B$ gives $x = \frac{47}{7}$ and $y = \frac{13}{7}$. Thus, $(\frac{47}{7}, -\frac{13}{7}, 0)$ is a particular solution of $AX = B$. By *part* (b) of Theorem 6-4.5, the solution set of $AX = B$ is

$$\{ a(11, -2, 7) + (\tfrac{47}{7}, -\tfrac{13}{7}, 0) \mid a \in R \}$$
$$= \{ (11a + \tfrac{47}{7}, \ -2a - \tfrac{13}{7}, \ 7a) \mid a \in R \}$$
$$= \left\{ \left(\frac{77a + 47}{7}, \ -\frac{14a + 13}{7}, \ 7a \right) \ \middle| \ a \in R \right\}$$

which agrees with the answer given in Section 3-2.

Problem Set 6-4

In Problems 1 through 10 verify Theorem 6-4.2 for each matrix and so obtain the rank of each matrix.

1. $\begin{pmatrix} 2 & 0 \\ 0 & 1 \end{pmatrix}$ 2. $\begin{pmatrix} -3 & 0 \\ 0 & 2 \end{pmatrix}$ 3. $\begin{pmatrix} -1 & 2 \\ 3 & 1 \end{pmatrix}$ 4. $\begin{pmatrix} 2 & -3 \\ 4 & -6 \end{pmatrix}$

5. $\begin{pmatrix} 1 & -2 & 0 \\ 3 & 1 & 0 \end{pmatrix}$ 6. $\begin{pmatrix} 1 & 0 & 1 \\ 0 & 1 & 0 \\ 0 & 0 & 1 \end{pmatrix}$ 7. $\begin{pmatrix} 1 & 0 & 0 \\ 0 & -3 & 0 \\ 0 & 0 & 1 \end{pmatrix}$

8. $\begin{pmatrix} 2 & 0 & 0 \\ 0 & -5 & 0 \\ 0 & 0 & 3 \end{pmatrix}$ 9. $\begin{pmatrix} 1 & 1 & 1 \\ 0 & 1 & 0 \\ 1 & 0 & 1 \end{pmatrix}$ 10. $\begin{pmatrix} 2 & 3 & -5 \\ 1 & -2 & 0 \\ -3 & 1 & 4 \end{pmatrix}$

In Problems 11 through 20 determine $dim \ f(V)$ and $dim \ (ker f)$, that is, the rank of f and the nullity of f, for the given linear mappings. Use the standard bases of the vector spaces.

11. $f[(x, y)] = (2x, y)$, R^2 into R^2

12. $f[(x, y)] = (-3x, 2y)$, R^2 into R^2

13. $f[(x, y)] = (-x + 2y, 3x + y)$, R^2 into R^2

14. $f[(x, y)] = (2x - 3y, 4x - 6y)$, R^2 into R^2

15. $f[(x, y, z)] = (x - 2y, 3x + y)$, R^3 into R^2

16. $f[(x, y, z)] = (x + z, y, z)$, R^3 into R^3

17. $f[(x, y, z)] = (x, -3y, z)$, R^3 into R^3

18. $f[(x, y, z)] = (2x, -5y, 3z)$, R^3 into R^3

19. $f[(x, y, z)] = (x + y + z, y, x + z)$, R^3 into R^3

20. $f[(x, y, z)] = (2x + 3y - 5z, x - 2y, -3x + y + 4z)$, R^3 into R^3

In Problems 21 through 24 obtain the dimension of the solution space for each system, then solve each system.

21. $\begin{cases} -x + 2y = 0 \\ 3x + y = 0 \end{cases}$

22. $\begin{cases} 2x - 3y = 0 \\ 4x - 6y = 0 \end{cases}$

23. $\begin{cases} x + y + z = 0 \\ y = 0 \\ x + z = 0 \end{cases}$

24. $\begin{cases} 2x + 3y - 5z = 0 \\ x - 2y = 0 \\ -3x + y + 4z = 0 \end{cases}$

In Problems 25 through 28 first verify that $S \neq \emptyset$, then solve each system by applying *part* (b) of Theorem 6–4.5. (A particular solution can be obtained by inspection.)

25. $\begin{cases} -x + 2y = 3 \\ 3x + y = 5 \end{cases}$

26. $\begin{cases} 2x - 3y = 5 \\ 4x - 6y = 10 \end{cases}$

27. $\begin{cases} x + y + z = 6 \\ y = 2 \\ x + z = 4 \end{cases}$

28. $\begin{cases} 2x + 3y - 5z = 0 \\ x - 2y = -1 \\ -3x + y + 4z = 2 \end{cases}$

29. Prove *part* (c) of Theorem 6–4.4.

30. Prove *part* (d) of Theorem 6–4.4.

6-5. INVERSE OF A LINEAR MAPPING

Recall that if f is a one-to-one mapping from a set A onto a set B, there is a natural one-to-one mapping h from B onto A (see Problem 18 of Problem Set 6–1A). Thus, if $y \in B$ we pair y with that $x \in A$ such that $f(x) = y$. In notation, the mapping h is defined by $h(y) = x$ if and only if $f(x) = y$. What is hf and what is fh? Now, if

$$x \in A, \text{ then } (hf)(x) = h[f(x)] = h(y) = x$$

and if

$$y \in B, \text{ then } (fh)(y) = f[h(y)] = f(x) = y$$

Thus, hf is the identity mapping on A and fh is the identity mapping on B. The mapping h is called the *inverse* of f and is denoted by $h = f^{-1}$. If $A = B$, notice that $ff^{-1} = f^{-1}f = I$, the identity mapping on A.

Illustration 1

If $A = \{1, 2, 3, 4, 5\}$, $B = \{6, 7, 8, 9, 10\}$, and f is defined by $f(x) = x + 5$ for all $x \in A$, then f^{-1} is the mapping specified by $f^{-1}(y) = y - 5$, for all $y \in B$. Thus,

f	f^{-1}
$1 \to 6$	$6 \to 1$
$2 \to 7$	$7 \to 2$
$3 \to 8$	$8 \to 3$
$4 \to 9$	$9 \to 4$
$5 \to 10$	$10 \to 5$

143

Illustration 2

If $A = Z^+$, $B = \{2x \mid x \in Z^+\}$, and $f(x) = 2x$ for all $x \in A$, then f^{-1} is described by $f^{-1}(y) = y/2$ for all $y \in B$.

In the context of vector spaces, if f is a linear mapping is f^{-1} a linear mapping? The following theorem answers the question for f a one-to-one onto linear mapping.

THEOREM 6–5.1. *If f is a one-to-one linear mapping from a vector space V over a field F onto a vector space W over F, then f^{-1} is a one-to-one linear mapping from W onto V.*

Proof: From Problem 1 of this section, f^{-1} is a one-to-one mapping from W onto V. Thus, all we need to prove is that f^{-1} is a linear mapping. If $\mathbf{w}_1, \mathbf{w}_2 \in W$, there exist $\mathbf{v}_1, \mathbf{v}_2 \in V$ such that

$$f(\mathbf{v}_1) = \mathbf{w}_1$$

and

$$f(\mathbf{v}_2) = \mathbf{w}_2$$

Thus,

$$f^{-1}(\mathbf{w}_1) = \mathbf{v}_1$$

and

$$f(\mathbf{w}_2) = \mathbf{v}_2$$

Since f is a linear mapping,

$$f(\mathbf{v}_1 + \mathbf{v}_2) = f(\mathbf{v}_1) + f(\mathbf{v}_2) = \mathbf{w}_1 + \mathbf{w}_2$$

which leads to

$$f^{-1}(\mathbf{w}_1 + \mathbf{w}_2) = \mathbf{v}_1 + \mathbf{v}_2 = f^{-1}(\mathbf{w}_1) + f^{-1}(\mathbf{w}_2)$$

Next, if $\mathbf{w} \in W$, there exists a $\mathbf{v} \in V$ such that $f(\mathbf{v}) = \mathbf{w}$. Then, $f^{-1}(\mathbf{w}) = \mathbf{v}$. If $c \in F$, then

$$f(c\mathbf{v}) = cf(\mathbf{v}) = c\mathbf{w}$$

from which

$$f^{-1}(c\mathbf{w}) = c\mathbf{v} = cf^{-1}(\mathbf{w})$$

Therefore, f^{-1} is a linear mapping.

Under the conditions of Theorem 6–5.1, f^{-1} is a linear mapping and f^{-1} is the inverse of the mapping f. Thus, we call f^{-1} the *inverse* of the linear mapping f. If V and W each have dimension n, and the hypothesis of Theorem 6–5.1 is satisfied, then f is said to be *nonsingular.* Let $[\mathbf{v}_1, \mathbf{v}_2, \ldots, \mathbf{v}_n]$ and $[\mathbf{w}_1, \mathbf{w}_2, \ldots, \mathbf{w}_n]$ be ordered bases of V and W, respectively. If $F = R$, then with respect to these two bases the matrices of f and f^{-1} are each

$n \times n$. Thus, suppose

$$A = \begin{pmatrix} a_{11} & a_{12} & \cdots & a_{1n} \\ a_{21} & a_{22} & \cdots & a_{2n} \\ \vdots & \vdots & \ddots & \vdots \\ a_{n1} & a_{n2} & \cdots & a_{nn} \end{pmatrix} \quad \text{and} \quad B = \begin{pmatrix} b_{11} & b_{12} & \cdots & b_{1n} \\ b_{21} & b_{22} & \cdots & b_{1n} \\ \vdots & \vdots & \ddots & \vdots \\ b_{n1} & b_{n2} & \cdots & b_{nn} \end{pmatrix}$$

How are A and B related? Since the matrix of ff^{-1} is I and the matrix of a product of two linear mappings is the product of the matrices of the mappings, we have $AB = I$. Since the matrix of $f^{-1}f$ is also I, then $BA = I$. Therefore, $B = A^{-1}$. Thus, the matrix of f^{-1} is the inverse of the matrix of f.

Illustration 3

Describe f^{-1} for the linear mapping f of Illustration 3 in Section 6–2. Since $A = \begin{pmatrix} 2 & 1 \\ 1 & -4 \end{pmatrix}$ we have immediately $A^{-1} = \dfrac{1}{9}\begin{pmatrix} 4 & 1 \\ 1 & -2 \end{pmatrix}$. Then,

$$f^{-1}(\mathbf{i}) = (4\mathbf{i} + 1\mathbf{j})/9$$

and

$$f^{-1}(\mathbf{j}) = (1\mathbf{i} - 2\mathbf{j})/9$$

Now, $f^{-1}[(x, y)]$ can be obtained from

$$\frac{1}{9}\begin{pmatrix} 4 & 1 \\ 1 & -2 \end{pmatrix}\begin{pmatrix} x \\ y \end{pmatrix} = \frac{1}{9}\begin{pmatrix} 4x + y \\ x - 2y \end{pmatrix}$$

as $f^{-1}[(x, y)] = ([4x + y]/9, [x - 2y]/9)$. For example, if $f[(3, -5)] = (1, 23)$, then $f^{-1}[(1, 23)] = ([4 \cdot 1 + 23]/9, [1 - 2(23)]/9) = (\frac{27}{9}, -\frac{45}{9}) = (3, -5)$, as required.

Illustration 4

Consider R^3 with ordered bases $[\mathbf{i}, \mathbf{j}, \mathbf{k}]$ and $[\mathbf{u}, \mathbf{v}, \mathbf{w}]$, where $\mathbf{u} = (1, 1, 1)$, $\mathbf{v} = (0, 1, 1)$, and $\mathbf{w} = (0, 1, 0)$. Now f defined by

$$f(\mathbf{i}) = \mathbf{u} + \mathbf{v}$$
$$f(\mathbf{j}) = \mathbf{u} + \mathbf{w}$$

and

$$f(\mathbf{k}) = \mathbf{v} + \mathbf{w}$$

is a one-to-one linear mapping from R^3 onto R^3. (You can easily show this.) The matrix of f with respect to the given bases is

$$A = \begin{pmatrix} 1 & 1 & 0 \\ 1 & 0 & 1 \\ 0 & 1 & 1 \end{pmatrix}$$

The matrix of f^{-1} is then

$$A^{-1} = \frac{1}{2}\begin{pmatrix} 1 & 1 & -1 \\ 1 & -1 & 1 \\ -1 & 1 & 1 \end{pmatrix}$$

145

The coordinates of $f[\,(x, y, z)\,]$ and $f^{-1}[\,(x, y, z)\,]$ are obtained from

$$\begin{pmatrix} 1 & 1 & 0 \\ 1 & 0 & 1 \\ 0 & 1 & 1 \end{pmatrix} \begin{pmatrix} x \\ y \\ z \end{pmatrix} = \begin{pmatrix} x + y \\ x + z \\ y + z \end{pmatrix}$$

and

$$\frac{1}{2}\begin{pmatrix} 1 & 1 & -1 \\ 1 & -1 & 1 \\ -1 & 1 & 1 \end{pmatrix} \begin{pmatrix} x \\ y \\ z \end{pmatrix} = \frac{1}{2}\begin{pmatrix} x + y - z \\ x - y + z \\ -x + y + z \end{pmatrix}$$

Thus,

$$f[\,(x, y, z)\,] = (x + y, \; x + z, \; y + z)$$

and

$$f^{-1}[\,(x, y, z)\,] = ([\,x + y - z\,]/2, \; [\,x - y + z\,]/2, \; [\,-x + y + z\,]/2)$$

For example,

$$f[\,(3, -2, 7)\,] = (3 - 2, \; 3 + 7, \; -2 + 7) = (1, 10, 5)$$

and

$$f^{-1}[\,(1, 10, 5)\,] = ([\,1 + 10 - 5\,]/2, \; [\,1 - 10 + 5\,]/2, \\ [\,-1 + 10 + 5\,]/2) = (3, -2, 7)$$

as expected.

Problem Set 6–5

1. If f is a one-to-one mapping from a set A onto a set B, argue that f^{-1} is a one-to-one mapping from B onto A.

2. If g is a one-to-one mapping from a set A onto a set B and f is a one-to-one mapping from B onto a set C, prove that $(fg)^{-1}$ is a one-to-one mapping from C onto A and $(fg)^{-1} = g^{-1}f^{-1}$.

3. If V, W, and U are vector spaces over R, g is a nonsingular mapping from V onto W, and f is a nonsingular mapping from W onto U, prove that fg is a nonsingular mapping from V onto U and $(fg)^{-1} = g^{-1}f^{-1}$.

In the following problems obtain the matrix of f^{-1} (if it exists) with respect to the standard ordered bases of the vector spaces. Determine an explicit formula for f^{-1}.

4. $f(x) = -x$, R^1 into R^1

5. $f(x) = 5x$, R^1 into R^1

6. $f(x) = -2x$, R^1 into R^1

7. $f(x) = mx$ for $m \neq 0$, R^1 into R^1

8. $f[\,(x, y)\,] = (x + y, y)$, R^2 into R^2

9. $f[\,(x, y)\,] = (y, x)$, R^2 into R^2

10. $f[\,(x, y)\,] = (x, -y)$, R^2 into R^3

11. $f[\,(x, y)\,] = (-x, y)$, R^2 into R^2

12. $f[\,(x, y)\,] = (-x, -y)$, R^2 into R^2

13. $f[\,(x, y)\,] = c(x, y)$ for $c \neq 0$, R^2 into R^2

14. $f[\,(x, y)\,] = (2x + 3y, y)$, R^2 into R^2

15. $f[\,(x, y)\,] = (3x - 2y, 5x + y)$, R^2 into R^2

16. $f[\,(x, y)\,] = (x \cos \theta + y \sin \theta,\ -x \sin \theta + y \cos \theta)$ for θ constant, R^2 into R^2

17. $f[\,(x, y, z)\,] = (x, y, 0),\ R^3$ into R^3

18. $f[\,(x, y, z)\,] = (x, z),\ R^3$ into R^2

19. $f[\,(x, y, z)\,] = (x, y, z),\ R^3$ into R^3

20. $f[\,(x, y, z)\,] = (0, 0, 0),\ R^3$ into R^3

21. $f[\,(x, y, z)\,] = (3x + 2y + z,\ 2y + 2z,\ -z),\ R^3$ into R^3

22. $f[\,(x, y, z)\,] = (x, \frac{1}{2}y, \frac{1}{3}z),\ R^3$ into R^3

23. $f[\,(x, y, z)\,] = (3x + y,\ x - y + 2z,\ x + y + z),\ R^3$ into R^3

24. $f[\,(x, y, z)\,] = (x + 2y - z,\ 3y + z,\ -4z),\ R^3$ into R^3

6–6. CHANGE OF BASIS

Let V and W be vector spaces of dimension n and m, respectively, over R. Let f be a particular linear mapping from V into W. If A is the matrix of f with respect to the pair of ordered bases $[\,\mathbf{v}_1, \mathbf{v}_2, \ldots, \mathbf{v}_n\,]$ and $[\,\mathbf{w}_1, \mathbf{w}_2, \ldots, \mathbf{w}_m\,]$ and B is the matrix of f with respect to the pair of ordered bases $[\,\mathbf{v}'_1, \mathbf{v}'_2, \ldots, \mathbf{v}'_n\,]$ and $[\,\mathbf{w}'_1, \mathbf{w}'_2, \ldots, \mathbf{w}'_m\,]$, how are A and B related? This question is answered in the following theorem, which will not be proved.

THEOREM 6–6.1. *If $f \in T(V, W)$ has matrices A and B with respect to two pairs of ordered bases of V and W, then there exist non-singular matrices P and Q such that $B = Q^{-1}AP$. If $V = W$, then $Q = P$ and $B = P^{-1}AP$.*

This theorem leads to the concept of similarity for square matrices.

DEFINITION 6–6.1. *If A is an $n \times n$ matrix, then B is similar to A if and only if there exists a nonsingular matrix P such that $B = P^{-1}AP$.*

Now B has dimension $n \times n$. You can easily prove that for n fixed *is similar to* is an equivalence relation on the set of all $n \times n$ matrices. For example, if B is similar to A, then A is similar to B, since from $B = P^{-1}AP$ we have $PBP^{-1} = A$. Then, $(P^{-1})^{-1} = P$ gives $A = (P^{-1})^{-1}BP^{-1}$.

Since only mappings in $T(V, V)$ are considered and the matrices are each relative to one basis, we state the following theorem.

THEOREM 6–6.2. *Let V be a vector space over R and let $[\,\mathbf{v}_1, \mathbf{v}_2, \ldots, \mathbf{v}_n\,]$ be an ordered basis of V. If f is a linear mapping from V into V and A is the matrix of f with respect to $[\,\mathbf{v}_1, \mathbf{v}_2, \ldots, \mathbf{v}_n\,]$, then an $n \times n$ matrix B is the matrix of f with respect to some basis of V if and only if B is similar to A.*

147

Illustration 1

Let an $f \in T(R^2, R^2)$ be defined by $f[\,(x, y)\,] = (x + y,\ 2x - 3y)$, for all $x, y \in R$. Obtain the matrix A of f relative to the ordered basis $[\,\mathbf{i}, \mathbf{j}\,]$, the matrix B of f relative to the ordered basis $[\,\mathbf{u}, \mathbf{v}\,]$, and the nonsingular matrix P such that $B = P^{-1}AP$ if $\mathbf{i} = (1, 0)$, $\mathbf{j} = (0, 1)$, $\mathbf{u} = (1, -1)$, and $\mathbf{v} = (1, 2)$. Now,

$$f(\mathbf{i}) = (1, 2) = 1\mathbf{i} + 2\mathbf{j}$$

and

$$f(\mathbf{j}) = (1, -3) = 1\mathbf{i} - 3\mathbf{j}$$

give the matrix

$$A = \begin{pmatrix} 1 & 2 \\ 1 & -3 \end{pmatrix}^t = \begin{pmatrix} 1 & 1 \\ 2 & -3 \end{pmatrix}$$

of f relative to the basis $[\,\mathbf{i}, \mathbf{j}\,]$. Using systems of equations we can obtain

$$f(\mathbf{u}) = (0, 5) = (-\tfrac{5}{3})\mathbf{u} + (\tfrac{5}{3})\mathbf{v}$$

and

$$f(\mathbf{v}) = (3, -4) = (\tfrac{10}{3})\mathbf{u} - \tfrac{1}{3}\mathbf{v}$$

Then,

$$B = \begin{pmatrix} -\tfrac{5}{3} & \tfrac{5}{3} \\ \tfrac{10}{3} & -\tfrac{1}{3} \end{pmatrix}^t = \begin{pmatrix} -\tfrac{5}{3} & \tfrac{10}{3} \\ \tfrac{5}{3} & -\tfrac{1}{3} \end{pmatrix}$$

is the matrix of f relative to the basis $[\,\mathbf{u}, \mathbf{v}\,]$. Another useful way to obtain B is as follows. Notice that

$$\mathbf{u} = (1, -1) = \mathbf{i} - \mathbf{j}$$

and

$$\mathbf{v} = (1, 2) = \mathbf{i} + 2\mathbf{j}$$

Then,

$$\mathbf{i} = \tfrac{2}{3}\mathbf{u} + \tfrac{1}{3}\mathbf{v}$$

and

$$\mathbf{j} = -\tfrac{1}{3}\mathbf{u} + \tfrac{1}{3}\mathbf{v}$$

Hence,

$$f(\mathbf{u}) = f(\mathbf{i} - \mathbf{j}) = f(\mathbf{i}) - f(\mathbf{j}) = -\tfrac{5}{3}\mathbf{u} + \tfrac{5}{3}\mathbf{v}$$

and

$$f(\mathbf{v}) = f(\mathbf{i} + 2\mathbf{j}) = f(\mathbf{i}) + 2f(\mathbf{j}) = \tfrac{10}{3}\mathbf{u} - \tfrac{1}{3}\mathbf{v}$$

as above. Next, let $g \in T(R^2, R^2)$ be defined by

$$g(\mathbf{i}) = \mathbf{u} = \mathbf{i} - \mathbf{j}$$

and

$$g(\mathbf{j}) = \mathbf{v} = \mathbf{i} + 2\mathbf{j}$$

The matrix P of g relative to the basis $[\,\mathbf{i}, \mathbf{j}\,]$ is then

$$P = \begin{pmatrix} 1 & 1 \\ -1 & 2 \end{pmatrix}$$

Now,

$$P^{-1} = \begin{pmatrix} \tfrac{2}{3} & -\tfrac{1}{3} \\ \tfrac{1}{3} & \tfrac{1}{3} \end{pmatrix}$$

and

$$P^{-1}AP = \begin{pmatrix} \frac{2}{3} & -\frac{1}{3} \\ \frac{1}{3} & \frac{1}{3} \end{pmatrix} \begin{pmatrix} 1 & 1 \\ 2 & -3 \end{pmatrix} \begin{pmatrix} 1 & 1 \\ -1 & 2 \end{pmatrix}$$

$$= \begin{pmatrix} \frac{2}{3} & -\frac{1}{3} \\ \frac{1}{3} & \frac{1}{3} \end{pmatrix} \begin{pmatrix} 0 & 3 \\ 5 & -4 \end{pmatrix}$$

$$= \begin{pmatrix} -\frac{5}{3} & \frac{10}{3} \\ \frac{5}{3} & -\frac{1}{3} \end{pmatrix}$$

$$= B$$

Illustration 2

Let an $f \in T(R^3, R^3)$ be defined by

$$f[\,(x, y, z)\,] = (2x - y, \; x - y + z, \; 3y + z)$$

If $\mathbf{i} = (1, 0, 0)$, $\mathbf{j} = (0, 1, 0)$, $\mathbf{k} = (0, 0, 1)$, $\mathbf{u} = (1, 0, 0)$, $\mathbf{v} = (1, -1, 0)$, and $\mathbf{w} = (1, 0, 1)$, determine the matrix A of f relative to the ordered basis $[\,\mathbf{i}, \mathbf{j}, \mathbf{k}\,]$ and the matrix B of f relative to the ordered basis $[\,\mathbf{u}, \mathbf{v}, \mathbf{w}\,]$. Also, obtain the nonsingular matrix P such that $P^{-1}AP = B$. First,

$$f(\mathbf{i}) = (2, 1, 0) = 2\mathbf{i} + \mathbf{j} + 0\mathbf{k}$$
$$f(\mathbf{j}) = (-1, -1, 3) = -1\mathbf{i} - 1\mathbf{j} + 3\mathbf{k}$$

and

$$f(\mathbf{k}) = (0, 1, 1) = 0\mathbf{i} + 1\mathbf{j} + 1\mathbf{k}$$

The matrix A of f relative to the basis $[\,\mathbf{i}, \mathbf{j}, \mathbf{k}\,]$ is then

$$A = \begin{pmatrix} 2 & 1 & 0 \\ -1 & -1 & 3 \\ 0 & 1 & 1 \end{pmatrix}^t = \begin{pmatrix} 2 & -1 & 0 \\ 1 & -1 & 1 \\ 0 & 3 & 1 \end{pmatrix}$$

Next, systems of equations provide

$$f(\mathbf{u}) = (2, 1, 0) = 3\mathbf{u} - 1\mathbf{v} + 0\mathbf{w}$$
$$f(\mathbf{v}) = (3, 2, -3) = 8\mathbf{u} - 2\mathbf{v} - 3\mathbf{w}$$

and

$$f(\mathbf{w}) = (2, 2, 1) = 3\mathbf{u} - 2\mathbf{v} + 1\mathbf{w}$$

Therefore, the matrix B of f relative to the basis $[\,\mathbf{u}, \mathbf{v}, \mathbf{w}\,]$ is

$$B = \begin{pmatrix} 3 & -1 & 0 \\ 8 & -2 & -3 \\ 3 & -2 & 1 \end{pmatrix}^t = \begin{pmatrix} 3 & 8 & 3 \\ -1 & -2 & -2 \\ 0 & -3 & 1 \end{pmatrix}$$

We could have obtained B as follows. Since

$$\mathbf{u} = (1, 0, 0) = \mathbf{i}$$
$$\mathbf{v} = (1, -1, 0) = \mathbf{i} - \mathbf{j}$$

and

$$\mathbf{w} = (1, 0, 1) = \mathbf{i} + \mathbf{k}$$

we have

$$\mathbf{i} = \mathbf{u}$$
$$\mathbf{j} = \mathbf{u} - \mathbf{v}$$

and

$$\mathbf{k} = -\mathbf{u} + \mathbf{w}$$

Hence,

$$f(\mathbf{u}) = f(\mathbf{i}) = 2\mathbf{i} + \mathbf{j} = 3\mathbf{u} - \mathbf{v} + 0\mathbf{w}$$

$$f(\mathbf{v}) = f(\mathbf{i} - \mathbf{j}) = f(\mathbf{i}) - f(\mathbf{j}) = 3\mathbf{i} + 2\mathbf{j} - 3\mathbf{k} = 8\mathbf{u} - 2\mathbf{v} - 3\mathbf{w}$$

and

$$f(\mathbf{w}) = f(\mathbf{i} + \mathbf{k}) = f(\mathbf{i}) + f(\mathbf{k}) = 2\mathbf{i} + 2\mathbf{j} + \mathbf{k} = 3\mathbf{u} - 2\mathbf{v} + \mathbf{w}$$

as before. Finally, let $g \in T(R^3, R^3)$ be defined by

$$g(\mathbf{i}) = \mathbf{u} = \mathbf{i}$$

$$g(\mathbf{j}) = \mathbf{v} = \mathbf{i} - \mathbf{j}$$

and

$$g(\mathbf{k}) = \mathbf{w} = \mathbf{i} + \mathbf{k}$$

Now, the matrix P of g relative to the basis $[\,\mathbf{i}, \mathbf{j}, \mathbf{k}\,]$ is

$$P = \begin{pmatrix} 1 & 0 & 0 \\ 1 & -1 & 0 \\ 1 & 0 & 1 \end{pmatrix}^{t} = \begin{pmatrix} 1 & 1 & 1 \\ 0 & -1 & 0 \\ 0 & 0 & 1 \end{pmatrix}$$

You can easily verify that

$$P^{-1} = \begin{pmatrix} 1 & 1 & -1 \\ 0 & -1 & 0 \\ 0 & 0 & 1 \end{pmatrix}$$

and that $P^{-1}AP = B$.

Problem Set 6–6

In Problems 1 through 5 obtain the matrix A of f relative to the ordered basis $[\,\mathbf{i}, \mathbf{j}\,]$, where $\mathbf{i} = (1, 0)$ and $\mathbf{j} = (0, 1)$, and the matrix B of f relative to the ordered basis $[\,\mathbf{u}, \mathbf{v}\,]$, where $\mathbf{u} = (1, -1)$ and $\mathbf{v} = (1, 2)$. Also determine the nonsingular matrix P such that $P^{-1}AP = B$.

1. $f[\,(x, y)\,] = (2x + 3y,\ 2x - 3y)$, for all $x, y \in R$
2. $f[\,(x, y)\,] = (y, x)$, for all $x, y \in R$
3. $f[\,(x, y)\,] = (x, -y)$, for all $x, y \in R$
4. $f[\,(x, y)\,] = (-x, -y)$, for all $x, y \in R$
5. $f[\,(x, y)\,] = (x, y)$, for all $x, y \in R$

If Problems 6 through 10 let $\mathbf{i} = (1, 0, 0)$, $\mathbf{j} = (0, 1, 0)$, $\mathbf{k} = (0, 0, 1)$, $\mathbf{u} = (1, 0, 0)$, $\mathbf{v} = (1, -1, 0)$, and $\mathbf{w} = (1, 0, 1)$. Obtain the matrix A of f relative to the ordered basis $[\,\mathbf{i}, \mathbf{j}, \mathbf{k}\,]$ and the matrix B of f relative to the ordered basis $[\,\mathbf{u}, \mathbf{v}, \mathbf{w}\,]$. Also determine the nonsingular matrix P such that $P^{-1}AP = B$.

6. $f[\,(x, y, z)\,] = (y, x, z)$, for all $x, y, z \in R$
7. $f[\,(x, y, z)\,] = (x, z, y)$, for all $x, y, z \in R$
8. $f[\,(x, y, z)\,] = (x + y,\ y - z,\ z - x)$, for all $x, y, z \in R$
9. $f[\,(x, y, z)\,] = (3x, 5y, -2z)$, for all $x, y, z \in R$
10. $f[\,(x, y, z)\,] = (2x - 3y,\ 2y - 3z,\ 2z - 3x)$, for all $x, y, z \in R$
11. If A is $n \times n$, argue that A is similar to A.
12. If A is similar to B and B is similar to C, prove that A is similar to C.

7

Some Applications of Linear Algebra

Suppose you are asked to obtain the distance between two points in space. If the coordinates of the points with respect to some rectangular coordinate system are known, the distance formula for space will provide an answer. Here, the distance formula is used as a *model*. This model works well at times and at other times it does not work well at all. For example, if one point is in Boston and the other is in Tokyo, the distance formula will not give an accurate measure of the distance between the points. Here, a better approximation could be obtained by using measurement along a circle rather than along a straight line. In any case, since measurements are used to obtain the coordinates of the points, the model provides only an approximation to the distance between the points.

In this chapter, we will discuss some models that describe certain situations. We will not be concerned with how well the models describe the situations. All of our models will be *linear models* and consist of systems of linear equations, inequalities, or differential equations. The models will be linear in that each function defined by an equation, inequality, or differential equation will have the properties of Eq. (6-1.1a). To recall the properties of linear functions, we state them again as

$$f(x + y) = f(x) + f(y)$$

(7-1.1)

$$f(cx) = cf(x)$$

Illustration 1

Which of $z_1 = 2x$, $z_2 = 3x + y$, $2x - 3y < 5$, $z_3 = a_{11}x + a_{12}y$, $z_4 = a_{21}x + a_{22}y$, $\dfrac{dx}{dt} = x(t) + 2y(t)$, and $\dfrac{dy}{dt} = 3x(t) - 5y(t)$ can be in a linear model? The answer is all of them can be in linear models. It should be clear that $f(x) = 2x$, $f[\,(x, y)\,] = 3x + y$, $f[\,(x, y)\,] = 2x - 3y$, $f[\,(x, y)\,] = a_{11}x + a_{12}y$, and $f[\,(x, y)\,] = a_{21}x + a_{22}y$ are linear functions. Is it clear that $f[\,(x, y)\,] = x(t) + 2y(t)$ is linear? To see this, we will compute

$$
\begin{aligned}
f[\,(x_1, y_1) + (x_2, y_2)\,] &= f[\,(x_1 + x_2, y_1 + y_2)\,] \\
&= (x_1 + x_2)(t) + 2(y_1 + y_2)(t) \\
&= x_1(t) + x_2(t) + 2y_1(t) + 2y_2(t) \\
&= [\,x_1(t) + 2y_1(t)\,] + [\,x_2(t) + 2y_2(t)\,] \\
&= f[\,(x_1, y_1)\,] + f[\,(x_2, y_2)\,]
\end{aligned}
$$

and

$$
\begin{aligned}
f[\,c(x, y)\,] &= f[\,(cx, cy)\,] \\
&= (cx)(t) + 2(cy)(t) \\
&= cx(t) + 2cy(t) \\
&= c[\,x(t) + 2y(t)\,] \\
&= cf[\,(x, y)\,]
\end{aligned}
$$

Similar computations would show that $f[\,(x, y)\,] = 3x(t) - 5y(t)$ is a linear function. In fact, you can show that for particular real numbers a and b, $f[\,(x, y)\,] = ax(t) + by(t)$ is a linear function.

Illustration 2

Can any of $z_1 = 3x + 5$, $z_2 = 4xy$, $z_3 = e^x$, or $z_4 = \sin x$ be in a linear model? The answer is no, since $f(x) = 3x + 5$, $f[\,(x, y)\,] = 4xy$, $f(x) = e^x$, and $f(x) = \sin x$ are not linear functions. You can easily verify this.

All of the linear models that we will consider will either consist of a system of linear equations or inequalities or lead to them. In the system

(7-1.2)
$$
\begin{cases} a_{11}x + a_{12}y = b_1 \\ a_{21}x + a_{22}y = b_2 \end{cases}
$$

usually a_{11}, a_{12}, a_{21}, and a_{22} are known. If b_1 and b_2 are also known, then x and y must satisfy system (7-1.2). If b_1 and b_2 are not known, then system (7-1.2) shows how x, y, b_1, and b_2 are related.

7-2. LINEAR PROGRAMMING

Suppose that a company has two machines and wants to produce one or both of two types of products. Let us agree that both machines must be used for each unit of each product. Suppose we know the time needed for each unit on each machine, the total time available for each machine per day, and the unit profit for each product. How many units of the products should be produced each day to realize maximum profit? We will solve this problem for a specific example in the following illustration.

Illustration 1

Solve the problem above for the information given in Table 7-2.1. This table shows that each unit of product X requires 1 hour on machine A

TABLE 7-2.1

Machine	Product X	Product Y	Time Available Per Day
A	1	5	20
B	4	2	18
Unit Profit	1	2	

and 4 hours on machine B. Each unit of product Y required 5 hours on machine A and 2 hours on machine B. The total time available for machine A is 20 hours per day and for machine B is 18 hours per day. The unit profit for product X is \$1.00 and for product Y is \$2.00. Let x and y denote the number of units of products X and Y, respectively. Now, we want to obtain x and y such that profit, z, will be a maximum. Notice that since machine A cannot be used more than 20 hours per day, then $x + 5y \leq 20$. Since the time available for machine B is 18 hours, then $4x + 2y \leq 18$. Clearly, $x \geq 0$ and $y \geq 0$. The profit can be expressed as $z = x + 2y$. Thus, we are led to the linear model

$$\begin{cases} x + 5y \leq 20 \\ 4x + 2y \leq 18 \\ x \geq 0 \\ y \geq 0 \\ z = x + 2y \end{cases}$$

We will solve this system graphically (see Fig. 7-2.1). Each point, (x, y), in the shaded region is a *feasible* solution. We want to obtain the *optimal* solution, that feasible solution for which z is a maximum. Notice that the slopes of the lines defined by $x + 5y = 20$, $4x + 2y = 18$, and $z = x + 2y$ (for z constant) are $m_1 = -\frac{1}{5}$, $m_2 = -2$, and $m_3 = -\frac{1}{2}$. Since $-2 < -\frac{1}{2} < -\frac{1}{5}$, the optimal solution is obtained from the system of

153

linear equations

$$\begin{cases} x + 5y = 20 \\ 4x + 2y = 18 \end{cases}$$

to be $x = \frac{25}{9}$ and $y = \frac{31}{9}$. This point, $(\frac{25}{9}, \frac{31}{9})$, is a corner of the region of feasible solutions. This is always the case and leads to such topics as convex polyhedra, simplices, and general linear programming. In actuality, we would use $x = 3$ and $y = 3$ or in nine days produce 25 of product X and 31 of product Y.

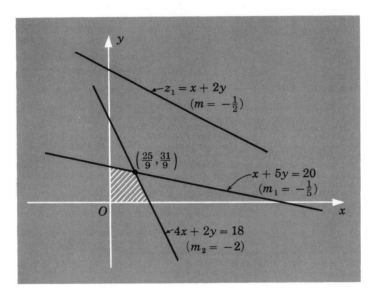

Figure 7–2.1

Illustration 2

Let us set up a linear model for the following distribution problem. Suppose a manufacturer has distribution centers in Atlanta and Chicago and retail outlets in New York and Dallas. If there are 100 units at Atlanta and 110 units at Chicago and 150 units are needed in New York and 60 in Dallas, how should the units be distributed to minimize cost. The total shipping costs in dollars are shown in Table 7–2.2. Let x, y, z, and w denote the number of units shipped from Atlanta to New York,

TABLE 7–2.2

	New York	Dallas
Atlanta	80	60
Chicago	50	70

Atlanta to Dallas, Chicago to New York, and Chicago to Dallas, respectively.

We can now set up the linear model

$$\begin{cases} x + y = 100 \\ z + w = 110 \\ x + z = 150 \\ y + w = 60 \\ x \geq 0 \\ y \geq 0 \\ z \geq 0 \\ w \geq 0 \end{cases}$$

$$C = 80x + 60y + 50z + 70w$$

where C is the cost. We do not know enough about linear programming to give a method that minimizes C. However, in this problem the obvious answer is $x = 40$, $y = 60$, $z = 110$, and $w = 0$.

Problem Set 7-2

Solve the following linear programming problems by graphing.

1. $\begin{cases} x + 2y \leq 6 \\ x \geq 0 \\ y \geq 0 \end{cases}$

    (a) Maximize $z = 2x + y$
    (b) Maximize $z = -2x + y$
    (c) Minimize $z = 2x + y$

2. $\begin{cases} x + 2y \leq 8 \\ 3x - 4y \leq 12 \\ x \geq 0 \\ y \geq 0 \end{cases}$

    (a) Maximize $z = 3x + y$
    (b) Maximize $z = -3x + y$

3. $\begin{cases} x + y \leq 5 \\ 2x - 3y \leq 6 \\ x \geq 0 \\ y \geq 0 \end{cases}$

    Maximize $z = 2x + y$

4. $\begin{cases} x + y \geq 3 \\ 2x + y \leq 6 \\ x \geq 0 \\ y \geq 0 \end{cases}$

    (a) Maximize $z = -x + y$
    (b) Maximize $z = x + y$
    (c) Minimize $z = (\frac{3}{2})x + y$
    (d) Minimize $z = (-\frac{1}{2})x + y$

5. A firm makes two products A and B and for each product two machines X and Y must be used. For each unit of A, X must be used for 1 hour and Y must be used for 2 hours. For each unit of B, X and Y must each be used for 3 hours. The machines X and Y are available for 12 and 18 hours per day, respectively. If the unit profit for A is \$20 and the unit profit for B is \$40, how many of each product should be made each day to maximize the firm's profit?

155

6. A farmer wishes to plant two crops A and B on $173\frac{1}{3}$ acres of land. The seed for A and B cost \$5 and \$10 per acre, respectively. The labor cost for A is \$25 per acre and for B the labor cost is \$20 per acre. Suppose the income for crop A is \$130 per acre and the income for crop B is \$160 per acre. If the farmer spends no more than \$1200 for seed and \$4000 for labor, how many acres of each crop should the farmer plant to maximize his profit?

7. A breakfast cereal company purchases mixed lots of corn, then grades the corn as premium, regular, or unusable. The company needs at least 100 tons of premium-grade and 55 tons of regular-grade corn. Suppose corn can be bought from suppliers A and B in any desired amount. From supplier A, 60% is premium grade, 30% is regular grade, and 10% is unusable. From supplier B, 50% is premium grade, 30% is regular grade, and 20% is unusable. If A charges \$200 per ton and B charges \$150 per ton, how much corn should be bought from each supplier to fulfill the company's needs at minimum cost?

7-3. AN INTERINDUSTRY MODEL

In this section we consider a simplified version of a linear model of the national economy. The original model was developed by Professor Wassily Leontief in the 1930s. For our purposes, suppose X_1, X_2, and X_3 are three industries and each produce exactly one type of product. For example, X_1 might be the automobile industry, X_2 the steel industry, and X_3 the rubber industry. We suppose that to produce its product each industry buys from the others and produces just enough to provide for the other industries and all other consumers. No surpluses are allowed here.

Suppose industry X_j $(j = 1, 2, 3)$ requires y_{ij} units from industry X_i $(i = 1, 2, 3)$ and the demand from all other consumers on X_i is b_i. Then, X_1 requires y_{11} units from X_1, X_2 requires y_{12} units from X_1, X_3 requires y_{13} units from X_1, and all other consumers require b_1 units from X_1. If x_1 denotes the number of units output of industry X_1, then

$$x_1 = y_{11} + y_{12} + y_{13} + b_1$$

Similarly, X_1 requires y_{21} units from X_2, X_2 requires y_{22} units from X_2, X_3 requires y_{23} units from X_2, and all other consumers require b_2 units from X_2. If x_2 denotes the number of units output of industry X_2, then

$$x_2 = y_{21} + y_{22} + y_{23} + b_2$$

If x_3 is the number of units output of industry X_3, a similar discussion gives

$$x_3 = y_{31} + y_{32} + y_{33} + b_3$$

The balance equation for each industry is then a member of the system

(7-3.1)
$$\begin{cases} x_1 = y_1 + y_{12} + y_{13} + b_1 \\ x_2 = y_{21} + y_{22} + y_{23} + b_2 \\ x_3 = y_{31} + y_{32} + y_{33} + b_3 \end{cases}$$

Notice that these equations allow for an industry to use some of its own product.

Next, an important assumption is made. We assume that the amount of good i needed to produce good j is directly proportional to the amount of good j produced. Thus, we assume that

(7-3.2) $$y_{ij} = a_{ij}x_j$$

where the constant of proportionality, a_{ij}, depends on the technology of industry X_j. From Eq. (7-3.2), $y_{11} = a_{11}x_1$, $y_{12} = a_{12}x_2$, $y_{13} = a_{13}x_3$, $y_{21} = a_{21}x_1$, $y_{22} = a_{22}x_2$, $y_{23} = a_{23}x_3$, $y_{31} = a_{31}x_1$, $y_{32} = a_{32}x_2$, and $y_{33} = a_{33}x_3$. Substituting these in system (7-3.1) gives

$$\begin{cases} x_1 = a_{11}x_1 + a_{12}x_2 + a_{13}x_3 + b_1 \\ x_2 = a_{21}x_1 + a_{22}x_2 + a_{23}x_3 + b_2 \\ x_3 = a_{31}x_1 + a_{32}x_2 + a_{33}x_3 + b_3 \end{cases}$$

from which we have the linear model

(7-3.3)
$$\begin{cases} (1 - a_{11})x_1 - a_{12}x_2 - a_{13}x_3 = b_1 \\ -a_{21}x_1 + (1 - a_{22})x_2 - a_{23}x_3 = b_2 \\ -a_{31}x_1 - a_{32}x_2 + (1 - a_{33})x_3 = b_3 \end{cases}$$

In matrix notation, system (7-3.3) is $AX = B$ where

$$A = \begin{pmatrix} 1 - a_{11} & -a_{12} & -a_{13} \\ -a_{21} & 1 - a_{22} & -a_{23} \\ -a_{31} & -a_{32} & 1 - a_{33} \end{pmatrix}, \quad X = \begin{pmatrix} x_1 \\ x_2 \\ x_3 \end{pmatrix}, \quad \text{and} \quad B = \begin{pmatrix} b_1 \\ b_2 \\ b_3 \end{pmatrix}$$

If B is specified and A is nonsingular, then the number of units x_1, x_2, and x_3 needed from each industry can be determined from $X = A^{-1}B$. The answer depends, of course, on the technologies, a_{ij}, of the industries.

Next, let us think of a_{ij} as the number of units of industry X_i needed to produce one unit of industry X_j. If p_i is the price of one unit of X_i, the cost of materials needed to produce one unit of X_j is

(7-3.4) $$a_{1j}p_1 + a_{2j}p_2 + a_{3j}p_3 \qquad (j = 1, 2, 3)$$

The cost of materials to produce one unit of X_1, X_2, and X_3 is

$$a_{11}p_1 + a_{21}p_2 + a_{31}p_3$$

$$a_{12}p_1 + a_{22}p_2 + a_{32}p_3$$

and

$$a_{13}p_1 + a_{23}p_2 + a_{33}p_3$$

respectively. The *value added*, r_j, by industry X_j is the difference between the price of one unit of X_j and the cost of materials needed to produce this one unit. Thus, we have

$$\begin{cases} p_1 - (a_{11}p_1 + a_{21}p_2 + a_{31}p_3) = r_1 \\ p_2 - (a_{12}p_1 + a_{22}p_2 + a_{32}p_3) = r_2 \\ p_3 - (a_{13}p_1 + a_{23}p_2 + a_{33}p_3) = r_3 \end{cases}$$

This system is rewritten as the linear model

(7-3.5)
$$\begin{cases} (1 - a_{11})p_1 - a_{21}p_1 - a_{31}p_3 = r_1 \\ - a_{12}p_1 + (1 - a_{22})p_2 - a_{32}p_3 = r_2 \\ - a_{13}p_1 - a_{23}p_2 + (1 - a_{33})p_3 = r_3 \end{cases}$$

In matrix notation, system (7-3.5) is $A^t P = B$ where A is as before, $P = \begin{pmatrix} p_1 \\ p_2 \\ p_3 \end{pmatrix}$, and $B = \begin{pmatrix} r_1 \\ r_2 \\ r_3 \end{pmatrix}$. Notice that if A^t is nonsingular, the technologies of the industries are known, and the values added are known, then the prices can be determined.

7-4. REGRESSION ANALYSIS

Suppose we wish to obtain the line that contains the origin and *best fits* the set of points $S = \{ (1, 2), (2, 1), (3, 4) \}$. The line we seek has equation $y = mx$, where the slope m must be determined. This model, $y = mx$, is clearly linear. By *best fit* we mean the line for which the sum of the squares of the vertical deviations of the given points from the line is a minimum (see Fig. 7-4.1). This line is sometimes called the *least squares line*. From Fig. 7-4.1, notice

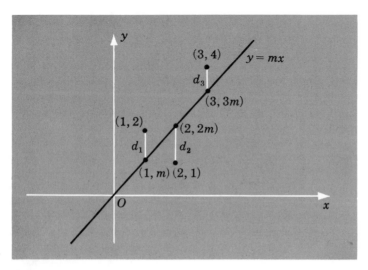

Figure 7-4.1

that the vertical deviations are $d_1 = 2 - m$, $d_2 = 1 - 2m$, and $d_3 = 4 - 3m$. If we set $z = d_1^2 + d_2^2 + d_3^2$, then

$$z = \sum_{i=1}^{i=3} d_i^2 = (2 - m)^2 + (1 - 2m)^2 + (4 - 3m)^2$$

$$= 4 - 2m + m^2 + 1 - 4m + 4m^2 + 16 - 24m + 9m^2$$

$$= 14m^2 - 30m + 21$$

Now, we need to minimize $z = 14m^2 - 30m + 21$. The simplest way to minimize z is to use calculus. The derivative of z with respect to z is $\dfrac{dz}{dm} = 28m - 30$. Now, z will be a minimum when $\dfrac{dz}{dm} = 0$ because the parabola with equation $z = 14m^2 - 30m + 21$ opens upward. Setting $28m - 30 = 0$, we have $m = \frac{30}{28} = \frac{15}{14}$. The equation of the least squares line is then $y = (\frac{15}{14})x$.

If you do not know calculus, you can still minimize z by completing the square as follows. If $a > 0$, consider

$$z = am^2 + 2bm + c$$
$$= (a^2m^2 + 2abm + ac)/a$$
$$= (a^2m^2 + 2abm + b^2 - b^2 + ac)/a$$
$$= [(a^2m^2 + 2abm + b^2) + (ac - b^2)]/a$$
$$= [(am + b)^2 + (ac - b^2)]/a$$

Since $(am + b)^2 \geq 0$, z will be a minimum when $am + b = 0$, that is, when $m = -b/a$. Notice that for $z = 14m^2 + 2(-15)m + 21$ we have $a = 14$, $b = -15$, and $c = 21$. Then, $m = -(-15)/14 = 15/14$, as before. If you know calculus, from $z = am^2 + 2bm + c$, we have $\dfrac{dz}{dm} = 2am + 2b$. Setting $\dfrac{dz}{dm} = 0$ gives $m = -b/a$ again.

If a line is to be fitted to N points and N is large, expanding $\sum_{i=1}^{i=N} d_i^2$ would be tedious. However, the work can be neatly arranged as follows. As before, we want to obtain the line that contains to origin and for which the sum of the squares of the vertical deviations of the given points from the line is a minimum. Let $S = \{(x_1, y_1), (x_2, y_2), \ldots, (x_N, y_N)\}$ and let $y = mx$ be the equation of the line we seek (see Fig. 7-4.2). Now, $d_i = y_i - mx_i$, and if z denotes the sum of the squares of the vertical deviations of the points from the line, we have

$$z = \sum_{i=1}^{i=N} d_i^2 = \sum_{i=1}^{i=N} (y_i - mx_i)^2$$

$$= \sum_{i=1}^{i=N} (y_i^2 - 2mx_iy_i + m^2x_i^2)$$

$$= \sum_{i=1}^{i=N} y_i^2 - 2m \sum_{i=1}^{i=N} x_iy_i + m^2 \sum_{i=1}^{i=N} x_i^2$$

$$= \left(\sum_{i=1}^{i=N} x_i^2\right) m^2 - 2\left(\sum_{i=1}^{i=N} x_iy_i\right) m + \sum_{i=1}^{i=N} y_i^2$$

159

This is a quadratic in m. From the previous discussion, z will be a minimum when

(7-4.1)
$$m = \frac{\sum\limits_{i=1}^{i=N} x_i y_i}{\sum\limits_{i=1}^{i=N} x_i^2}$$

By calculus, $\dfrac{dz}{dm} = 2m \sum_{i=1}^{i=N} x_i^2 - 2 \sum_{i=1}^{i=N} x_i y_i$. Setting $\dfrac{dz}{dm} = 0$, we again obtain the m of Eq. (7-4.1).

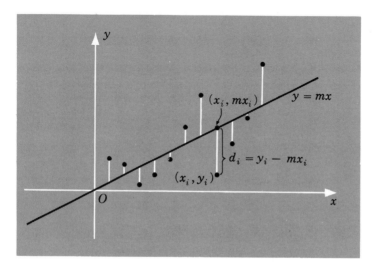

Figure 7-4.2

Illustration 1

Obtain the least squares line for $S = \{(1, 2), (2, 5), (3, 1), (4, 6), (5, 3)\}$. This model is the linear equation $y = mx$, where m is to be determined. To use Eq. (7-4.1), we arrange the work as given in Table 7.4-1. From Eq. (7-4.1) and Table 7-4.1, $m = \frac{54}{55}$. Therefore, $y = \left(\frac{54}{55}\right)x$ is the equation of the least squares line.

TABLE 7-4.1

x_i	y_i	x_i^2	$x_i y_i$
1	2	1	2
2	5	4	10
3	1	9	3
4	6	16	24
5	3	25	15
$\sum\limits_{i=1}^{i=5} x_i^2 = 55$		$54 = \sum\limits_{i=1}^{i=5} x_i y_i$	

Sometimes a line with equation $y = mx + b$ is fitted to a set of points using the least squares method. This line is also called the least squares line. For this line, m and b must be determined. We will not use $y = mx + b$ for a model since this model is not linear.

Next, let us fit a plane containing the origin to a set of points $S = \{(x_1, y_1, z_1), (x_2, y_2, z_2), \ldots, (x_N, y_N, z_N)\}$ using the least squares method. The equation we seek will be $z = ax + by$, where a and b must be determined. (This model, $z = ax + by$, is clearly linear.) We will obtain a and b such that the sum of the squares of the vertical deviations of the points in S from the plane will be a minimum. In this case, the vertical deviations are $d_i = z_i - (ax_i + by_i)$, and if we let $w = \sum_{i=1}^{i=N} d_i^2$, then

$$
\begin{aligned}
w &= \sum_{i=1}^{i=N} d_i^2 = \sum_{i=1}^{i=N} [z_i - (ax_i + by_i)]^2 \\
&= \sum_{i=1}^{i=N} (z_i^2 + a^2 x_i^2 + b^2 y_i^2 - 2ax_i y_i - 2by_i z_i + 2abx_i y_i) \\
&= \sum_{i=1}^{i=N} z_i^2 + a^2 \sum_{i=1}^{i=N} x_i^2 + b^2 \sum_{i=1}^{i=N} y_i^2 - 2a \sum_{i=1}^{i=N} x_i y_i \\
&\quad - 2b \sum_{i=1}^{i=N} y_i z_i + 2ab \sum_{i=1}^{i=N} x_i y_i
\end{aligned}
$$

The partial derivatives, $\dfrac{\partial w}{\partial a}$ and $\dfrac{\partial w}{\partial b}$, are helpful here. To obtain $\dfrac{\partial w}{\partial a}$ $\left(\dfrac{\partial w}{\partial b}\right)$ treat $b(a)$ as a constant and take the derivative of w with respect to $a(b)$. The minimum w will be attained when $\dfrac{\partial w}{\partial a} = 0$ and $\dfrac{\partial w}{\partial b} = 0$. Setting

$$
\frac{\partial w}{\partial a} = 2a \sum_{i=1}^{i=N} x_i^2 - 2 \sum_{i=1}^{i=N} x_i z_i + 2b \sum_{i=1}^{i=N} x_i y_i = 0
$$

and

$$
\frac{\partial w}{\partial b} = 2b \sum_{i=1}^{i=N} y_i^2 - 2 \sum_{i=1}^{i=N} y_i z_i + 2a \sum_{i=1}^{i=N} x_i y_i = 0
$$

leads to

(7-4.2)
$$
\begin{cases}
a \displaystyle\sum_{i=1}^{i=N} x_i^2 + b \sum_{i=1}^{i=N} x_i y_i = \sum_{i=1}^{i=N} x_i z_i \\[2mm]
a \displaystyle\sum_{i=1}^{i=N} x_i y_i + b \sum_{i=1}^{i=N} y_i^2 = \sum_{i=1}^{i=N} y_i z_i
\end{cases}
$$

From this system of equations we can usually solve for a and b.

Illustration 2

Obtain the least squares plane for $S = \{(1, 2, 3), (4, 2, 0), (3, 1, 5), (0, 4, 1)\}$. The plane has equation $z = ax + by$ where we must solve for a and b. To use system (7–4.2) we arrange the work as shown in Table 7–4.2.

TABLE 7–4.2

x_i	y_i	z_i	x_i^2	y_i^2	$x_i y_i$	$x_i z_i$	$y_i z_i$
1	2	3	1	4	2	3	6
4	2	0	16	4	8	0	0
3	1	5	9	1	3	15	5
0	4	1	0	16	0	0	4
			26	25	13	18	15
			$\sum\limits_{i=1}^{i=4} x_i^2$	$\sum\limits_{i=1}^{i=4} y_i^2$	$\sum\limits_{i=1}^{i=4} x_i y_i$	$\sum\limits_{i=1}^{i=4} x_i z_i$	$\sum\limits_{i=1}^{i=4} y_i z_i$

With the information from this table, system (7–4.2) gives

$$26a + 13b = 18$$
$$13a + 25b = 15$$

from which $a = \frac{255}{481}$ and $b = \frac{156}{481} = \frac{12}{37}$. Therefore, the equation of the least squares plane is $z = \left(\frac{255}{481}\right)x + \left(\frac{12}{37}\right)y$ or $255x + 156y - 481z = 0$.

Problem Set 7–4

Obtain the equation of the least squares line or plane, whichever is applicable, for the following sets of points.

1. $\{\,(1, 2),\ (2, 1)\,\}$
2. $\{\,(1, 2),\ (2, 4)\,\}$
3. $\{\,(1, 3),\ (2, 3),\ (3, 5),\ (4, 9)\,\}$
4. $\{\,(1, 2),\ (2, 5),\ (3, 3),\ (4, 7)\,\}$
5. $\{\,(1, 3),\ (2, 10),\ (3, 4),\ (4, 9),\ (5, 5)\,\}$
6. $\{\,(1, 1),\ (2, 3),\ (3, 1),\ (4, 2),\ (5, 3),\ (6, 5),\ (7, 10)\,\}$
7. $\{\,(1, 2, 3),\ (1, 1, 0),\ (2, 1, 3)\,\}$
8. $\{\,(1, 1, 1),\ (2, 2, 2),\ (3, 3, 3)\,\}$
9. $\{\,(1, 3, 2),\ (2, 2, 4),\ (3, 1, 5),\ (4, 0, 7)\,\}$
10. $\{\,(0, 1, 3),\ (0, 2, 3),\ (0, 3, 5),\ (0, 4, 9)\,\}$

7–5. SYSTEMS OF LINEAR DIFFERENTIAL EQUATIONS

If a particle moves in a plane such that at any instant its velocity component in the direction of each coordinate axis is equal to the other coordinate, what are the possible paths of the particle? We assume that a path is described by

$$\begin{cases} x = x(t) \\ y = y(t) \end{cases}$$

a system of parametric equations with parameter t. The velocity component in the direction of the positive x-axis is $\dfrac{dx}{dt}$ and the velocity component in the direction of the positive y-axis is $\dfrac{dy}{dt}$. To solve the problem, we then use the linear model

$$\begin{cases} \dfrac{dx}{dt} = y \\[2mm] \dfrac{dy}{dt} = x \end{cases}$$

a system of linear differential equations. We will shortly see how to obtain the path described by $x = e^t$, $y = e^t$ and the path described by $x = e^{-t}$, $y = -e^{-t}$. From these two paths we will see that all possible paths (one path for each pair of real numbers c_1 and c_2) are described by

$$\begin{cases} x = c_1 e^t + c_2 e^{-t} \\ y = c_1 e^t - c_2 e^{-t} \end{cases}$$

Let us now consider the system

(7-5.1)
$$\begin{cases} \dfrac{dx}{dt} = a_{11}x + a_{12}y \\[2mm] \dfrac{dy}{dt} = a_{21}x + a_{22}y \end{cases}$$

where a_{11}, a_{12}, a_{21}, and a_{22} are particular real numbers (constants) and x and y are differentiable functions of t on some interval $T \subseteq R$. In matrix notation system (7-5.1) is

(7-5.1a)
$$\dot{X} = AX$$

where $A = \begin{pmatrix} a_{11} & a_{12} \\ a_{21} & a_{22} \end{pmatrix}$, $X = \begin{pmatrix} x \\ y \end{pmatrix}$, and $\dot{X} = \begin{pmatrix} \dot{x} \\ \dot{y} \end{pmatrix} = \begin{pmatrix} \dfrac{dx}{dt} \\[2mm] \dfrac{dy}{dt} \end{pmatrix}$.

Notice that the derivative of a vector (a 2×1 matrix) is used here. If the components of a vector Y are differentiable functions on an interval T then the *derivative* of the vector Y is that vector $\dot{Y}$ obtained from Y by replacing each component in Y by its derivative. A matrix is *continuous on* T if and only if each of its entries is continuous on T. A *solution* of Eq. (7-5.1a) is a vector that is differentiable on T and satisfies Eq. (7-5.1a). If $t_0 \in T$, then $X(t_0) = \begin{pmatrix} x(t_0) \\ y(t_0) \end{pmatrix}$.

Illustration 1

If $U = \begin{pmatrix} u_1 \\ u_2 \end{pmatrix}$ and $V = \begin{pmatrix} v_1 \\ v_2 \end{pmatrix}$ are solutions of Eq. (7-5.1a) on an interval T, let us show that $U + V$ is also a solution on T. Now, $\dot{U} = AU$ and

$\dot{V} = AV$. Then,

$$\frac{d(U + V)}{dt} = \frac{d\begin{pmatrix} u_1 + v_1 \\ u_2 + v_2 \end{pmatrix}}{dt} = \begin{pmatrix} \dfrac{d(u_1 + v_1)}{dt} \\ \dfrac{d(u_2 + v_2)}{dt} \end{pmatrix}$$

$$= \begin{pmatrix} \dot{u}_1 + \dot{v}_1 \\ \dot{u}_2 + \dot{v}_2 \end{pmatrix}$$

$$= \begin{pmatrix} \dot{u}_1 \\ \dot{u}_2 \end{pmatrix} + \begin{pmatrix} \dot{v}_1 \\ \dot{v}_2 \end{pmatrix}$$

$$= \dot{U} + \dot{V}$$

$$= AU + AV$$

$$= A(U + V)$$

You can easily show that for c, a particular real number, cU is a solution of Eq. (7–5.1a) over T.

We will now state some theorems about the solutions of Eq. (7–5.1a), then solve some systems.

THEOREM 7–5.1. *If* $B = \begin{pmatrix} b_1 \\ b_2 \end{pmatrix}$, *where* b_1 *and* b_2 *are given real numbers, and* t_0 *is any point in* T, *then there is exactly one solution* X *of Eq. (7–5.1a) such that* $X(t_0) = B$.

COROLLARY 7–5.1. *If* $X(t_0) = \begin{pmatrix} 0 \\ 0 \end{pmatrix}$ *for some* t_0 *in* T, *then* $X = \begin{pmatrix} 0 \\ 0 \end{pmatrix}$.

The solutions $U = \begin{pmatrix} u_1 \\ u_2 \end{pmatrix}$ and $V = \begin{pmatrix} v_1 \\ v_2 \end{pmatrix}$ of Eq. (7–5.1a) on T are linearly independent means that every linear combination $c_1 U + c_2 V = O$ if and only if $c_1 = c_2 = 0$. Since

$$c_1 U + c_2 V = c_1 \begin{pmatrix} u_1 \\ u_2 \end{pmatrix} + c_2 \begin{pmatrix} v_1 \\ v_2 \end{pmatrix}$$

$$= \begin{pmatrix} c_1 u_1 \\ c_1 u_2 \end{pmatrix} + \begin{pmatrix} c_2 v_1 \\ c_2 v_2 \end{pmatrix}$$

$$= \begin{pmatrix} c_1 u_1 + c_2 v_1 \\ c_1 u_2 + c_2 v_2 \end{pmatrix}$$

then U and V are linearly independent if and only if the system

$$\begin{cases} c_1 u_1 + c_2 v_1 = 0 \\ c_1 u_2 + c_2 v_2 = 0 \end{cases}$$

has only the solution $c_1 = c_2 = 0$. Notice that U and V are linearly independent if u_1 and v_1 are linearly independent and u_2 and v_2 are linearly independent. Does the converse hold? If U and V are not linearly independent, they are said to be linearly dependent.

THEOREM 7-5.2. *The vectors U and V are linearly independent solutions of Eq. (7–5.1a) if and only if*

$$\det \begin{pmatrix} u_1 & v_1 \\ u_2 & v_2 \end{pmatrix} = u_1 v_2 - v_1 u_2 \neq 0$$

THEOREM 7-5.3. *There exist two linearly independent solutions U and V of Eq. (7–5.1a) and every solution of Eq. (7–5.1a) is a linear combination of U and V.*

THEOREM 7-5.4. *If U and V are any two linearly independent solutions of Eq. (7–5.1a), then every solution of Eq. (7–5.1a) is a linear combination of U and V.*

In the following illustrations the interval T will be R. We will discuss methods to solve systems of two linear differential equations.

Illustration 2

Solve the system

$$\begin{cases} \dfrac{dx}{dt} = 3x - 2y \\ \dfrac{dy}{dt} = 4x - 3y \end{cases}$$

In matrix notation the system is $\dot{X} = AX$ where $A = \begin{pmatrix} 3 & -2 \\ 4 & -3 \end{pmatrix}$ and $X = \begin{pmatrix} x \\ y \end{pmatrix}$. We will determine a and b, neither zero, and λ such that $X = \begin{pmatrix} ae^{\lambda t} \\ be^{\lambda t} \end{pmatrix}$ is a solution. Since $\dot{X} = \begin{pmatrix} a\lambda e^{\lambda t} \\ b\lambda e^{\lambda t} \end{pmatrix}$, we have

$$\begin{pmatrix} a\lambda e^{\lambda t} \\ b\lambda e^{\lambda t} \end{pmatrix} = \begin{pmatrix} 3 & -2 \\ 4 & -3 \end{pmatrix} \begin{pmatrix} ae^{\lambda t} \\ be^{\lambda t} \end{pmatrix}$$

Then,

$$0 = \begin{pmatrix} 3 & -2 \\ 4 & -3 \end{pmatrix} \begin{pmatrix} ae^{\lambda t} \\ be^{\lambda t} \end{pmatrix} - \begin{pmatrix} a\lambda e^{\lambda t} \\ b\lambda e^{\lambda t} \end{pmatrix}$$

$$= \begin{pmatrix} 3 & -2 \\ 4 & -3 \end{pmatrix} \begin{pmatrix} a \\ b \end{pmatrix} e^{\lambda t} - \lambda \begin{pmatrix} a \\ b \end{pmatrix} e^{\lambda t}$$

$$= \left[\begin{pmatrix} 3 & -2 \\ 4 & -3 \end{pmatrix} - \lambda \begin{pmatrix} 1 & 0 \\ 0 & 1 \end{pmatrix} \right] \begin{pmatrix} a \\ b \end{pmatrix} e^{\lambda t}$$

$$= \begin{pmatrix} 3 - \lambda & -2 \\ 4 & -3 - \lambda \end{pmatrix} \begin{pmatrix} a \\ b \end{pmatrix} e^{\lambda t}$$

Since $e^{\lambda t} \neq 0$, we have

$$\begin{pmatrix} 3 - \lambda & -2 \\ 4 & -3 - \lambda \end{pmatrix} \begin{pmatrix} a \\ b \end{pmatrix} = 0$$

If you look at A you can see how to write this equation immediately from A. Notice that $\begin{pmatrix} 3 - \lambda & -2 \\ 4 & -3 - \lambda \end{pmatrix} = A - \lambda I$ where $I = \begin{pmatrix} 1 & 0 \\ 0 & 1 \end{pmatrix}$.

165

This equation will have a nontrivial solution for a and b if and only if

$$\begin{vmatrix} 3 - \lambda & -2 \\ 4 & -3 - \lambda \end{vmatrix} = 0$$

Then, $\lambda^2 - 1 = 0$ from which $\lambda = \pm 1$. For $\lambda = 1$, we have

$$\begin{pmatrix} 2 & -2 \\ 4 & -4 \end{pmatrix} \begin{pmatrix} a \\ b \end{pmatrix} = O$$

and the only restriction on a and b is that they be equal. Thus, if we let $a = b = 1$, then $X_1 = \begin{pmatrix} e^t \\ e^t \end{pmatrix}$ is a solution of the given system of equations.

For $\lambda = -1$, we have

$$\begin{pmatrix} 4 & -2 \\ 4 & -2 \end{pmatrix} \begin{pmatrix} a \\ b \end{pmatrix} = O$$

and the only restriction on a and b is that $b = 2a$. If we choose $a = 1$, then $b = 2$ and $X_2 = \begin{pmatrix} e^{-t} \\ 2e^{-t} \end{pmatrix}$ is a solution. Now, X_1 and X_2 are linearly independent over R because

$$\begin{vmatrix} e^t & e^{-t} \\ e^t & 2e^{-t} \end{vmatrix} = 2 - 1 = 1 \neq 0 \qquad \textit{By Theorem 7–5.2}$$

By Theorem 7–5.4, every solution is a linear combination of X_1 and X_2. The *general solution* is then

$$c_1 X_1 + c_2 X_2 = c_1 \begin{pmatrix} e^t \\ e^t \end{pmatrix} + c_2 \begin{pmatrix} e^{-t} \\ 2e^{-t} \end{pmatrix} = \begin{pmatrix} c_1 e^t + c_2 e^{-t} \\ c_1 e^t + 2c_2 e^{-t} \end{pmatrix}$$

Illustration 3

Solve the system

$$\begin{cases} \dfrac{dx}{dt} = 2x - y \\ \dfrac{dy}{dt} = x \end{cases}$$

In matrix notation the system is $\dot{X} = AX$ where $A = \begin{pmatrix} 2 & -1 \\ 1 & 0 \end{pmatrix}$ and $X = \begin{pmatrix} x \\ y \end{pmatrix}$. As in Illustration 2 we will try to obtain λ and nonzero numbers a and b such that $X_1 = \begin{pmatrix} ae^{\lambda t} \\ be^{\lambda t} \end{pmatrix}$ is a solution. Substituting X_1 and $\dot{X}_1$ in $\dot{X} = AX$ leads to

$$\begin{pmatrix} 2 - \lambda & -1 \\ 1 & -\lambda \end{pmatrix} \begin{pmatrix} a \\ b \end{pmatrix} = O$$

In order that $a \neq 0$ and $b \neq 0$, we must have

$$\begin{vmatrix} 2 - \lambda & -1 \\ 1 & -\lambda \end{vmatrix} = 0$$

Thus, $\lambda^2 - 2\lambda + 1 = 0$ from which $\lambda = 1$. For $\lambda = 1$, we have

$$\begin{pmatrix} 1 & -1 \\ 1 & -1 \end{pmatrix} \begin{pmatrix} a \\ b \end{pmatrix} = O$$

which shows that $a = b$. If we let $a = b = 1$, then $X_1 = \begin{pmatrix} e^t \\ e^t \end{pmatrix}$ is a solution of the system over R.

Since only one value of λ was obtained, we need to try something different. We will try to obtain values for a, b, c, and d such that $X_2 = \begin{pmatrix} (at + b)e^t \\ (ct + d)e^t \end{pmatrix}$ is a solution of the given system. Substituting X_2 in $\dot{X} = AX$ leads to

$$\begin{pmatrix} (c - a)t + a - b + d \\ (c - a)t + a - b + d \end{pmatrix} = \begin{pmatrix} 0 \\ 0 \end{pmatrix}$$

Thus, we conclude that

$$\begin{cases} c - a = 0 \\ a - b + d = 0 \end{cases}$$

Here, $a = c$ and we can choose b and d. If we choose $b = 0$ and $d = -1$, then $a = 1 = c$. With these values, $X_2 = \begin{pmatrix} te^t \\ (t - 1)e^t \end{pmatrix}$. Since

$$\begin{vmatrix} e^t & te^t \\ e^t & (t - 1)e^t \end{vmatrix} = -e^{2t} \neq 0$$

X_1 and X_2 are linearly independent over R. Therefore, the general solution is

$$c_1 X_1 + c_2 X_2 = \begin{pmatrix} c_1 e^t + c_2 te^t \\ c_1 e^t + c_2(t - 1)e^t \end{pmatrix}$$

Illustration 4

Solve the system

$$\begin{cases} \dfrac{dx}{dt} = 4y \\ \dfrac{dy}{dt} = -2x + 4y \end{cases}$$

In matrix notation the system is $\dot{X} = AX$ where $A = \begin{pmatrix} 0 & 4 \\ -2 & 4 \end{pmatrix}$ and $X = \begin{pmatrix} x \\ y \end{pmatrix}$. As before, we try for a solution of the form $X = \begin{pmatrix} ae^{\lambda t} \\ be^{\lambda t} \end{pmatrix}$. This leads to $det\,(A - \lambda I) = 0$ for the determination of a, b, and λ. Since

$$det\,(A - \lambda I) = \begin{vmatrix} -\lambda & 4 \\ -2 & 4 - \lambda \end{vmatrix} = 0$$

we have $\lambda^2 - 4\lambda + 8 = 0$. Thus, $\lambda = 2 \pm 2i$, a pair of conjugate complex numbers. For $\lambda = 2 + 2i$,

$$\begin{pmatrix} -2 - 2i & 4 \\ -2 & 2 - 2i \end{pmatrix} \begin{pmatrix} a \\ b \end{pmatrix} = O$$

from which

$$\begin{cases} -(1 + i)a + 2b = 0 \\ -a + (1 - i)b = 0 \end{cases}$$

Thus, $a = (1 - i)b$. If we let $b = 1 + i$, then $a = 2$ and $X = \begin{pmatrix} 2e^{(2+2i)t} \\ (1 + i)e^{(2+2i)t} \end{pmatrix}$ is a solution. To verify that X satisfies the system simply

167

treat i as a constant when obtaining derivatives. Two solutions can be obtained from X by using the Euler relation

$$e^{(a+bi)t} = e^{at}(\cos bt + i \sin bt)$$

By the Euler relation,

$$2e^{(2+2i)t} = 2e^{2t}(\cos 2t + i \sin 2t) = 2e^{2t} \cos 2t + 2(e^{2t} \sin 2t)i$$

and

$$(1 + i)e^{(2+2i)t} = (1 + i)e^{2t}(\cos 2t + i \sin 2t)$$
$$= e^{2t}(\cos 2t - \sin 2t) + e^{2t}(\cos 2t + \sin 2t)i$$

Now, in order for X to be a solution, the real parts and the imaginary parts of $2e^{(2+2i)t}$ and $(1 + i)e^{(2+2i)t}$ must form solutions. Thus, $X_1 = \begin{pmatrix} 2e^{2t} \cos 2t \\ e^{2t}(\cos 2t - \sin 2t) \end{pmatrix}$ and $X_2 = \begin{pmatrix} 2e^{2t} \sin 2t \\ e^{t}(\cos 2t + \sin 2t) \end{pmatrix}$ are solutions. You can verify that X_1 and X_2 are linearly independent over R. The general solution is then

$$c_1 X_1 + c_2 X_2 = \begin{pmatrix} 2e^{2t}(c_1 \cos 2t + c_2 \sin 2t) \\ e^{2t}[\, c_1(\cos 2t - \sin 2t) + c_2(\cos 2t + \sin 2t)\,] \end{pmatrix}$$

Here, $\lambda = 2 - 2i$ was not needed since the Euler relation provided two linearly independent solutions for $\lambda = 2 + 2i$.

By the three preceding illustrations we have shown how system (7–5.1) or Eq. (7–5.1a) can be solved. From the equation

(7–5.2) $\qquad det\,(A - \lambda I) = \begin{vmatrix} a_{11} - \lambda & a_{12} \\ a_{21} & a_{22} - \lambda \end{vmatrix} = 0$

the two values of λ must be real and distinct or real and equal or conjugate complex numbers. In the illustrations, we considered each possibility. Equation (7–5.2) is sometimes called the *characteristic equation* of the system (7–5.1), and its roots, say λ_1 and λ_2, are *characteristic roots* of the system.

Problem Set 7–5

Solve the following systems.

1. $\begin{cases} \dfrac{dx}{dt} = 3x - 2y \\ \dfrac{dy}{dt} = x \end{cases}$

2. $\begin{cases} \dfrac{dx}{dt} = x + 2y \\ \dfrac{dy}{dt} = 3x + 2y \end{cases}$

3. $\begin{cases} \dfrac{dx}{dt} = x - y \\ \dfrac{dy}{dt} = 2x + 4y \end{cases}$

4. $\begin{cases} \dfrac{dx}{dt} = -13x + 30y \\ \dfrac{dy}{dt} = -5x + 12y \end{cases}$

5. $\begin{cases} \dfrac{dx}{dt} = 2x - y \\ \dfrac{dy}{dt} = -3x \end{cases}$

6. $\begin{cases} \dfrac{dx}{dt} = y \\ \dfrac{dy}{dt} = -x + 2y \end{cases}$

7.
$$\begin{cases} \dfrac{dx}{dt} = 3x - y \\ \dfrac{dy}{dt} = 4x - y \end{cases}$$

8.
$$\begin{cases} \dfrac{dx}{dt} = 4x - y \\ \dfrac{dy}{dt} = x + 2y \end{cases}$$

9.
$$\begin{cases} \dfrac{dx}{dt} = 3x - y \\ \dfrac{dy}{dt} = x + y \end{cases}$$

10.
$$\begin{cases} \dfrac{dx}{dt} = 5x + 4y \\ \dfrac{dy}{dt} = -x + y \end{cases}$$

11.
$$\begin{cases} \dfrac{dx}{dt} = x - 3y \\ \dfrac{dy}{dt} = 3x + y \end{cases}$$

12.
$$\begin{cases} \dfrac{dx}{dt} = x - 4y \\ \dfrac{dy}{dt} = x + y \end{cases}$$

13.
$$\begin{cases} \dfrac{dx}{dt} = 3x + 2y \\ \dfrac{dy}{dt} = -5x + y \end{cases}$$

14.
$$\begin{cases} \dfrac{dx}{dt} = 2x - 5y \\ \dfrac{dy}{dt} = x - 2y \end{cases}$$

15.
$$\begin{cases} \dfrac{dx}{dt} = x + 2y \\ \dfrac{dy}{dt} = -x + 3y \end{cases}$$

Fundamentals of Set Theory

In this short appendix, we discuss only that part of set theory that is used in this book. Some examples of sets we have used are:

i. E^2, the set of all vectors in a Euclidean plane,
ii. R^2, the set of all ordered pairs of real numbers,
iii. E^3, the set of all vectors in space,
iv. R^3, the set of all ordered triples of real numbers,
v. R^n, the set of all ordered n-tuples of real numbers,
vi. Z^+, the set of all positive integers,
vii. R, the set of all real numbers,
viii. the set of all $m \times n$ matrices,
ix. S, the solution set of a system of linear equations,
x. $P[R]$, the set of all real-valued polynomial functions over R,
xi. a basis of a vector space, and
xii. $T(V, W)$, the set of all linear mappings from V into W.

Although the term *set* will not be defined, each of the above sets is *well-defined* in that we know, (intuitively), or can determine what is in and what is not in the set. No ambiguity is allowed here. Notice that the collection of all college deans is not a well-defined set. Do we include the dean of men, dean of women, dean of Arts and Sciences, the Graduate Dean, . . . , from a given college? Also, are deans from two-year colleges included? A set must be described in a way that eliminates ambiguity. If A is a set, the notation

$a \in A$ indicates that a is contained in or is an element of A, while $a \notin A$ indicates that a is not contained in or is not an element of A.

In Theorem 3–1.1 equality of two sets is used. Thus, we need to know when two sets are equal. Set equality is the simplest kind of equality, since *two sets are equal* if and only if they are *identical* in the sense that they contain exactly the same elements. In notation, if A is a set and B is a set, then $A = B$ means if $x \in A$, then $x \in B$ and if $x \in B$, then $x \in A$. You can easily verify that equality of sets is an equivalence relation. No order is generally assigned to elements of a set. Thus, if two people solve a system of two linear equations in two unknowns, one may obtain the solution set $S_1 = \{(3, -2), (0, 6)\}$, while the other may obtain the solution set $S_2 = \{(0, 6), (3, -2)\}$. This poses no difficulty, for clearly $S_1 = S_2$.

If we want to merely name a set, usually upper case letters, such as A, B, or V are used. However, if the elements of a set need to be exhibited, braces, $\{\}$, are used with the elements either designated as stated above, or a rule (or rules) is given that specifies the elements in the set. For example, if A consists of the integers 1, 2, 3, 4, 5, and 6, one description of A is $A = \{1, 2, 3, 4, 5, 6\}$. Here, the elements of A are simply listed. Another description of A is $A = \{x \mid x \in Z^+ \text{ and } x < 7\}$. Here, the rules $x \in Z^+$ and $x < 7$ must both be satisfied by an x in order for x to be in A. If either rule is not satisfied by an x, then $x \notin A$.

Illustration 1

If $A = \{-5, -2, 0, 1, 4\}$, then $-5 \in A$, $-2 \in A$, $0 \in A$, $1 \in A$, and $4 \in A$. If $x \neq -5, -2, 0, 1,$ or 4, then $x \notin A$. For example, $3 \notin A$.

Illustration 2

Describe the set of all positive even integers. One description is $\{2, 4, 6, 8, \ldots\}$, if we understand exactly what the ellipsis points, $\ldots$, mean. Another description is $\{2x \mid x \in Z^+\}$.

Illustration 3

Describe the set of all odd integers. One description is $\{\ldots, -3, -1, 1, 3, \ldots\}$, while another is $\{2x - 1 \mid x \in Z\}$. Here, Z denotes the set of all integers.

Illustration 4

What are a and b, if $A = \{-3, 0, a\}$, $B = \{1, b, -3\}$, and $A = B$? We see immediately that $a = 1$ and $b = 0$, since 1 must be in A and 0 must be in B.

As we know, each positive integer is a real number. Symbolically, we write $Z^+ \subseteq R$, which is read Z^+ *is a subset of* R. In defining a basis B of a vector space V, recall that we specified that $B \subseteq V$. Much was learned about V by considering only the basis vectors. More generally, if A is a set and B is a set, then A is a subset of $B (A \subseteq B)$ if and only if each element in A is also in B. Thus, $A \subseteq B$ means if $x \in A$, then $x \in B$. You can easily show that $A = B$ if and only if $A \subseteq B$ and $B \subseteq A$.

Illustration 5

If $A = \{0, 1, 5\}$ and $B = \{0, 1, 2, 3, 4, 5\}$ then $A \subseteq B$ since each element in A is also in B. Here, $4 \in B$ but $4 \notin A$. Thus, B is not a subset of A.

Recall that the intersection of two subspaces of a vector space V is a subspace of V (see Theorem 5–4.2), but the union of two subspaces is not necessarily a subspace of V. If A is a set and B is a set, then $A \cup B$ (read A union B) and $A \cap B$ (read A intersect B) are defined as

$$A \cup B = \{x \mid x \in A \text{ or } x \in B\}$$

and

$$A \cap B = \{x \mid x \in A \text{ and } x \in B\}$$

Thus, $A \cup B$ is the set of all elements that are in *either* A or B (or both), while $A \cap B$ is the set of all elements that are in both A and B. In order for $A \cap B$ to always be a set, we must agree that a set with no element is still a set. This situation occurs if A and B have no common element. As usual, the *empty set* is denoted by $\emptyset$. Notice that the following comparisons hold for any sets A and B.

i. $A \subseteq A$,

ii. $\emptyset \subseteq A$,

iii. $A \cap B \subseteq A$ and $A \cap B \subseteq B$, and

iv. $A \subseteq A \cup B$ and $B \subseteq A \cup B$.

Illustration 6

If $A = \{1, 5, 7\}$ and $B = \{-2, 0, 1, 6, 7\}$ obtain $A \cup B$ and $A \cap B$. Now,

$$A \cup B = \{-2, 0, 1, 5, 6, 7\}$$

and

$$A \cap B = \{1, 7\}$$

Illustration 7

List all subsets of $A = \{1, 5, 7\}$. The subsets are $\emptyset$, $\{1\}$, $\{5\}$, $\{7\}$, $\{1, 5\}$, $\{1, 7\}$, $\{5, 7\}$, and $\{1, 5, 7\}$. Notice that A has three elements and the number of subsets of A is $2^3 = 8$. More generally, if B has n elements, the number of subsets of B is 2^n. (You can show this.)

You can easily verify that $(A \cup B) \cup C = A \cup (B \cup C)$ for any sets A, B, and C. We agree that either of these is equal to $A \cup B \cup C$. Also, since $(A \cap B) \cap C = A \cap (B \cap C)$ (show this), then either is equal to $A \cap B \cap C$. More generally, if $A_1, A_2, \ldots, A_n$ are sets, then

$$\bigcup_{i=1}^{i=n} A_i = A_1 \cup A_2 \cup \cdots \cup A_n$$
$$= \{x \mid x \in A_i \text{ for some } i = 1, 2, 3, \ldots, n\}$$

and

$$\bigcap_{i=1}^{i=n} A_i = A_1 \cap A_2 \cap \cdots \cap A_n$$
$$= \{x \mid x \in A_i \text{ for each } i = 1, 2, 3, \ldots, n\}$$

Therefore, the union of a finite number of sets is the set of all elements that are in *at least one* of the sets A_i, while the intersection of a finite number of sets is the set of all elements that are in *every* set A_i.

Illustration 8

Argue that $A \cap (B \cup C) = (A \cap B) \cup (A \cap C)$ for any sets A, B, and C. If $x \in A \cap (B \cup C)$, then $x \in A$ and $x \in B \cup C$. Thus, $x \in A$ and $x \in B$ or $x \in C$. In case $x \in B$, then $x \in A \cap B$; in case $x \in C$, then $x \in A \cap C$. In either case, $x \in (A \cap B) \cup (A \cap C)$. Consequently, $A \cap (B \cup C) \subseteq (A \cap B) \cup (A \cap C)$.

Next, if $x \in (A \cap B) \cup (A \cap C)$, then $x \in A \cap B$ or $x \in A \cap C$. In case $x \in A \cap B$, then $x \in A$ and $x \in B$. Hence, $x \in A$ and $x \in B \cup C$, which implies that $x \in A \cap (B \cup C)$. In case $x \in A \cap C$, then $x \in A$ and $x \in C$. Thus, $x \in A$ and $x \in B \cup C$ from which $x \in A \cap (B \cup C)$. In either case, $x \in A \cap (B \cup C)$ and we have $(A \cap B) \cup (A \cap C) \subseteq A \cap (B \cup C)$. With the two parts of the proof, we have $A \cap (B \cup C) = (A \cap B) \cup (A \cap C)$.

Answers to Selected Problems

CHAPTER 1

Section 1–2

1. (a) $(3, -5)$ (b) $(-3, 5)$ (c) $(0, 0)$
   (d) $(-3, 5)$ (e) $(3, -5)$ (f) $(1, 0)$
3. (a) $(6, 2 - \sqrt{3})$ (b) $(4, 2 + \sqrt{3})$ (c) $(5 - \sqrt{3}, 1)$
   (d) $(9, 6)$ (e) $(1, 6)$ (f) $(1, -2)$
7. (a) $(5, -5)$ (b) $\mathbf{w}$ (c) $(1, -5)$
   (d) $\mathbf{0}$ (e) $(8, -10)$ (f) $(-20, 15)$
   (g) $(-12, 20)$ (h) $(1, -2)$ (i) $(1, -2)$
   (j) $(-11, -3)$ (k) $(23, -10)$ (l) $(4, -12)$

Section 1–3

1. (a) -5 (b) -17 3. (a) -22 (b) -22
5. (a) 0 (b) 0 7. $3\pi/4$
9. π 11. $163.8°$
13. $0, \mathbf{0}$ 15. $\frac{7}{5}$, $(-\frac{21}{25})\mathbf{i} + (-\frac{28}{25})\mathbf{j}$
17. $0, \mathbf{0}$ 19. 5, $\mathbf{v} = 4\mathbf{i} - 3\mathbf{j}$
21. $\frac{38}{5}$, $(\frac{152}{25})\mathbf{i} + (\frac{114}{25})\mathbf{j}$ 23. Let $x \in R$ and $y = \frac{5}{7}x$.

31. 15 square units

33. 16 square units

35. 15.5 square units

37. $5\sqrt{2}/2$

39. 6

Section 1-4

1. $(-1, \frac{3}{2})$

3. $(\frac{4}{5}, -\frac{6}{5})$

5. $(-\frac{5}{2}, \frac{15}{4})$, $(-7, \frac{21}{2})$

7. $\mathbf{v} = (0, 6r)$, $x = 0$

9. $\mathbf{v} = (-2q + 10r, 0) = (-2 + 12r, 0)$, $y = 0$

11. $\mathbf{v} = (-4q + 2r, -6q + 7r) = (-4 + 6r, -6 + 13r)$,
     $13x - 6y + 16 = 0$

13. $\mathbf{v} = (aq + ar, bq + dr) = (a, b + [d - b]r)$, $x = a$

15. $\mathbf{v} = (aq + cr, bq + dr) = (a + [c - a]r, b + [d - b]r)$,
     $(d - b)x + (a - c)y = ad - bc$

Section 1-5

3. (a) $(1, 2, 3)$ (b) $(4, -2, 9)$ (c) $\mathbf{v} = (-3, 5, -2)$
    (d) $(-15, 25, -10)$ (e) $(0, 4, 16)$ (f) $(6, 1, 11)$
    (g) $(-12, 26, 16)$ (h) $(24, -31, 15)$

5. (a) -37 (b) 3   (c) -17
    (d) -54 (e) -148 (f) 0
    (g) 0   (h) 5   (i) 37
    (j) 38   (k) -26 (l) -26

7. $\pi/2$

9. $\pi/2$

11. $136.9°$

13. $43.1°$

15. $\frac{37}{7}$, $(\frac{111}{49})\mathbf{i} + (\frac{74}{49})\mathbf{j} - (\frac{222}{49})\mathbf{k}$

17. $\frac{37}{9}$, $(\frac{259}{81})\mathbf{i} - (\frac{148}{81})\mathbf{j} - (\frac{148}{81})\mathbf{k}$

19. $\frac{37}{9}$, $(-\frac{259}{81})\mathbf{i} + (\frac{148}{81})\mathbf{j} + (\frac{148}{81})\mathbf{k}$

21. $\mathbf{0}, \mathbf{0}$

23. $10\mathbf{i} + 13\mathbf{j} - \mathbf{k}$

25. $\mathbf{k}$

27. $-22\mathbf{i} - 13\mathbf{j} + 10\mathbf{k}$

29. $\mathbf{0}$

31. $60\mathbf{i} + 78\mathbf{j} - 6\mathbf{k}$

Section 1-6

1. $\cos \alpha = \frac{4}{9}$, $\cos \beta = -\frac{7}{9}$, $\cos \gamma = -\frac{4}{9}$

3. $\cos \alpha = \frac{1}{3}$, $\cos \beta = -\frac{2}{3}$, $\cos \gamma = \frac{2}{3}$

5. $\cos \alpha = -\frac{1}{3}$, $\cos \beta = \frac{2}{3}$, $\cos \gamma = -\frac{2}{3}$

7. $\cos \alpha = 0$, $\cos \beta = 1$, $\cos \gamma = 0$

9. $\cos \alpha = \frac{4}{5}$, $\cos \beta = 0$, $\cos \gamma = -\frac{3}{5}$

11. $\cos \alpha = \frac{3}{7}$, $\cos \beta = \frac{2}{7}$, $\cos \gamma = -\frac{6}{7}$

13. $\cos \alpha = \pm\frac{2}{3}$

15. $\cos \alpha = \pm\frac{1}{3}$

17. $\cos \beta = \pm\frac{4}{9}$

19. $(5, 7, 2)$, $(10, 14, 4)$, $(-5, -7, -2)$

21. $(5, 3, 3)$, $(5, 6, 3)$, $(5, -3, 3)$

23. $(5, 10, 7)$, $(5, 12, 7)$, $(5, 6, 7)$

25. $(6, 10, 7)$, $(7, 12, 7)$, $(4, 6, 7)$

27. $(5, 9, 9)$, $(5, 10, 11)$, $(5, 7, 5)$

29. (a) $[\,k, 12k, 10k\,]$ for $k \in R$, $k \neq 0$
    (b) $[\,9k, 0, -4k\,]$ for $k \in R$, $k \neq 0$
    (c) $[\,0, 4k, -3k\,]$ for $k \in R$, $k \neq 0$
    (d) $[\,4k, -3k, 5k\,]$ for $k \in R$, $k \neq 0$
    (e) $[\,10k, k, -8k\,]$ for $k \in R$, $k \neq 0$
    (f) $[\,6k, -12k, 14k\,]$ or $[\,3k, -6k, 7k\,]$ for $k \in R$, $k \neq 0$
    (g) $[\,3k, 0, -4k\,]$ for $k \in R$, $k \neq 0$
    (h) $[\,4k, k, -3k\,]$ for $k \in R$, $k \neq 0$

31. $x = -3 + 9t$, $y = -5$, and $z = 2 - 4t$ for $t \in R$; the symmetric form does not apply.

33. $x = 4t$, $y = -3t$, and $z = 5t$ for $t \in R$; $x/4 = y/(-3) = z/5$

35. $x = 3 + 6t$, $y = -6 - 12t$, and $z = 7 + 14t$ for $t \in R$ or $x = 3 + 3t$, $y = -6 - 6t$, and $z = 7 + 7t$ for $t \in R$; $(x - 3)/3 = (y + 6)/(-6) = (z - 7)/7$

37. $x = 4 + 4t$, $y = 3 + t$, and $z = -3t$ for $t \in R$; $(x - 4)/4 = (y - 3)/1 = z/(-3)$

39. $x = 3 + t$, $y = 4 - 3t$, and $z = 6t$ for $t \in R$; $(x - 3)/1 = (y - 4)/(-3) = z/6$

41. $x = 5 + 2t$, $y = 8$, and $z = 7$ for $t \in R$; the symmetric form does not apply.

43. $x = 5$, $y = 8$, and $z = 7 + 2t$ for $t \in R$; the symmetric form does not apply.

45. $x = 5 + t$, $y = 8$, and $z = 7 + 2t$ for $t \in R$; the symmetric form does not apply.

47. $x = -6 - 4t$, $y = -3 - 7t$, and $z = 2 + 6t$ for $t \in R$; $(x + 6)/(-4) = (y + 3)/(-7) = (z - 2)/6$

Section 1–7

1. $2x + y - 6z = 49$
3. $2x - y + 3z + 28 = 0$
5. $4x - 2y + 7z = 94$
7. $3x - 2y + 4z + 3 = 0$
9. $x - 3y - 7z + 39 = 0$
11. $3y - 4z = 0$, $x \in R$
13. $43x + 58y + 4z = 135$
15. $\frac{12}{7}$
17. 6
19. $2\sqrt{3}$
21. $\frac{22}{7}$
23. $7x - 3y + z = 39$
25. $(4, -\frac{17}{3}, -18)$
27. $(16, 20, 10)$
29. $(x - 4)/2 = (y - 1)/1 = (z + 2)/(-3)$
31. $(x - \frac{12}{5})/13 = (y + 1)/15 = (z - \frac{14}{5})/36$

CHAPTER 2

Section 2–1

1. $a = 5$, $b = 1$, $c = 0$, $d = -2$, $e = -1$, $f = 3$, $x = 3$, $y = -5$, and $z = 7$.

3. (a) $(3, 3, 3, 2)$
   (b) $(2, -1, 3, 5)$
   (c) $(-1, 3, 3, 4)$
   (d) $(-1, 3, 3, 4)$
   (e) $(4, 16, 0, -12)$
   (f) $(12, 0, 0, -6)$

(g) (16, 16, 0, −18)   (h) (0, 0, 0, 0)

(i) (−7, −23, 9, 34)   (j) (−4, 13, −15, −33)

(k) (2, 0, 0, −1)

5. No, C is 3×3 and D is 3×2.

7. $\begin{pmatrix} 15 & -6 \\ 9 & 0 \\ -12 & 6 \end{pmatrix}$

9. $\begin{pmatrix} 4 & -1 & 4 \\ 0 & 1 & 0 \\ 5 & -4 & 8 \end{pmatrix}$

11. $\begin{pmatrix} -25 & 15 & -5 \\ 0 & -30 & 20 \\ -5 & 10 & -35 \end{pmatrix}$

13. $\begin{pmatrix} 0 & 0 & 0 \\ 0 & 0 & 0 \\ 0 & 0 & 0 \end{pmatrix}$

15. $\begin{pmatrix} 5 & 4 & 17 \\ 0 & -13 & 12 \\ 22 & -14 & 19 \end{pmatrix}$

17. $\begin{pmatrix} -25 & 10 \\ -15 & 0 \\ 20 & -10 \end{pmatrix}$

19. $\begin{pmatrix} 0 & 0 \\ 0 & 0 \\ 0 & 0 \end{pmatrix}$

43. $(a_1, a_2, a_3, a_4) \cdot (x_1, x_2, x_3, x_4) = a_1 x_1 + a_2 x_2 + a_3 x_3 + a_4 x_4$,
    $(a_1, a_2, \ldots, a_n) \cdot (x_1, x_2, \ldots, x_n) = a_1 x_1 + a_2 x_2 + \cdots + a_n x_n$

Section 2–2

1. (a) $8 + 16 + 24 + 32 = 80$

   (b) $-3 - 6 - 9 - 12 - 15 = -45$

   (c) $6 + 6 + 6 = 18$

   (d) $a + ar + ar^2 + \cdots + ar^{n-1}$

   (e) $1 + x + \dfrac{x^2}{2!} + \dfrac{x^3}{3!} + \cdots + \dfrac{x^n}{n!}$

   (f) $x - \dfrac{x^3}{3!} + \dfrac{x^5}{5!} - \dfrac{x^7}{7!} + \cdots + \dfrac{(-1)^{n-1} x^{2n-1}}{(2n-1)!}$

   (g) $1 - \dfrac{x^2}{2!} + \dfrac{x^4}{4!} - \dfrac{x^6}{6!} + \cdots + \dfrac{(-1)^n x^{2n}}{(2n)!}$

3. (11), a 1×1 matrix

5. EB is not defined.

7. $\begin{pmatrix} 6 & -4 \\ 2 & 0 \\ 0 & -8 \end{pmatrix}$

9. $\begin{pmatrix} 5 & 0 \\ 13 & -14 \\ -1 & 2 \end{pmatrix}$

11. BB is not defined.

13. $\begin{pmatrix} 2 & -6 \\ 20 & -30 \\ 0 & 6 \end{pmatrix}$

15. $\begin{pmatrix} 8 & -12 \\ 6 & 0 \\ 6 & -12 \end{pmatrix}$

17. $\mathbf{v}_1 = 3(2, -1)$, and
    $\mathbf{v}_2 = -5(2, -1)$.

19. $\mathbf{v}_1 = 1(2, 0) - 4(0, 2)$,
    $\mathbf{v}_2 = 2(2, 0) + 0(0, 2)$, and
    $\mathbf{v}_3 = 3(2, 0) - 2(0, 2)$.

21. $\mathbf{v}_1 = 3(2, 0) - 2(0, 2)$,
    $\mathbf{v}_2 = 1(2, 0) + 0(0, 2)$, and
    $\mathbf{v}_3 = 0(2, 0) - 4(0, 2)$.

23. $\mathbf{v}_1 = -1(1, -4) + 0(2, 0) + 2(3, -2)$,
    $\mathbf{v}_2 = 2(1, -4) + 1(2, 0) + 3(3, -2)$, and
    $\mathbf{v}_3 = 0(1, -4) + 1(2, 0) - 1(3, -2)$.

25. $\mathbf{v}_1 = -1(-1, 0, 2) + 0(2, 1, 3) + 2(0, 1, -1)$,
    $\mathbf{v}_2 = 2(-1, 0, 2) + 1(2, 1, 3) + 3(0, 1, -1)$, and
    $\mathbf{v}_3 = 0(-1, 0, 2) + 1(2, 1, 3) - 1(0, 1, -1)$.

27. No. Let $C = \begin{pmatrix} 0 & 2 \\ 0 & 2 \end{pmatrix}$, $A = \begin{pmatrix} 0 & 1 \\ 0 & 2 \end{pmatrix}$, $B = \begin{pmatrix} 0 & 0 \\ 0 & 2 \end{pmatrix}$. Then, $CA = CB$, but $A \neq B$.

Section 2–3

1. A, A

3. $-3A, -3A$

5. $\begin{pmatrix} 12 & -5 \\ -8 & 4 \end{pmatrix}$, $\begin{pmatrix} 12 & -20 \\ -2 & 4 \end{pmatrix}$

7. $5A, 5A$

9. $\begin{pmatrix} 15 & 12 & 4 \\ -10 & -3 & 0 \\ 5 & -6 & -6 \end{pmatrix}$, $\begin{pmatrix} 15 & -20 & 10 \\ 6 & -3 & 0 \\ 2 & 4 & -6 \end{pmatrix}$

11. $\begin{pmatrix} 3 & -12 & 2 \\ -2 & 3 & 0 \\ 1 & 6 & -3 \end{pmatrix}$, $\begin{pmatrix} 3 & -4 & 2 \\ -6 & 3 & 0 \\ 1 & 2 & -3 \end{pmatrix}$

13. $\begin{pmatrix} 3 & -4 & 8 \\ -2 & 1 & -4 \\ 1 & 2 & -1 \end{pmatrix}$, $\begin{pmatrix} 5 & 0 & -4 \\ -2 & 1 & 0 \\ 1 & 2 & -3 \end{pmatrix}$

15. $\begin{pmatrix} 15 & -4 & -10 \\ -5 & 1 & 0 \\ -5 & 2 & 15 \end{pmatrix}$, $\begin{pmatrix} 3 & -4 & 2 \\ -11 & 13 & -6 \\ -5 & -10 & 15 \end{pmatrix}$

17. $-2B$

19. $\begin{pmatrix} 6 & -9 & 15 \\ 0 & -12 & 24 \end{pmatrix}$

CHAPTER 3

Section 3–1A

1. (a) $\begin{pmatrix} 5 & -1 \\ 3 & 7 \end{pmatrix}$

(b) $\begin{pmatrix} 1 & 3 & -1 \\ 2 & -1 & 4 \end{pmatrix}$

(c) $\begin{pmatrix} 1 & 0 \\ 0 & 1 \end{pmatrix}$

(d) $\begin{pmatrix} 5 & 1 \\ 0 & 0 \\ 2 & -3 \end{pmatrix}$

(e) $\begin{pmatrix} 2 & -7 \\ 1 & 5 \\ -4 & 1 \end{pmatrix}$

(f) $\begin{pmatrix} 1 & 5 \\ 2 & -7 \\ -4 & 1 \end{pmatrix}$

(g) $\begin{pmatrix} -4 & 1 \\ 2 & -7 \\ 1 & 5 \end{pmatrix}$

(h) $\begin{pmatrix} 3 & -2 \\ 2 & 5 \end{pmatrix}$

(i) $(1 \ -5 \ 1 \ 7)$

(j) $\begin{pmatrix} 2 & -7 & 0 & 3 \\ 1 & 0 & 5 & -1 \\ -4 & 3 & 0 & 0 \\ 0 & 1 & -1 & 5 \\ 1 & -1 & 1 & -1 \end{pmatrix}$

3. $3x - y = 0(x + 3y) + 1(3x - y)$,
$x + 3y = 1(x + 3y) + 0(3x - y)$,
$x + 3y = 0(3x - y) + 1(x + 3y)$,
$3x - y = 1(3x - y) + 0(x + 3y)$

5. $3x - y = 1(-10y) + 3(x + 3y)$,
$x + 3y = 0(-10y) + 1(x + 3y)$,
$-10y = 1(3x - y) - 3(x + 3y)$,
$x + 3y = 0(3x - y) + 1(x + 3y)$

7. $3x - y = 1(3x - y) + 0(0x + 0y) + 0(x + 3y)$,
$x + 3y = 0(3x - y) + 0(0x + 0y) + 1(x + 3y)$,
$3x - y = 1(3x - y) + 0(x + 3y)$,
$0x + 0y = 0(3x - y) + 0(x + 3y)$,
$x + 3y = 0(3x - y) + 1(x + 3y)$

9. All except *part c*.   11. $S = \{(0, 0)\}$

13. $S = \{(0, 5k, 3k) \mid k \in R\}$

15. $S = \{(k, K, 4k + 3K) \mid k, K \in R\}$

17. $S = \{(-7k, 13k, 11k) \mid k \in R\}$ 19. $S = \{(0, 0, 0)\}$

Section 3–1B

1. The matrices in *parts* (*a*), (*c*), and (*d*) are reduced matrices.
   (b) Definition 3–1.1, *part* (*a*) does not hold. $(0 \quad 1 \quad \frac{1}{2})$
   (e) Definition 3–1.1, *part* (*c*) does not hold. $\begin{pmatrix} 0 & 0 & 1 \\ 0 & 0 & 0 \end{pmatrix}$
   (f) Definition 3–1.1, *parts* (*a*) and (*b*) do not hold. $\begin{pmatrix} 1 & 0 & 0 \\ 0 & 0 & 1 \end{pmatrix}$
   (g) Definition 3–1.1, *part* (*a*) does not hold. $\begin{pmatrix} 1 & 0 & 0 & 0 \\ 0 & 1 & 0 & 0 \\ 0 & 0 & 0 & 1 \end{pmatrix}$
   (h) Definition 3–1.1, *part* (*c*) does not hold. $\begin{pmatrix} 1 & 5 & 0 & 0 \\ 0 & 0 & 1 & 0 \\ 0 & 0 & 0 & 1 \\ 0 & 0 & 0 & 0 \end{pmatrix}$

3. $\begin{pmatrix} 1 & 0 \\ 0 & 1 \end{pmatrix}$, $S = \{(0, 0)\}$

5. $\begin{pmatrix} 1 & 0 & 0 \\ 0 & 1 & -\frac{5}{3} \end{pmatrix}$, $S = \{(0, y, (\frac{3}{5})y) \mid y \in R\}$

7. $\begin{pmatrix} 1 & \frac{3}{4} & -\frac{1}{4} \\ 0 & 0 & 0 \end{pmatrix}$, $S = \{(x, y, z) \mid x = (-\frac{3}{4})y + (\frac{1}{4})z\}$

9. $\begin{pmatrix} 1 & 0 & \frac{7}{11} \\ 0 & 1 & -\frac{13}{11} \end{pmatrix}$, $S = \{((-\frac{7}{11})z, (\frac{13}{11})z, z) \mid z \in R\}$

11. $\begin{matrix} 1 & 0 & 0 & 0 \\ 0 & 1 & 0 & 0 \\ 0 & 0 & 1 & 0 \\ 0 & 0 & 0 & 1 \\ 0 & 0 & 0 & 0 \end{matrix}$, $S = \{(0, 0, 0, 0)\}$

13. The reduced matrix has at least one row of zeros.

15. $\begin{pmatrix} 0 & 0 \\ 0 & 0 \end{pmatrix}$, $\begin{pmatrix} 0 & 1 \\ 0 & 0 \end{pmatrix}$, $\begin{pmatrix} 1 & a \\ 0 & 0 \end{pmatrix}$ for $a \in R$, and $\begin{pmatrix} 1 & 0 \\ 0 & 1 \end{pmatrix}$

17. $\begin{pmatrix} 0 & 0 & 0 \\ 0 & 0 & 0 \\ 0 & 0 & 0 \end{pmatrix}$, $\begin{pmatrix} 0 & 0 & 1 \\ 0 & 0 & 0 \\ 0 & 0 & 0 \end{pmatrix}$, $\begin{pmatrix} 0 & 1 & a \\ 0 & 0 & 0 \\ 0 & 0 & 0 \end{pmatrix}$, $\begin{pmatrix} 0 & 1 & 0 \\ 0 & 0 & 1 \\ 0 & 0 & 0 \end{pmatrix}$,

$\begin{pmatrix} 1 & a & b \\ 0 & 0 & 0 \\ 0 & 0 & 0 \end{pmatrix}$, $\begin{pmatrix} 1 & a & 0 \\ 0 & 0 & 1 \\ 0 & 0 & 0 \end{pmatrix}$, $\begin{pmatrix} 1 & 0 & a \\ 0 & 1 & b \\ 0 & 0 & 0 \end{pmatrix}$, $\begin{pmatrix} 1 & 0 & 0 \\ 0 & 1 & 0 \\ 0 & 0 & 1 \end{pmatrix}$,

for $a, b \in R$.

$S = \emptyset$

$k \in R \}$

$S = \emptyset$

11. $\begin{pmatrix} 1 & 0 \\ -2 & 1 \end{pmatrix}$

13. $\begin{pmatrix} 4 & 0 \\ 0 & 1 \end{pmatrix}$

15. $\begin{pmatrix} 1 & 0 & 0 \\ 0 & -3 & 0 \\ 0 & 0 & 1 \end{pmatrix}$

17. $\begin{pmatrix} 1 & 0 & -1 \\ 0 & 1 & 0 \\ 0 & 0 & 1 \end{pmatrix}$

19. $\begin{pmatrix} 1 & 0 & 0 \\ 0 & 1 & 0 \\ 0 & 0 & -2 \end{pmatrix}$

23. $\frac{1}{13}\begin{pmatrix} 3 & -2 \\ 5 & 1 \end{pmatrix}$

25. $\begin{pmatrix} \frac{1}{3} & 0 & 0 \\ 0 & 1 & 0 \\ 0 & 0 & 1 \end{pmatrix}$

27. $\begin{pmatrix} 1 & 0 & 0 \\ 0 & 0 & 1 \\ 0 & 1 & 0 \end{pmatrix}$

29. $\begin{pmatrix} \frac{1}{2} & 0 & 0 \\ 0 & 0 & 1 \\ 0 & 1 & 0 \end{pmatrix}$

31. No inverse exists.

33. No inverse exists.

Section 3–3B

1. $\frac{1}{39}\begin{pmatrix} 4 & 3 \\ 5 & -6 \end{pmatrix}$

3. $\frac{1}{3}\begin{pmatrix} 0 & 1 \\ 1 & 0 \end{pmatrix}$

5. No inverse exists.

7. $\frac{1}{8}\begin{pmatrix} 6 & -2 & 4 \\ -1 & 3 & -2 \\ 3 & -1 & 6 \end{pmatrix}$

9. $\frac{1}{2}\begin{pmatrix} 1 & 0 & 1 \\ -1 & 1 & 0 \\ 0 & 1 & -1 \end{pmatrix}$

11. $S = \{ (\frac{11}{39}, \frac{43}{39}) \}$

13. $S = \{ (-4, 3) \}$

15. $S = \emptyset$

17. $S = \{ (5, -3, 2) \}$

19. $S = \{ (-2, 5, 1) \}$

21. $S = \{ (68a + 41b - 13c, \ -31a - 19b + 6c, \ -5a - 3b + c) \}$

181

CHAPTER 4

Section 4–1

1. 10   3. -10 5. 30   7. 10

9. 1   11. 30   13. 0

15. $M[-2] = 7$, $C[-2] = -7$; $M[1] = -9 = C[1]$; $M[7] = 6$, $C[7] = -6$

17. $M[3] = -17 = C[3]$; $M[-2] = 7$, $C[-2] = -7$; $M[0] = -39 = C[0]$

19. $M[4] = -4 = C[4]$; $M[7] = 6$, $C[7] = -6$; $M[-3] = -7 = C[-3]$

21. 9   23. 1   25. abc 27. -60

29. 20   31. -40 33. 14   35. -78

Section 4–2

1. -20 3. 50   5. -40 7. -30

9. *Property 6*   11. *Property 4*   13. *Property 2*   15. $x = \pm 4$

17. $x = 0$, $x = \pm 2\sqrt{2}$

19. $\begin{pmatrix} 2 & 26 & -6 \\ -7 & 9 & 1 \\ 5 & 5 & 5 \end{pmatrix}$
     21. $\begin{pmatrix} 6 & 7 & -3 \\ -2 & 1 & 11 \\ 4 & -2 & -2 \end{pmatrix}$

23. $\begin{pmatrix} -38 & 14 & 36 & 56 \\ -17 & 7 & 15 & 21 \\ 46 & -14 & -48 & -70 \\ 56 & -14 & -56 & -84 \end{pmatrix}$

Section 4–3

13. $S = \{ (x, y) \mid x = 3y \}$ 15. $S = \emptyset$

17. $S = \{ (0, 0, 0) \}$ 19. $S = \emptyset$

21. $S = \emptyset$

23. $S = \left\{ (x, y, z) \,\middle|\, z \in R,\ x = \dfrac{17 - z}{5},\ \text{and}\ y = \dfrac{4z + 7}{5} \right\}$

Section 4–4

23. $S = \{ (1, -1, 3) \}$ 25. $S = \{ (3, 0, -1) \}$

27. $S = \{ (1, 1, 1, 1) \}$

CHAPTER 5

Section 5–1B

18 through 25. None of the sets contains an additive identity. All sets except that of Problem 25 are not closed under addition. Are any of the sets closed under scalar multiplication?

Section 5–2

1. $7\mathbf{v}_1 + 3\mathbf{v}_2$
3. $2\mathbf{v}_1 = \mathbf{u} + \mathbf{v}, \ 2\mathbf{v}_2 = \mathbf{u} - \mathbf{v}, \ 5\mathbf{v}_1 + 3\mathbf{v}_2 = 4\mathbf{u} + \mathbf{v}, \ \text{and} \ -2\mathbf{v}_1 + 3\mathbf{v}_2 = (\frac{1}{2})\mathbf{u} - (\frac{5}{2})\mathbf{v}$
5. $\{ (-x, -y) \mid x, y \in R \} = \{ (x, y) \mid x, y \in R \}$
7. $\{ (3x, 2x) \mid x \in R \}$
9. $\{ (x + y + z, z, y + z) \mid x, y, z \in R \}$
11. $\{ (x + 2y, 2x + z, y + 2z) \mid x, y, z \in R \}$
13. $\{ (x + z, 3y + 6z, -2x + 5y + 8z) \mid x, y, z \in R \}$
$$= \{ (x, 3y, -2x + 5y) \mid x, y, \in R \}$$

15. Yes   17. No   19. Yes
21. Yes   23. No   25. Independent
27. Dependent   29. Independent   31. Independent
33. Dependent

Section 5–3

1. $\{ (2, -3), (1, 3) \}$ 3. $\{ (-3, 5), (5, 0) \}$
5. $\{ (1, 0, 0), (0, 1, 0), (0, 0, -1) \}$
7. $\{ (1, 1, 1), (0, 1, 1), (0, -2, -4) \}$
9. $\{ (5, 0), (0, 1) \}$ 11. $\{ (1, 0, 0), (0, 0, 5), (0, 1, 0) \}$
13. $\{ (1, 1, 1), (0, 1, 1), (0, 1, 0) \} \text{ or } \{ (1, 1, 1), (0, 1, 1), (0, 0, 1) \}$
15. $\{ (-3, 2, -4), (5, -2, 10), (1, 0, 0) \}, \ \{ (-3, 2, -4), (5, -2, 10), (0, 1, 0) \}, \text{ or } \{ (-3, 2, -4), (5, -2, 10), (0, 0, 1) \}$

Section 5–4

1. Yes, of R^2 3. No   5. No
7. Yes, of R^3 9. No   11. No
13. Yes   15. No   17. No
25. (a) $\{ (x, 0) \mid x \in R \}$ (b) R^2 (c) $\{ (x, y, 0) \mid x, y \in R \}$
     (d) $\{ (0, 0, 0) \}$ (e) R^2 (f) $\{ (0, 0) \}$
27. No   29. Yes

Section 5-5

1. (5), (10), (12), (0), (−5), (−10), (x); (1), (2), ($\frac{12}{5}$), (−1), (−2), ($x/5$)

3. ($x/2, -y/3$) 5. ($-x/2, -y/3$)

7. $\left(\dfrac{x+y}{2}, \dfrac{x-y}{2}\right)$ 9. ($x/3, y/2, z/5$)

11. (x, z, y) 13. (z, x, y)

15. $\left(\dfrac{x+y-z}{2}, \dfrac{x-y+z}{2}, \dfrac{y-x+z}{2}\right)$

CHAPTER 6

Section 6-1A

1. R, $\{4\}$ 3. R, all nonnegative real numbers.

5. All real numbers except −5, all real numbers except 1.

7. $\{x \mid x \in R \text{ and } x \geq 2\}$, $\{x \mid x \in R \text{ and } x \leq 0\}$

9. $\{x \mid x \in R \text{ and } x > 0\}$, R 11. R, $\{x \mid x \in R \text{ and } x \geq 0\}$

13. $\{x \mid x \in R \text{ and } x \neq \dfrac{\pi}{2} + k\pi \text{ for } k \in Z\}$

15. (a) If $x \in Z^+$, let $f(x) = -x$.
    (b) Let $f(1) = f(2) = -1$ and for $x > 2$, let $f(x) = -x + 1$.

17. (a) If $x \in Z^+$, let $f(x) = 2x - 1$.
    (b) Let $f(1) = f(2) = 1$ and for $x > 2$, let $f(x) = 2x - 3$.

Section 6-1B

1. Yes 3. Yes 5. Yes

7. No 9. No 11. Yes

13. Yes 15. No 17. No

19. The first four are reflections and the fifth is a rotation.

21. Yes

27. (a) $5\mathbf{i} + 2\mathbf{j} - 3\mathbf{k}$ (b) (5, 2, −3) (c) $(x + y)\mathbf{i} + x\mathbf{j} - y\mathbf{k}$
    (d) (0, 0, 0) (e) (0, 0, 0)

29. (a) 1 (b) −1 (c) −7
    (d) $x - y - 7z$ (e) $\{(y + 7z, y, z) \mid y, z \in R\}$

Section 6-1C

1. R, R 3. (0, 0), R^2

5. If $c = 0$, the kernel is R^2 and the range is $\{(0, 0)\}$. If $c \neq 0$, the kernel is $\{(0, 0)\}$ and the range is R^2.

7. (a) Here, f is not a linear mapping.
   (b) $\{\,(x, 3x) \mid x \in R\,\}$, R^1 (c) $\{\,(x, -x) \mid x \in R\,\}$, R^1
   (d) $\{\,(0, y) \mid y \in R\,\}$, R^1

9. $\{\,(x, [\tfrac{3}{2}]\,x, [\tfrac{5}{2}]\,x) \mid x \in R\,\}$, R^2

Section 6–2

1. (a) $\begin{pmatrix} 0 & 1 \\ 1 & 0 \end{pmatrix}$ (b) $\begin{pmatrix} 1 & 0 \\ 0 & -1 \end{pmatrix}$ (c) $\begin{pmatrix} -1 & 0 \\ 0 & 1 \end{pmatrix}$ (d) $\begin{pmatrix} -1 & 0 \\ 0 & -1 \end{pmatrix}$

3. (a) $\begin{pmatrix} 3 & -2 & 0 \\ 5 & 0 & -2 \end{pmatrix}$ (b) $\begin{pmatrix} 1 & 0 & 0 \\ 0 & 0 & 1 \end{pmatrix}$

5. (a) $\begin{pmatrix} 1 & -1 & 0 & 0 \\ 0 & 1 & -1 & 0 \\ 0 & 0 & 1 & -1 \\ -1 & 0 & 0 & 1 \end{pmatrix}$ (b) $\begin{pmatrix} 3 & 0 & 0 & 0 \\ 2 & 1 & 0 & 0 \\ 0 & 1 & -2 & 0 \\ 0 & 0 & 0 & 1 \end{pmatrix}$

7. $\begin{pmatrix} 1 & 0 \\ -1 & -1 \end{pmatrix}$ 9. $\begin{pmatrix} -1 & 0 \\ 1 & -1 \end{pmatrix}$ 11. $\begin{pmatrix} 5 & -3 \\ -8 & 8 \end{pmatrix}$

13. $\begin{pmatrix} 1 & 0 & 0 \\ -1 & 0 & 1 \end{pmatrix}$ 15. $f[\,(x, y)\,] = (x - 3y,\ y)$

17. $f[\,(x, y)\,] = (3x - y,\ x,\ -2x + 5y)$

19. $f[\,(x, y, z)\,] = (0, 0, 0)$

21. $f[\,(x, y, z, w)\,] = (2y - 3z + w,\ x + 2w,\ w)$

Section 6–4

1. 2   3. 2   5. 2   7. 3   9. 2

11. 2, 0   13. 2, 0   15. 2, 1   17. 3, 0   19. 2, 1

21. $0,\ S = \{\,(0, 0)\,\}$ 23. $1,\ S = \{\,(x, 0, -x) \mid x \in R\,\}$

25. $S = \{\,(1, 2) + (0, 0)\,\} = \{\,(1, 2)\,\}$

27. $S = \{\,(2, 2, 2) + (x, 0, -x) \mid x \in R\,\}$
     $= \{\,(2 + x,\ 2,\ 2 - x) \mid x \in R\,\}$

Section 6–5

5. $(\tfrac{1}{5})$, $f^{-1}(x) = (\tfrac{1}{5})x$ 7. $\left(\dfrac{1}{m}\right)$, $f^{-1}(x) = \dfrac{1}{m}\,x$

9. $\begin{pmatrix} 0 & 1 \\ 1 & 0 \end{pmatrix}$, $f^{-1}[\,(x, y)\,] = (y, x)$

11. $\begin{pmatrix} -1 & 0 \\ 0 & 1 \end{pmatrix}$, $f^{-1}[\,(x, y)\,] = (-x, y)$

13. $\begin{pmatrix} \dfrac{1}{c} & 0 \\ 0 & \dfrac{1}{c} \end{pmatrix}$, $f^{-1}[\,(x, y)\,] = \dfrac{1}{c}\,(x, y)$

15. $\dfrac{1}{13}\begin{pmatrix} 1 & 2 \\ -5 & 3 \end{pmatrix}$, $f^{-1}[\,(x, y)\,] = \tfrac{1}{13}(x + 2y,\ -5x + 3y)$

17. f^{-1} does not exist.

19. $\begin{pmatrix} 1 & 0 & 0 \\ 0 & 1 & 0 \\ 0 & 0 & 1 \end{pmatrix}$, $f^{-1}[(x, y, z)] = (x, y, z)$

21. $\dfrac{1}{6}\begin{pmatrix} 2 & -2 & -2 \\ 0 & 3 & 6 \\ 0 & 0 & -6 \end{pmatrix}$, $f^{-1}[(x, y, z)] = \frac{1}{6}(2x - 2y - 2z, \; 3y + 6z, \; -6z)$

23. $\dfrac{1}{8}\begin{pmatrix} 3 & 1 & -2 \\ -1 & -3 & 6 \\ -2 & 2 & 4 \end{pmatrix}$,

 $f^{-1}[(x, y, z)] = \frac{1}{8}(3x + y - 2z, \; -x - 3y + 6z, \; -2x + 2y + 4z)$

Section 6–6

1. $A = \begin{pmatrix} 2 & 3 \\ 2 & -3 \end{pmatrix}$, $B = \dfrac{1}{3}\begin{pmatrix} -7 & 20 \\ 4 & 4 \end{pmatrix}$, $P = \begin{pmatrix} 1 & 1 \\ -1 & 2 \end{pmatrix}$

3. $A = \begin{pmatrix} 1 & 0 \\ 0 & -1 \end{pmatrix}$, $B = \dfrac{1}{3}\begin{pmatrix} 1 & 4 \\ 2 & -1 \end{pmatrix}$, $P = \begin{pmatrix} 1 & 1 \\ -1 & 2 \end{pmatrix}$

5. $A = B = \begin{pmatrix} 1 & 0 \\ 0 & 1 \end{pmatrix}$, $P = \begin{pmatrix} 1 & 1 \\ -1 & 2 \end{pmatrix}$

7. $A = \begin{pmatrix} 1 & 0 & 0 \\ 0 & 0 & 1 \\ 0 & 1 & 0 \end{pmatrix}$, $B = \begin{pmatrix} 1 & 2 & 2 \\ 0 & 0 & -1 \\ 0 & -1 & 0 \end{pmatrix}$, $P = \begin{pmatrix} 1 & 1 & 1 \\ 0 & -1 & 0 \\ 0 & 0 & 1 \end{pmatrix}$

9. $A = \begin{pmatrix} 3 & 0 & 0 \\ 0 & 5 & 0 \\ 0 & 0 & -2 \end{pmatrix}$, $B = \begin{pmatrix} 3 & -2 & 5 \\ 0 & 5 & 0 \\ 0 & 0 & -2 \end{pmatrix}$, $P = \begin{pmatrix} 1 & 1 & 1 \\ 0 & -1 & 0 \\ 0 & 0 & 1 \end{pmatrix}$

CHAPTER 7

Section 7–2

1. (a) $x = 6$, $y = 0$; $z = 12$ (b) $x = 0$, $y = 3$; $z = 3$
   (c) $x = 0$, $y = 0$; $z = 0$
2. (a) $x = \frac{28}{5}$, $y = \frac{6}{5}$; $z = 18$ (b) $x = 0$, $y = 4$; $z = 4$
3. $x = \frac{21}{5}$, $y = \frac{4}{5}$; $z = -\frac{13}{10}$
4. (a) $x = 0$, $y = 6$; $z = 6$ (b) $x = 0$, $y = 6$; $z = 6$
   (c) $x = 0$, $y = 3$; $z = 3$ (d) $x = 3$, $y = 0$; $z = -\frac{3}{2}$
5. 6 of product A and 2 of product B. Maximum profit is $200 per day.
6. $106\frac{2}{3}$ acres of crop A and $66\frac{2}{3}$ acres of crop B. Maximum profit is $19,333.33.
7. $83\frac{2}{3}$ tons from A and 100 tons from B. Minimum cost is $31,666.67.

Section 7–4

1. $4x - 5y = 0$ 2. $y = 2x$ 3. $y = 2x$
4. $49x - 30y = 0$ 5. $86x - 55y = 0$ 6. $133x - 140y = 0$

7. $9x + 9y - 11z = 0$

8. No unique answer. $z = ax + by$, where $a + b = 1$.

9. $69x + 5y - 40z = 0$

10. No unique answer. $z = ax + 2y$, where $a \in R$.

Section 7–5

1. $\begin{pmatrix} c_1 e^t + 2c_2 e^{2t} \\ c_1 e^t + c_2 e^{2t} \end{pmatrix}$

2. $\begin{pmatrix} c_1 e^{-t} + c_2 e^{4t} \\ -c_1 e^{-t} + (\frac{3}{2})c_2 e^{4t} \end{pmatrix}$

3. $\begin{pmatrix} c_1 e^{2t} + c_2 e^{3t} \\ -c_1 e^{2t} - 2c_2 e^{3t} \end{pmatrix}$

4. $\begin{pmatrix} 2c_1 e^{2t} + 3c_2 e^{-3t} \\ c_1 e^{2t} + c_2 e^{-3t} \end{pmatrix}$

5. $\begin{pmatrix} c_1 e^{-t} + c_2 e^{3t} \\ 3c_1 e^{-t} - c_2 e^{3t} \end{pmatrix}$

6. $\begin{pmatrix} c_1 e^t + c_2 t e^t \\ c_1 e^t + c_2(t + 1)e^t \end{pmatrix}$

7. $\begin{pmatrix} c_1 e^t + c_2 t e^t \\ 2c_1 e^t + c_2(2t - 1)e^t \end{pmatrix}$

8. $\begin{pmatrix} c_1 e^{3t} + c_2(t + 1)e^{3t} \\ c_1 e^{3t} + c_2 t e^{3t} \end{pmatrix}$

9. $\begin{pmatrix} c_1 e^{2t} + c_2 t e^{2t} \\ c_1 e^{2t} + c_2(t - 1)e^{2t} \end{pmatrix}$

10. $\begin{pmatrix} -2c_1 e^{3t} + c_2(2t + 1)e^{3t} \\ c_1 e^{3t} - c_2 t e^{3t} \end{pmatrix}$

11. $\begin{pmatrix} e^t(c_1 \cos 3t + c_2 \sin 3t) \\ e^t(c_1 \sin 3t - c_2 \cos 3t) \end{pmatrix}$

12. $\begin{pmatrix} 2e^t(-c_1 \sin 2t + c_2 \cos 2t) \\ e^t(c_1 \cos 2t + c_2 \sin 2t) \end{pmatrix}$

13. $\begin{pmatrix} 2e^{2t}(c_1 \cos 3t + c_2 \sin 3t) \\ e^{2t}[-c_1(\cos 3t + 3 \sin 3t) + c_2(3 \cos 3t - \sin 3t)] \end{pmatrix}$

14. $\begin{pmatrix} c_1(2 \cos t - \sin t) + c_2(\cos t + 2 \sin t) \\ c_1 \cos t + c_2 \sin t \end{pmatrix}$

15. $\begin{pmatrix} c_1 e^{2t}(\cos t + \sin t) + c_2 e^{2t}(\sin t - \cos t) \\ c_1 e^{2t} \cos t + c_2 e^{2t} \sin t \end{pmatrix}$

187

Index

189